McGRAW-HILL RYERSON
MATHEMATICS 8
MAKING CONNECTIONS

Authors

Elizabeth Ainslie
Hon. B.Sc., B.Ed.
Toronto District School
Board

Wayne Erdman
B.Math., B.Ed.
Toronto District School
Board

Dan Gilfoy
B.Sc. (Agr.), B.Ed.
Halifax Regional School
Board

Honi Huyck
B.Sc., B.Ed.
Belle River, Ontario

Stacey Lax
B.A., B.Ed., M.Ed.
York Region District School
Board

Brian McCudden
M.A., M.Ed., Ph.D.
Toronto, Ontario

Kelly Ryan
Hon. B.Sc., B.Ed.
Toronto District School
Board

Jacob Speijer
B.Eng., M.Sc.Ed., P.Eng.
District School Board of
Niagara

Sandy Szeto
B.Sc., B.Ed.
Toronto District School
Board

Michael Webb
B.Sc., M.Sc., Ph.D.
Toronto, Ontario

**Assessment/Pedagogy
Consultants**
Elizabeth Ainslie
Toronto District School
Board

Brian McCudden
Toronto, Ontario

**Combined Grades
Consultant**
Jonathan Dean
Hamilton-Wentworth
District School Board

**Special Education
Consultants**
Pauline Creighton
District School Board of
Niagara

Deirdre Gordon
Hastings and Prince Edward
District School Board

Technology Consultant
Honi Huyck
Belle River, Ontario

**Mental Mathematics
Consultant**
Joan Manuel
District 10, St. Stephen,
New Brunswick

Literacy Consultant
Anne Burnham MacLeod
District 18, Fredericton,
New Brunswick

**English as a Second
Language Consultant**
Jane E. Sims
Toronto, Ontario

Advisors
Chris Dearling
OISE-University of Toronto

Catherine Little
Toronto District School
Board

Shelley McCurdy
Simcoe Muskoka Catholic
District School Board

Tess Miller
Durham District School
Board

Troy Parkhouse
District School Board of
Niagara

Debbie Price
Greater Essex County
District School Board

Mary E. O'Neill
The Halifax Regional
School Board, Nova Scotia

McGraw-Hill
Ryerson

Toronto   Montréal   Boston   Burr Ridge, IL   Dubuque, IA   Madison, WI   New York
San Francisco   St. Louis   Bangkok   Bogotá   Caracas   Kuala Lumpur   Lisbon   London
Madrid   Mexico City   Milan   New Delhi   Santiago   Seoul   Singapore   Sydney   Taipei

McGraw-Hill Ryerson

McGraw-Hill Ryerson
Mathematics 8: Making Connections

ISBN 0-07-091761-2

http://www.mcgrawhill.ca

1 2 3 4 5 6 7 8 9 10 TCP 0 9 8 7 6 5

Printed and bound in Canada

Care has been taken to trace ownership of copyright material contained in this text. The publishers will gladly accept any information that will enable them to rectify any reference or credit in subsequent printings.

The Geometer's Sketchpad®, Key Curriculum Press, 1150 65th Street, Emeryville, CA 94608, 1-800-995-MATH.

TABS+, The Knowledge Tree Inc., 554 Merton Street, Toronto, ON, M4S 1B3, (416) 488-4359, *www.knowledgetree.ca*.

National Library of Canada Cataloging in Publication Data

Mathematics 8 : making connections / authors, Elizabeth Ainslie ... [et al.].

Includes index.
ISBN 0-07-091761-2

1. Mathematics—Textbooks. I. Ainslie, Elizabeth
II. Title: Mathematics eight.

QA107.2.M393 2004   510   C2004-903899-0

PUBLISHER: Diane Wyman
PROJECT MANAGER: Helen Mason
DEVELOPMENTAL EDITORS: Maggie Cheverie, Julia Cochrane, Jean Ford, Tom Gamblin, Jackie Lacoursiere, Jodi Rauch
MANAGER, EDITORIAL SERVICES: Linda Allison
SUPERVISING EDITOR: Crystal Shortt
COPY EDITOR: Julia Cochrane
PHOTO RESEARCH/PERMISSIONS: Maria DeCambra
PHOTO RESEARCH/SET-UP PHOTOGRAPHY: Roland W. Meisel
JUNIOR EDITOR: Matan Kezwer
EDITORIAL ASSISTANT: Erin Hartley
MANAGER, PRODUCTION SERVICES: Yolanda Pigden
PRODUCTION CO-ORDINATOR: Jennifer Wilke
COVER AND INTERIOR DESIGN: Pronk & Associates
ART DIRECTION: Tom Dart/First Folio Resource Group, Inc.
ELECTRONIC PAGE MAKE-UP: Tom Dart, Greg Duhaney, Claire Milne, and Adam Wood of First Folio Resource Group, Inc.
COVER IMAGE: Jonathan Ferrier/CORBIS/MAGMA

COPIES OF THIS BOOK MAY BE OBTAINED BY CONTACTING:

McGraw-Hill Ryerson Ltd.

WEB SITE:
http://www.mcgrawhill.ca

E-MAIL:
orders@mcgrawhill.ca

TOLL-FREE FAX:
1-800-463-5885

TOLL-FREE CALL:
1-800-565-5758

OR BY MAILING YOUR ORDER TO:
McGraw-Hill Ryerson
Order Department
300 Water Street
Whitby, ON L1N 9B6

Please quote the ISBN and title when placing your order.

Student Text ISBN:
0-07-091761-2

Acknowledgements

Reviewers and Field-Test Teachers

The publisher, authors, and editors of McGraw-Hill Ryerson Mathematics 8: Making Connections, wish to extend their sincere thanks to the students, teachers, consultants, and reviewers who contributed their time, energy, and expertise to the creation of this textbook. We are grateful for their thoughtful comments and suggestions about what worked best in their classrooms. This feedback throughout the development process has been invaluable in ensuring that the text and related teacher's resource meet the needs of students and teachers. We would also like to extend special thanks to the students of Kelly Ryan's school, who participated in set-up photography sessions for some of the visuals in this text.

Chris Aikman
Hastings and Prince Edward District School Board

Melanie Allport
Limestone District School Board

Gord Anderson
Greater Essex County District School Board

Dan Antflyck
Toronto District School Board

Paul Apsimon
Ottawa-Carleton District School Board

Nikki Arrindell
Toronto District School Board

Andrew Austin
Peterborough Victoria Northumberland and Clarington Catholic District School Board

Leslie Baker
Toronto District School Board

Tracey Bates
Ottawa-Carleton Catholic District School Board

Lucas Bertran
Brant Haldimand Norfolk Catholic District School Board

Peter Boross-Harmes
Toronto District School Board

David Brownlee
York Region District School Board

Elizabeth Burgess-Masse
York Region District School Board

Aldo Caraminico
Dufferin-Peel Catholic District School Board

Kevin Carlyle
Thames Valley District School Board

Richard Chaplinsky
Ottawa-Carleton Catholic District School Board

Steve Charbonneau
St. Clair Catholic District School Board

Rob Citro
Peterborough Victoria Northumberland and Clarington Catholic District School Board

Peter Cobb
Lambton Kent District School Board

Sarah Cruickshanks
Greater Essex County District School Board

Mark Daranjo
Durham Catholic District School Board

Jonathan Dean
Hamilton-Wentworth District School Board

Brenda Dillon
Algonquin and Lakeshore Catholic District School Board

Angela Esau
District School Board of Niagara

Ron Fleming
York Catholic District School Board

Marilyn Fox
Durham Catholic District School Board

Sherry Hanson
Toronto District School Board

Stephen Hua
Hamilton-Wentworth District School Board

Val Hudson
Simcoe County District School Board

Margaret Kimble
Trillium Lakelands District School Board

Sylvia Constancio Kwan
Toronto District School Board

Susan Lai
Toronto District School Board

George Letsos
Toronto District School Board

Cyril Lewin
Toronto District School Board

Contents

A Tour of Your Textbook

How is *Mathematics 8: Making Connections* set up?

Each chapter starts off with a **Chapter Problem** that connects math and your world. You will be able to solve the problem using the math skills that you learn in the chapter.

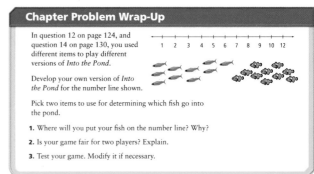

radius, diameter, circumference, and area of a circle and draw a circle given its area or circumference.

Chapter Problem

How far will you travel each time the drum spins around once? What information do you need to answer this question?

Think about other circular midway rides you have ridden on. In this chapter, you will learn how to calculate circular measures for these rides.

You are asked to answer questions related to the problem throughout the chapter.

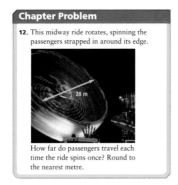

Chapter Problem

12. This midway ride rotates, spinning the passengers strapped in around its edge.

28 m

How far do passengers travel each time the ride spins once? Round to the nearest metre.

The **Chapter Problem Wrap-Up** is at the end of the chapter, on the second Practice Test page.

Chapter Problem Wrap-Up

In question 12 on page 124, and question 14 on page 130, you used different items to play different versions of *Into the Pond*.

Develop your own version of *Into the Pond* for the number line shown.

Pick two items to use for determining which fish go into the pond.

1. Where will you put your fish on the number line? Why?

2. Is your game fair for two players? Explain.

3. Test your game. Modify it if necessary.

The **Get Ready** pages provide a brief review of skills from previous grades that are important for success with this chapter.

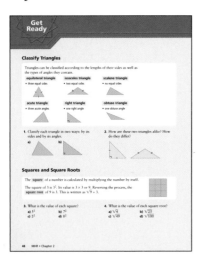

The **numbered sections** often start with a photo to connect the topic to a real setting. The purpose of this introduction is to help you make connections between the math in the section and the real world, or to make connections to previous knowledge.

A three-part lesson follows.

 Discover the Math

Is there a constant relationship among measures of ci

1. Choose five circular objects. Measure around the outside of e
What measurement is this?

 Key Ideas

- The measures of the internal angles in a triangle add to 18(
- You can use the sum of the internal angles to find unknow
measures in triangles.

Check Your Understanding

Practise

For help with questions 4 and 5, refer to Example 1.

4. What is the unknown angle measure in each triangle?

a)

35° 75°

15. a) Copy each equation and use the
Try This! symbols +, −, ÷, ×, and ( ) to make it
true.
- 5 ■ 9 ■ 7 = 3
- 3 ■ 5 ■ 4 = −8
- 20 ■ 4 ■ −6 = −4
b) Can you make any of the equations true
in more than one way? Explain.
c) What strategies did you try to answer
these questions? Which worked best?

9.4 **Use Databases to Solve Problems**

Focus on...
• databases

Use Technology

Explore the Pythagorean Relationship Using *The Geometer's Sketchpad*®

Focus on...
• exploring the Pythagorean relationship

1. Open *The Geometer's Sketchpad*® and begin a new sketch.

2. Construct a right triangle.
a) Use the **Straightedge** tool to create a horizontal line segment. Select
the line segment and one endpoint. From the **Construct** menu,
choose **Perpendicular Line**. Select the new line. From the **Construct**
menu choose **Point on Perpendicular Line**. If the point is below the
vertical line, move it up above. Select the perpendicular vertical line.

The first part helps you find answers to the key question.
- An activity is designed to help you build your own understanding
of the new concept and lead toward answers to the key question.

- **Examples** and **Solutions** demonstrate how to use the concept.

- A summary of the main new concepts is given in the **Key Ideas** box.

- Questions in the **Communicate the Ideas** section let you talk or write
about the concepts and assess whether you understand the ideas.

- **Practise**: these are straightforward questions to check your
knowledge and understanding of what you have learned.

- **Apply**: in these questions, you need to apply what you have learned
to solve problems.

- **Extend**: these questions may be a little more challenging and may
make connections to other lessons.

The last Apply question in each set of questions is designed to assess
your level of success with the section. Everyone should be able to
respond to at least some part of each 〈Try This!〉 question.

Numbered sections that have a green tab are based on the use of
technology such as scientific calculators, spreadsheets, or *The
Geometer's Sketchpad*®.

Some numbered sections are followed by a Use Technology feature.
This means some or part of the preceding section may be done using
the technology shown.

How does *Mathematics 8: Making Connections* help you learn?

Understanding Vocabulary

Key words are listed on the Chapter Opener. Perhaps you already know the meaning of some of them. Great! If not, watch for these terms highlighted the first time they are used in the chapter. The meaning is given close by in the margin.

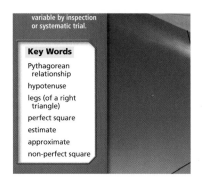

You have explored what is called the **Pythagorean relationship** . The sum of the areas of the squares on the two shorter sides, or **legs** , of a right triangle is equal to the area of the square on the **hypotenuse** .

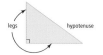

legs
• the two shorter sides of a right triangle
• legs meet at 90°

hypotenuse
• longest side of a right triangle
• opposite the right angle

Literacy Connections provide tips to help you read and interpret items in math. These tips will help you in other subjects as well.

> **Literacy Connections**
>
> **Writing Answers**
> Always include proper units in the final answer to any measurement problem.

Understanding Concepts

The Discover the Math activity is designed to help you construct your own understanding of new concepts. The key question tells you what the activity is about. Short steps, with illustrations, lead you to be able to make some conclusions in the last step, the **Reflect** question.

Discover the Math

How can you multiply integers using patterns?

Part 1: Multiply Opposite Integers

1. Copy and complete the multiplication statements to continue the pattern.

$4 \times 3 = 12$
$4 \times 2 = \blacksquare$
$4 \times 1 = \blacksquare$
$4 \times 0 = \blacksquare$
$4 \times (-1) = \blacksquare$
$4 \times (-2) = \blacksquare$

2. Describe the pattern. Explain how you used it to complete the last two multiplications.

3. Reflect

a) State a rule for multiplying a positive number by a negative number.
b) Would your rule hold for a negative number times a positive number? Explain.

11.2 Subtract Integers • MHR   **361**

The **Examples** and their worked **Solutions** include several tools to help you understand the work.

• Notes in a thought or speech bubble help you think through the steps.

• Sometimes different methods of solving the same problem are shown. One way may make more sense to you than the other.

• **Problem Solving Strategies** are pointed out.

• Calculator key press sequences are shown where appropriate.

Example 2: Apply Rates to Commission
Refer to Example 1. Devon hopes to earn $1000 by the end of the summer. What total value must he sell?

Total Sales

Solution
Method 1: Use Equivalent Ratios
40% commission means that he earns $40 for every $100 of sales.

$$\frac{\$40}{\$100} = \frac{\$1000}{\blacksquare}$$

Write the ratio commission sales

$$\frac{\$40}{\$100} = \frac{\$1000}{\blacksquare}$$ ×25

I need to find how many times larger $1000 is than $40.
1000 ÷ 40 = 25

$$= \frac{\$1000}{\$2500}$$

Multiply the denominator by 25.

To earn $1000 in commission, Devon must sell a total of $2500.

Method 2: Use Systematic Trial
40% is less than half. To earn a $1000 commission, Devon's total sales must be a little more than double $1000. Start by trying sales of $2200.

Strategies
Use a table or a chart to organize the trials.

Total Sales	Commission (40% of Total Sales)	
$2200	$880	Too low. C 2200 × 0.4 = 880
$2600	$1040	Just a little high.
$2500	$1000	That's it.

Devon must sell a total of $2500 to earn $1000.

The exercises begin with **Communicate the Ideas**. These two or three short questions focus your thinking on the **Key Ideas** you learned in the section. By discussing these questions in a group, or doing the action called for, you can see whether you understand the main points and are ready to start the exercises.

The first few questions in **Check Your Understanding** can often be done by following one of the worked Examples.

Key Ideas

■ The Pythagorean relationship connects the three sides of any right triangle.

■ The Pythagorean equation can be used to find the length of one of the sides of a right triangle if the other two sides are known.

$$c^2 = a^2 + b^2$$

Communicate the Ideas

1. **a)** Describe the steps you would use to find the length x.
   b) Estimate the value of x. Between which two whole numbers is it?

2. To find the length b, Crystal wrote

   $$b^2 = 10^2 + 8^2$$

   Is her method correct? If not, explain what she did wrong.

3. Darian wants to find the height, h, of this triangle. His method is to enter $\sqrt{81 - 49}$ into his calculator. Will his answer be correct? Explain why or why not.

Check Your Understanding

Practise
For help with questions 4 to 7, refer to Examples 1 and 2.

4. Find the length of the missing side in each triangle.
   a)   **b)**

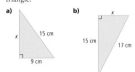

5. Find the length of the missing side in each triangle.
   a)   **b)**

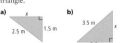

6. Find the length of the missing side in each triangle. Round your answers to the nearest tenth.
   a)   **b)**

What else will you find in *Mathematics 8: Making Connections*?

Two special sections at the beginning of the book will help you to be successful with the grade 8 course.

Problem Solving

This is an overview of the four steps you can use to approach solving problems. Samples of 12 problem solving strategies are shown. You can refer back to this section if you need help choosing a strategy to solve a problem. You are also encouraged to use your own strategies.

Problem Solving

How can you solve problems like the four below? Compare your ideas with the strategies that are shown on the following pages.

Problem 1
Dina's family owns and operates a small restaurant. They have many small square tables and folding chairs. What is the greatest number of people that can be seated when 10 tables are put together?

Problem 2
Amy's mother bought a basket of strawberries. Ben came in and ate half of them. Steve came home next and ate half of the remaining strawberries. Dora returned and ate half the number that remained. Amy came home last. She ate half of the remaining strawberries and left two whole strawberries for her mother. How many strawberries were orginally in the basket?

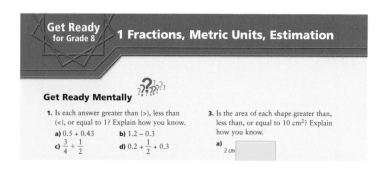

Get Ready for Grade 8

These six pages present a brief review of basic concepts from earlier grades and ways of thinking about the concepts.

Other Special Features

Did You Know?

The Canadian Shield is 500 million years old. It is made of Earth's oldest surface rock. That makes Canada one of the best places on Earth to find ancient craters.

Did You Know?

These are interesting facts related to math topics you are learning.

Making Connections

Types of Data

Data are any kind of mathematical information. Geometric data can tell about the location or shape of something. You will learn about other kinds of data in Chapters 9 and 10.

Making Connections

These activities link the current topic to careers, games, or to another subject.

18. Several Web sites provide proofs of the Pythagorean relationship. Go to www.mcgrawhill.ca/links/math8 and follow the links to find some of the proofs.

Internet Connect

You can find extra information related to some questions on the Internet. Log on to **www.mcgrawhill.ca/links/math8** and you will be able to link to recommended Web sites.

Each chapter ends with a **Chapter Review** and a **Practice Test**. The chapter review is organized by section number so you can look back if you need help with a question. The test includes the different types of questions that you will find on provincial tests: multiple choice, short answer, and extended response.

Task

These projects follow each pair of chapters. To provide a solution, you may need to combine skills from multiple chapters and your own creativity.

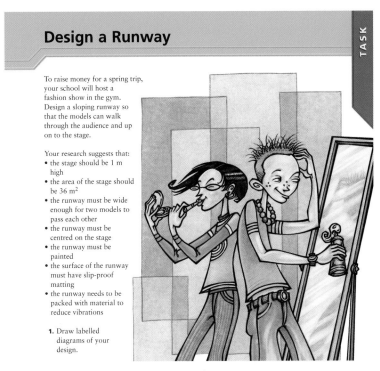

TASK

Design a Runway

To raise money for a spring trip, your school will host a fashion show in the gym. Design a sloping runway so that the models can walk through the audience and up on to the stage.

Your research suggests that:
- the stage should be 1 m high
- the area of the stage should be 36 m^2
- the runway must be wide enough for two models to pass each other
- the runway must be centred on the stage
- the runway must be painted
- the surface of the runway must have slip-proof matting
- the runway needs to be packed with material to reduce vibrations

1. Draw labelled diagrams of your design.

Reviews of the previous four chapters can be found following Chapters 4, 8, and 12.

Answers

Answers are provided to the odd-numbered Practise, Apply, and Extend questions, as well as, Reviews and Practice Tests. Sample answers are given for questions that have a variety of possible answers or that involve communication. If you need help, read the sample and then try to give an alternative response.

Answers are omitted for the Try This and the Chapter Problem questions because teachers may use these questions to assess your progress.

Glossary

Refer to the illustrated Glossary at the back of the text if you need to check the exact meaning of mathematical terms.

Problem Solving

How can you solve problems like the four below? Compare your ideas with the strategies that are shown on the following pages.

Problem 1

Dina's family owns and operates a small restaurant. They have many small square tables and folding chairs. What is the greatest number of people that can be seated when 10 tables are put together?

Problem 2

Amy's mother bought a basket of strawberries. Ben came in and ate half of them. Steve came home next and ate half of the remaining strawberries. Dora returned and ate half the number that remained. Amy came home last. She ate half of the remaining strawberries and left two whole strawberries for her mother. How many strawberries were orginally in the basket?

Problem 3

A road crew is repainting the solid yellow line down the centre of the road from Owen Sound to Tobermory. 1 L of the paint covers 4 m². How many litres of paint does the crew need?

Problem 4

Raj and his friend Matt live in a neighbourhood where the streets form a regular grid pattern. How many different routes are there from Raj's house to Matt's? Assume that Raj does not retrace his steps and always takes the shortest route.

People solve mathematical problems at home, at work, and at play. There are many different ways to solve problems. In *Mathematics 8: Making Connections*, you are encouraged to try different methods and to use your own ideas. Your method may be different but it may also work.

A Problem Solving Model

Where do you begin with problem solving? We suggest the following four-step process.

Understand

Read the problem.
• Think about the problem. Express it in your own words.
• What information do you have?
• What further information do you need?
• What is the problem asking you to do?

Plan

Select a strategy for solving the problem. You may sometimes need more than one strategy.
• Consider other problems you have solved successfully. Is this problem like one of them? Can you use a similar strategy? Strategies that you might use include

    – Make a picture or diagram   – Act it out
    – Make an organized list   – Use systematic trial
    – Look for a pattern   – Make an assumption
    – Make a model   – Find needed information
    – Work backward   – Choose a formula
    – Make a table or chart   – Solve a simpler problem

• Decide whether any of the following might help. Plan how to use them.
    – tools such as a ruler or a calculator
    – materials such as graph paper or a number line

Do It!

Solve the problem by carrying out your plan.
• Use mental math to estimate a possible answer.
• Do the calculations and record your steps.
• Explain and justify your thinking.
• Revise your plan if it does not work out.

Look Back

Examine your answer. Does it make sense?
• Is your answer close to your estimate?
• Does your answer fit the facts given in the problem?
• Is the answer reasonable? If not, make a new plan. Try a different strategy.
• Consider solving the problem a different way. Do you get the same answer?
• Compare your method with that of other students.

Problem Solving Strategies

Here are some different ways to solve the four problems on page xvi. Often you need to use more than one strategy to solve a problem. Your ideas on how to solve the problems might be different from any of these.

To see other examples of how to use these strategies, refer to the page references. These show where the strategy is used in other sections of *Mathematics 8: Making Connections*.

Problem 1

Dina's family owns and operates a small restaurant. They have many small square tables and folding chairs. What is the greatest number of people that can be seated when 10 tables are put together?

Strategy	Example	Other Examples

Make a picture or diagram

Make an organized list

Look for a pattern

Diagram	Number of Tables	Number of People
	1	4
	2	6
	3	8
	4	10

pages 36, 64, 402

pages 121, 127, 294

pages 187, 199, 215

When 10 tables are put together in a line, $4 + 2 \times 9$ people can be seated. This is 22 people.

> I can see a pattern. One table seats four people. With each extra table, two more people can be seated.

Look Back

> I should consider other possible arrangements of the tables.

When 3 tables are put together in an L-shape, 8 people can be seated. This is the same as when the tables are in a line.

When 4 tables are put together to form a square, 8 people can be seated. This is less than when the tables are in a line.

Conclusion: The greatest number of people that can be seated when 10 tables are put together is 22 people.

Make a model

> I got the same answer using square tiles for the tables and counters for the seats.

pages 18, 183, 249

Problem 2

Amy's mother bought a basket of strawberries. Ben came in and ate half of them. Steve came home next and ate half of the remaining strawberries. Dora returned and ate half the number that remained. Amy came home last. She ate half of the remaining strawberries and left two whole strawberries for her mother. How many strawberries were orginally in the basket?

Strategy	Example	Other Examples
Work backward **Make a table or chart**	Two strawberries were left for Amy's mother. The last person, Amy, must have eaten two. Half of 4 is 2. That's right. I will work backward from there.  | Person	Number Eaten	Remaining	Total
Amy	2	2	4
Dora	4	4	8
Steve	8	8	16
Ben	16	16	32 | **Look Back** Check that a basket containing 32 works. Ben: half of 32 = 16 Steve: half of 16 = 8 Dora: half of 8 = 4 Amy: half of 4 = 2 Mother: 2 16 + 8 + 4 + 2 + 2 = 32 It checks. There were 32 strawberries in the basket originally.	page 200 pages 167, 1688, 282,401
Act it out **Work backward**	Mother sees ● ● Amy sees ● ● ● ● Dora sees ● ● ● ● ● ● ● ● Steve sees ● ● ● ● ● ● ● ● ● ● ● ● ● ● ● ● So, Ben ate 16. I can act this out, using red counters to represent the strawberries. In the full basket, there were 32 strawberries.	pages 170, 215
Use systematic trial	Ben: half of 40 = 20 Steve: half of 20 = 10 Dora: half of 10 = 5 I'm going to guess and test. I will try 40 first. **Look Back** I need to change my starting number, because Amy would be eating $2\frac{1}{2}$ strawberries and leaving the same number for her mother. The problem says the mother got 2 whole berries. Since 2 is less than $2\frac{1}{2}$, I will start with a smaller number. When I repeat the steps with 32, I find it works perfectly. There were 32 strawberries in the basket originally.	pages 37, 38

Problem Solving Strategies

Problem 3	A road crew is repainting the solid yellow line down the centre of the road from Owen Sound to Tobermory. 1 L of the paint covers 4 m². How many litres of paint does the crew need?	

Strategy	Example	Other Examples
Make an assumption **Find needed information** **Choose a formula**	I'll assume that just one coat of paint is used. I need to find the distance from Owen Sound to Tobermory. I can use an Ontario road map. I can find the width of the centre yellow line by measuring one near my school.	page 233 pages 193, 233 pages 38, 69, 171, 254, 442

It is 113 km from Owen Sound to Tobermory.

The yellow line is 10 cm wide.
$A = l \times w$
$A = 113 \times 1000 \times 0.10$
$A = 11\ 300$
The area of the centre line is 11 300 m².

> The yellow line is approximately a long thin rectangle. I need to find its area. I am told that 1 L of paint covers 4 m², so I need to work in metres.
> 113 km = 113 × 1000 m
> 10 cm = 0.10 m

> Now I need to find how many litres of paint will cover 11 300 m². Each litre covers 4 m², so I need to divide the area by 4.

Number of litres $= \dfrac{11\ 300}{4}$
$= 2825$

To paint the centre line from Owen Sound to Tobermory, the crew needs approximately 2825 L of paint.

> I can use estimation to check that the answer is reasonable.

Look Back
Each kilometre is 1000 m.
1000 m × 0.10 m = 100 m²
For each kilometre, 100 ÷ 4 or 25 L of paint are needed.
So, for 100 km, 2500 L of paint are needed. This shows that the calculated answer is reasonable.

Problem 4

Raj and his friend Matt live in a neighbourhood where the streets form a regular grid pattern. How many different routes are there from Raj's house to Matt's? Assume that Raj does not retrace his steps and always takes the shortest route.

Strategy	Example	Other Examples
Solve a simpler problem	What if they lived one block apart?	pages 200, 234

Record the number of routes to get to each corner.

Look for a pattern

pages 361, 401

There are 2 possible routes in this case, each 2 blocks long.

What if they lived two blocks apart?

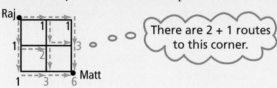

There are 2 + 1 routes to this corner.

There are 6 possible routes in this case, each 4 blocks long.

What if they lived three blocks apart?

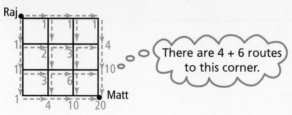

There are 4 + 6 routes to this corner.

There are 20 possible routes in this case, each 6 blocks long.

The last step: They actually live four blocks apart.

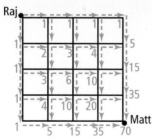

There are 70 possible routes in this case, each 8 blocks long.

Amazingly, there are 70 possible different routes from Raj's house to Matt's.

Get Ready Mentally

1. Is each answer greater than (>), less than (<), or equal to 1? Explain how you know.

a) 0.5 + 0.43   **b)** 1.2 − 0.3

c) $\dfrac{3}{4} + \dfrac{1}{2}$ **d)** $0.2 + \dfrac{1}{2} + 0.3$

2. Is the perimeter of each shape greater than, less than, or equal to 1 m? Explain how you know.

a)

10 cm

b)
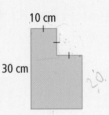
10 cm
30 cm

3. Is the area of each shape greater than, less than, or equal to 10 cm²? Explain how you know.

a)

2 cm
4 cm

b)
 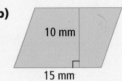
10 mm
15 mm

Get Ready by Thinking

1 g

1 cm

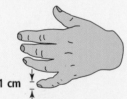
1 m

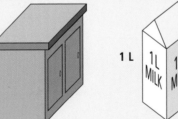
1 L

1 cm = 10 mm
1 m = 100 cm
1 g = 1000 mg
1 kg = 1000 g
1 L = 1000 mL

Choose the most reasonable estimate for each of the following. Share your estimates with a partner. Explain your thinking.

4. The volume of pop in a can is about

  A 250 mL   **B** 1.2 L
  C 350 mL   **D** 0.1 L

5. The height of a grade 8 student is about

  A 150 cm   **B** 0.6 m
  C 1800 mm   **D** 2.1 m

6. The thickness of a loonie is about

  A 0.5 cm   **B** 6 mm   **C** 0.1 m   **D** 2 mm

7. The mass of a lock is about

  A 500 g   **B** 150 g   **C** 50 mg   **D** 0.7 kg

8. The fraction of pizza that was eaten is about

  A $\dfrac{1}{5}$ **B** $\dfrac{1}{3}$

  C $\dfrac{1}{4}$ **D** $\dfrac{2}{3}$

Get Ready by Exploring

Materials
- centimetre grid paper
- scissors
- BLM Get Ready 8A Finger Puppets

9. Maya is designing some finger puppets for the drama club. She needs to cut two pieces of fabric for each puppet.

a) Determine the area of <u>felt</u> needed for each puppet. *32*

b) What do you notice about the areas? *the same*

c) What is the total area of felt used for these puppets?

10. For each puppet, Maya starts with a square piece of felt. She then cuts pieces from it and rearranges them. What is the area of the original square?

11. Look at the puppet designs on the worksheet. Show how the designs could be cut and rearranged back to squares.

Here are some hints to get you started on the first two puppets.
A: Cut and move one piece.
B: Cut and move one piece.

12. a) Draw a square with an area of 25 cm^2.

b) Design your own puppet by making two or three cuts and rearranging the pieces. Decorate your puppet. Draw another square to show your solution.

Get Ready by Reflecting

13. How is area different from perimeter?

14. Explain why Maya might want to know the perimeter of her puppets. Would they all have the same perimeter?

Get Ready Mentally

1. Write each fraction as a percent.

   a) $\dfrac{1}{2}$ **b)** $\dfrac{1}{4}$ **c)** $\dfrac{1}{5}$ **d)** $\dfrac{3}{5}$ $\times \frac{20}{100}$

2. Write each fraction as a decimal.

   a) $\dfrac{1}{4}$ **b)** $\dfrac{1}{5}$ **c)** $\dfrac{1}{10}$ **d)** $\dfrac{3}{10}$

3. Write each decimal as a percent.

   a) 0.25   **b)** 0.45   **c)** 0.9   **d)** 0.333

4. **a)** What does percent mean?
   b) Explain how to write a percent as a decimal.

5. Name three decimal numbers that are less than $\dfrac{1}{2}$.

Get Ready by Thinking

Origami is an ancient art. Square pieces of paper can be folded to form many different designs.

6. What is the area of a square piece of origami paper with each side length?

   a) 4 cm   **b)** 8 cm   **c)** 100 mm

7. Ashton is organizing his origami paper. What is the side length of a square piece with each area?

   a) 36 cm^2 **b)** 4 cm^2 **c)** 121 cm^2

8. What is the perimeter of a square piece of origami paper with each area?

   a) 16 cm^2 **b)** 25 cm^2 **c)** 49 mm^2

9. To make a paper crane, Kayle folds a piece of origami paper in half twice.

   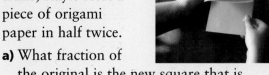

   a) What fraction of the original is the new square that is formed?
   b) Write your answer to part a) as a decimal and as a percent.

10. Shawana got 15 out of 20 marks for her design in an origami contest. Adwin got 19 out of 25 for precise folding. Explain how you could figure out who got the better mark.

Get Ready by Exploring

Elsa created a game called Math Spin for the Math Expo at school. To win, a player must spin the letters of the word MATH in the correct order.

Materials

• BLM Get Ready 8B Math Spinner

11. If you spin the spinner once, what is the probability that you will get each letter? Express each answer as a <u>fraction</u> and as a percent.

   a) a consonant
   b) the letter T

12. Aaliyah and Michael played the game. Their results are shown in the table.

Spin Number	Aaliyah	Micheal
1	Ⓜ	A
2	T	Ⓜ
3	Ⓐ	Ⓐ
4	H	A
5	Ⓣ	H
6	Ⓗ	Ⓣ

   a) Who won the game? How many spins did it take?
   b) What is the minimum number of spins needed to win a game of Math Spin?

13. **a)** Play Math Spin with a partner for 5 min. Record the results of each game, as well as the number of spins it took for someone to win, using a table.
   b) Determine the mean, median, and mode of the number of spins to win the game. Show your calculations.

14. Gather the game results from the whole class. Use them to repeat question 13b) for the whole class.

I already have an M. I have a one in four chance of getting an A on my next spin.

Get Ready by Reflecting

15. Is Math Spin a fair game? Explain how you know.

16. Describe how you could change this game so that it could be won in fewer spins.

Get Ready Mentally

1. List the next three numbers in each pattern.

a) 4, 9, 14, ...　　**b)** −2, −5, −8, ...

c) 1, 1, 2, 3, 5, ...　　**d)** 4, 2, 0, ...

e) 1, 4, 3, 6, 5, ...　　**f)** −15, −11, −7, ...

2. List the next three numbers in each pattern.

a) $\frac{1}{10}, \frac{1}{5}, \frac{3}{10}, ...$　　**b)** $\frac{1}{4}, \frac{1}{2}, \frac{3}{4}, 1, 1\frac{1}{4}, ...$

c) $3\frac{1}{2}, 3, 2\frac{1}{2}, ...$　　**d)** $\frac{1}{2}, -2, \frac{1}{3}, -3, \frac{1}{4}, ...$

Get Ready by Thinking

3. In each box, which number does not belong? Explain why.

a)

4	8	1
36	49	25

b)

2	11	13
5	3	6

c)

$\frac{2}{6}$	$\frac{4}{12}$	$\frac{3}{9}$
$\frac{6}{15}$	$\frac{10}{30}$	$\frac{7}{21}$

4. Each player at a chess tournament shakes hands once with every other player.

a) Copy and complete the table.

Number of Players	Number of Handshakes
1	0
2	1
3	3
4	
5	

b) Describe the pattern that relates the number of handshakes to the number of players.

c) How many handshakes would there be for 6 players? 10 players?

d) Describe the strategy you used to answer this question.

5. Squares can be divided into smaller squares using lines.

a) How many lines do you need to draw to get 36 smaller squares?

b) How many smaller squares will you get with 12 lines?

6. Describe what the number cruncher is doing to each set of numbers.

a)

In	Out
2	4
$\frac{1}{2}$	$2\frac{1}{2}$
−3	−1
7	9

b)

In	Out
3	5
6	11
$\frac{1}{2}$	0
10	19

Get Ready by Exploring

Ms. King asks each of her students to design a personal tile. The tiles will be joined together with clips at each vertex so that they can be displayed in the hallway.

Materials
• triangle dot paper

Ms. King arranged the tiles like this:

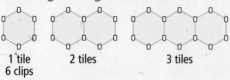

1 tile
6 clips

2 tiles

3 tiles

7. a) On triangle dot paper, sketch the arrangements for four to eight tiles, making sure to show the clips.

b) Copy and complete the table to show your results from part a).

Number of Tiles	Number of Clips
1	6
2	10
3	
4	
5	
6	
7	
8	

8. How many clips would Ms. King need for 12 students? Show two different ways to solve this.

9. a) Tiles cost $0.65 each and clips cost $0.07 each. How much would it cost to create a tile display for a class of 25 students?

b) Suggest another way to arrange the 25 tiles to save some money. Draw your arrangement on another piece of triangle dot paper.

10. a) What is the cost of your arrangement from question 9b)?

b) Describe some advantages and disadvantages of using your arrangement.

Get Ready by Reflecting

11. Describe a pattern that you have seen. How are the parts related? Explain using pictures, words, and numbers.

12. Write a paragraph about a real-life situation where you used a pattern to help solve a problem.

Measurement

- Interpret and evaluate measurement formulas.

- Define and measure radius, diameter, and circumference and explain their relationships.

- Develop the formulas for circumference and area of a circle.

- Estimate and calculate the radius, diameter, circumference, and area of a circle.

- Draw a circle given its area and/or circumference.

Geometry and Spatial Sense

- Construct a circle from various information.

Number Sense and Numeration

- Perform multi-step calculations, using calculators, and check them by estimation.

- Express repeated multiplication as powers.

Key Words

radius	r
diameter	d
circumference	C
pi	π

Measurement and Number Sense

Imagine you are strapped into this midway ride. As it spins faster and faster, your body presses against the back of the drum. You feel giddy and dizzy.

Why do many people think this ride is so much fun? How many times do you think the ride spins during the ride? How far do you think you travel during the ride?

In this chapter, you will develop formulas for circumference and area of a circle. You will estimate and calculate the radius, diameter, circumference, and area of a circle and draw a circle given its area or circumference.

Chapter Problem

How far will you travel each time the drum spins around once? What information do you need to answer this question?

Think about other circular midway rides you have ridden on. In this chapter, you will learn how to calculate circular measures for these rides.

Get Ready

Rounding With Units

To round a number, look at the digit to the right of the place value to which you are rounding. If the digit is 5 or greater, round up.

44.09 m rounded to the nearest tenth of a metre is 44.1 m.

> Look at the hundredths digit. 9 is greater than 5, so round the previous digit up.

13.2 cm rounded to the nearest centimetre is 13 cm.

> Look at the tenths digit. 2 is less than 5, so leave the previous digit as is.

1. Round to the nearest millimetre (mm).
   a) 25.6 mm   **b)** 4.336 mm

2. Round to the nearest hundredth of a kilometre (km).
   a) 2.485 km   **b)** 0.3109 km

3. Round to the nearest centimetre (cm).
   a) 37.605 cm   **b)** 0.89 cm

4. Round to the nearest tenth of a metre (m).
   a) 0.57 m   **b)** 1.27 m

Working With Ratios

A **ratio** is a comparison of two or more quantities with the same units. Ratios can appear in various forms. Suppose that your team wins 3 out of 4 of its games. The ratio 3 to 4 can be written as follows:

3:4   **ratio form**

$\dfrac{3}{4}$ **fraction form**

3 ÷ 4   **division statement**

5. A candy bag has 6 red and 4 blue jellybeans. Write the ratio of red to blue jellybeans in three different forms.

6. Rewrite each ratio.
   a) $\dfrac{5}{6}$, in ratio form
   b) 2 ÷ 5, in fraction form
   c) $\dfrac{5}{6}$, as a division statement
   d) 5:7, in fraction form
   e) 2 ÷ 13, in ratio form

Squaring a Number

The square of a number is the value of the number multiplied by itself.

$5^2 = 5 \times 5$
$= 25$ © 5 × 5 = 25. or © 5 x^2 25.

> Scientific and many graphing calculators have an x^2 button.

7. Evaluate.
  a) 3^2 **b)** 10^2 **c)** 2.5^2

8. Evaluate.
  a) 2.7^2 **b)** 0.3^2 **c)** 35^2 **d)** 100^2

Applying Area Formulas

Area is a measure of the space covered by a two-dimensional shape. The table gives the area formulas of some common shapes.

What is the area of this shape?

4.5 cm
8.0 cm

Shape	Name	Formula
	Square	$A = s \times s$ $A = s^2$
	Rectangle	$A = l \times w$
	Parallelogram	$A = b \times h$

Apply the formula for the area of a rectangle:

$A = l \times w$ **Substitute l = 8.0 and w = 4.5.**
$A = 8.0 \times 4.5$ **Substituted numbers are shown in red.**
$A = 36$

> That's about the size of a business card.

The area of the rectangle is 36 cm^2.

9. Find the area of each shape.
  a)
  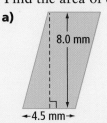
  8.0 mm
  4.5 mm
  b)
  1 cm
  1 cm

10. Find the area of each shape.
  a)
  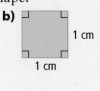
  6 mm
  10 mm
  4 mm
  7 mm
  b)
  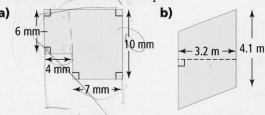
  3.2 m   4.1 m

Discover the Pi Relationship

Circles come in many different sizes. Every circle has a **radius**, a **diameter**, and a **circumference**.

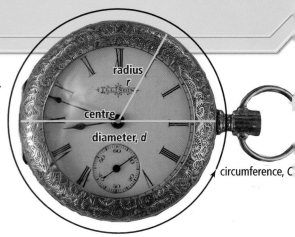

Discover the Math

Materials
- string
- scissors
- ruler
- paper and pencil
- circular objects

Optional:
- BLM 1.1A Discover the Pi Relationship

radius
- distance from the centre of a circle to the outside edge
- short form is r

diameter
- distance from one side of a circle to the other, through the centre.
- short form is d

circumference
- distance around a circle
- short form is C

Is there a constant relationship among measures of circles?

1. Choose five circular objects. Measure around the outside of each object. What measurement is this?

Place a piece of string around the outside of the object. Mark the length around the object.

Measure the length of the string.

2. Measure the maximum width of each object. What measurement is this?

Trace around the object to make a circle on a piece of paper.

Cut out the circle and fold it in half.

Measure across the fold.

3. Measure from the centre to the edge. What measurement is this?

Fold the circle in half again. Measure across the fold.

4. Record your measurements in a table like the one below.

Radius, r (cm)	Diameter, d (cm)	Circumference, C (cm)	$C \div d$
3.0	6.0	18.8	
5.5			

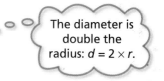

The diameter is double the radius: $d = 2 \times r$.

5. Reflect Look for any patterns or relationships.
a) Describe the relationships between C and d, d and r, and C and r.
b) Are these relationships constant? Explain.

Key Ideas

- The circumference of a circle is approximately three times its diameter.

- The ratio of the circumference to the diameter is constant for any circle. This constant value is called **pi**, often written as the symbol **π**.

- The value of π is approximately 3.14.

Communicate the Ideas

1. a) How many different ways can you measure a circle? What are these measures called?
b) The perimeter of any shape is the distance around its outside. How are the perimeter and circumference of a circle related?

2. If you increase the diameter of a circle, what happens to
a) the circumference?
b) the ratio of $C \div d$?

pi
- value of $\dfrac{C}{d}$
- short form is π

Literacy Connections

Writing Ratios
$\dfrac{C}{d}$ can also be written as $C \div d$.

Practise

3. State the diameter and the circumference of each circle.

a)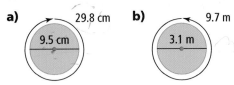
29.8 cm
9.5 cm

b)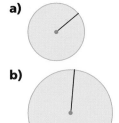
9.7 m
3.1 m

4. State the radius and the circumference of each circle.

a)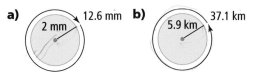
12.6 mm
2 mm

b)
37.1 km
5.9 km

5. Use string and a ruler to measure the diameter and the circumference of each circle.

a)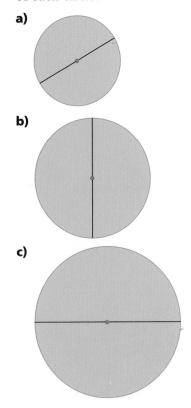

b)

c)

6. Calculate the circumference-to-diameter ratio for each circle in question 5.

7. Without measuring, what is the radius of each circle in question 5?

8. Use string and a ruler to measure the radius and circumference of each circle.

a)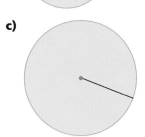

b)

c)

9. Calculate the circumference-to-radius ratio for each circle in question 8.

10. Without measuring, what is the diameter of each circle in question 8?

Apply

11. When you measure $C \div d$ for various circles, you might not always get exactly the value of π. Suggest reasons for this.

12. Find five circular objects in your classroom or at home.
  a) Describe a method for measuring the radius of each object.
  b) Use your method to measure each radius.
  c) Determine the ratio of circumference to radius for each circle by dividing $C \div r$.
  d) Compare your results with your prediction. Describe what you notice.

13. The playing area of a CD does not go all the way to the centre.

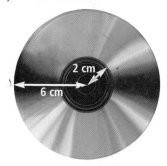

a) What is the ratio of the outside and inside radii?

b) How many times longer than the inside "track" of a CD is the outside "track"? Explain your reasoning.

14. Babylonian, Greek, and Egyptian mathematicians all estimated π. Research some of these early estimates. Use your local reference library, or go to **www.mcgrawhill.ca/links/math8** and follow the links.

Internet Connect

Did You Know?

Archimedes was the Greek mathematician who first recorded an estimate of π. He used polygons to show that π is between $\frac{223}{71}$ and $\frac{22}{7}$.

15. This dolphin pool has a circumference of 38 m. Estimate its diameter. Justify your choice of estimate.

 16. A circular garden has a pathway running through its centre. The pathway is 6.3 m long.
Try This!

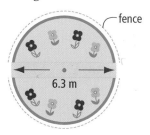

a) What is the radius?

b) Explain how you could determine the length of the fence around the garden.

c) Use your method to calculate the length of fence. Round your answer to the nearest tenth of a metre.

Extend

17. Soup cans usually have the same shape.

a) Predict which will be greater, the height of a soup can or its circumference.

b) Test your prediction using an actual soup can. Compare your findings with classmates.

c) Discuss reasons why the wrong prediction might be made in part a).

Circumference Relationships

Mousetrap-racers are a fun way to learn about design, motion, and math.

How far will a mouse-trap racer go if its wheels turn eight times? How does the size of the wheels affect the answer?

6 cm

Discover the Math

Materials
- string
- scissors
- compasses
- ruler
- paper and pencil

What formulas relate to circumference?

1. On a blank sheet of paper, draw a circle with diameter of your choice.

2. a) Explain how you can use the $C \div d = \pi$ relationship to find the circumference of this circle. Do not measure the circumference!

b) Use your method to calculate the circumference.

c) Measure the circumference.
Compare your answers to a) and b). Describe what you notice.

d) Does your calculation method work?
If not, try to improve it.

3. a) Use your method to calculate the circumference of a circle with a diameter of 18.0 cm.

b) Compare your answer with those of your classmates.

4. Reflect Explain how to find the circumference of a circle

a) if you know its diameter

b) if you know its radius

Example 1: Diameter and Circumference Formula

A "Pizza-Plus" has a thin string of cheese baked inside the crust. The string of cheese goes around the circumference of the pizza. What length of cheese is stuffed into the crust of the pizza? Round to the nearest centimetre.

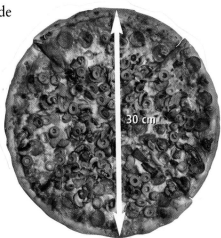

30 cm

Solution

Use the formula $C = \pi \times d$.
The diameter is 30 cm.

$C = \pi \times d$
$C = \pi \times 30$
$C = 94.247\ldots$
$C \doteq 94$

ⓒ π × 30 = 94.24777961

or

ⓒ 3.14 × 30 = 94.2

> This means the circumference is a bit more than 3 times the diameter.

Each pizza needs about 94 cm of cheese.

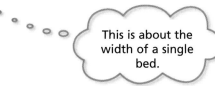

> This is about the width of a single bed.

Literacy Connections

Writing Answers
Always include proper units in the final answer to any measurement problem.

Literacy Connections

Reading ≐
The symbol ≐ means "is approximately equal to."

Example 2: Radius and Circumference Formula

Alysia is designing a mousetrap-racer for her science class.

a) Determine the circumference of each wheel. Round to the nearest centimetre.

b) How far will the mousetrap-racer go if the wheels spin eight full turns? Round to the nearest tenth of a metre.

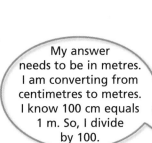

Solution

a) Use the formula $C = 2 \times \pi \times r$.
The radius of each wheel is 6 cm.

$C = 2 \times \pi \times r$

$C = 2 \times \pi \times 6$ Estimate: $2 \times 3 \times 6 = 36$

$C = 37.699...$

$C \doteq 38$

`c` `2` `×` `π` `×` `6` `=` `37.69911184`

The circumference of each wheel is about 38 cm.

b) *Method 1: Calculate the Distance*

The wheels will spin 8 times.
Multiply to get the total distance.

distance $= 8 \times 38$

         $= 304$

The total distance is 304 cm.
Convert to metres.

304 cm $= 3.04$ m

        $\doteq 3.0$ m

The mousetrap-racer will travel approximately 3.0 m.

> My answer needs to be in metres. I am converting from centimetres to metres. I know 100 cm equals 1 m. So, I divide by 100.

Method 2: Measure the Distance

• Take a single CD. Make a mark at one point on the circumference.

• Roll the CD carefully along a tape measure. Start with the mark at 0.

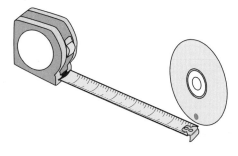

> **Strategies**
> Make a model

• Record the distance after eight complete rolls. Round to the nearest tenth of a metre.

The mousetrap-racer will travel approximately 3.0 m.

- If you know the diameter of a circle, you can calculate the circumference. Use the formula $C = \pi \times d$.

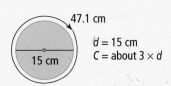

47.1 cm

$d = 15$ cm
$C = $ about $3 \times d$

15 cm

- If you know the radius of a circle, you can calculate the circumference. Use the formula $C = 2 \times \pi \times r$.

37.1 km

5.9 km

$r = 5.9$ km
$C = 2 \times$ about $3 \times r$

Communicate the Ideas

1. **a)** What formula could you use to calculate the circumference of this circle? Explain why.
   b) What other formula might you use? What would you have to do before using this formula?

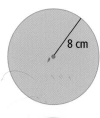

8 cm

2. **a)** What formula could you use to calculate the circumference of this circle? Explain why.
   b) What other formula might you use? What would you have to do before using this formula?

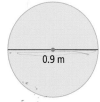

0.9 m

3. Suggest a method for finding the diameter of a circle if you know its circumference.

Check Your Understanding

Practise

Remember to include units of measure with all final answers. For help with questions 4 to 7, refer to Example 1.

4. Find the circumference of each circle. Round to the nearest centimetre.

a)

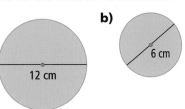

12 cm

b)

6 cm

5. A string of cheese goes around the circumference of a pizza. The pizza has a diameter of 20 cm. What length of cheese is stuffed into the pizza? Round to the nearest centimetre.

6. A string of cheese goes around the circumference of a pizza. The pizza has a diameter of 43.5 cm. What length of cheese is stuffed into the pizza? Round to the nearest tenth of a centimetre.

7. Find the circumference of a basketball hoop with diameter 0.5 m. Round to the nearest tenth of a metre.

For help with questions 8 and 9, refer to Example 2.

8. Find the circumference of each circle. Round to the nearest centimetre.

a)

b)

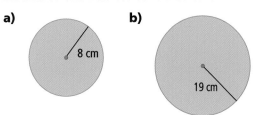

8 cm

19 cm

9. What is the circumference of a ring with radius 12 mm? Round to the nearest millimetre.

10. Find the circumference of each circle. Round to the nearest tenth of a metre.

a)

b)

0.9 m

2.5 m

c)

d)

3.3 m

4.7 m

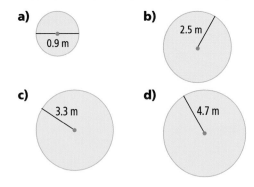

Apply

For questions 11 to 17, round your answers to the nearest unit.

11. A spoke of a bicycle wheel is 16 cm. What is the circumference of the wheel?

Chapter Problem

12. This midway ride rotates, spinning the passengers strapped in around its edge.

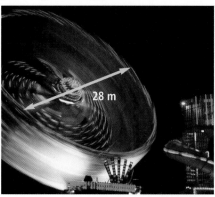

28 m

How far do passengers travel each time the ride spins once? Round to the nearest metre.

13. Here is a measurement problem, and Claudia's solution:

The diameter of a circle is 12 cm.
Find the circumference.
Solution
C = 2 x π x r
C = 2 x π x 12
C ≐ 75
The circumference is 75 cm.

What is wrong with Claudia's solution? How can she fix it?

14. Refer to Example 1. Ivan's favourite part of a "Pizza Plus" is the cheese-filled crust. His mother says that he can order either a large pizza or two small pizzas for himself and two friends.

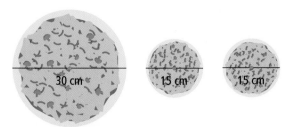

30 cm   15 cm   15 cm

a) Which option, if either, gives Ivan more stuffed cheese?

b) What else might affect Ivan's decision? Explain.

15. Refer to Example 2. Mateo and Yvonne are using old records for their mousetrap-racers. Mateo is using LPs, which have a diameter of 30 cm. His racer's wheels turn 5 times. Yvonne is using 45s, which have a diameter of 17.5 cm. Her racer's wheels turn 8.5 times. Whose racer travels the farthest?

Making Connections

The Race is On!

- Construct a mousetrap-racer using old CDs or card circles with radius 6 cm.
- Mark a point on the circumference of one front wheel.
- Use masking tape and a tape measure to create a start line and track.
- Place a ramp or a sloped stack of books just behind the start line.
- Position the racer on the ramp so that the mark on its front wheel touches the start line.
- Release the racer, and wait for it to come to a stop.
- Use your knowledge of circle relationships to calculate how many turns your racer's wheels have made.

16. The Saturn V moon rocket consisted of several stacked circular stages, of different diameters. The diagram shows these diameters.

Try This!

a) Name an object that is about 10 m long.
b) Find the circumference of each stage.
c) Why would an engineer need to know the circumference of each cylinder?

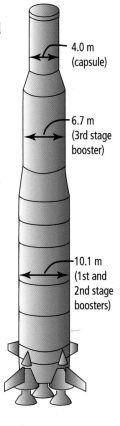

4.0 m (capsule)

6.7 m (3rd stage booster)

10.1 m (1st and 2nd stage boosters)

Extend

17. A semicircular outdoor theatre is being planned.

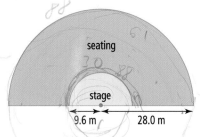

seating

stage

9.6 m   28.0 m

Each seat is to be a 0.5-m length of curved bench. How many more people can sit in the back row than in the front row? Describe how you found your answer.

1.3

Discover the Area of a Circle

Focus on...
- area of a circle
- estimating areas
- area formula for a circle

Lac a l'Eau Claire in Québec was formed around 300 million years ago when meteorites crashed to Earth. The photo shows the two circular craters that form the bed of this 20-m deep lake. Both craters have about the same diameter. About how much land does Lac a l'Eau Claire cover?

Discover the Math

How do you calculate the area of a circle?

1. Cassie drew a circle with radius 5 cm. She cut it up to estimate its area. What are the dimensions marked? Explain your answer.

2. Cassie then put the parts of her circle together, like this.

   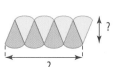

   a) Does Cassie's new shape have the same area as her original circle? Explain.

   b) What figure is closest to Cassie's new shape? How do you calculate the area of *that* shape?

   c) Use your answer to step 2b) to estimate the area of Cassie's circle.

3. **Reflect** Can you use Cassie's trick with any circle?

   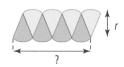

   a) Write an expression for the horizontal arrow in this diagram.

   b) Write a formula for the area of a circle with radius *r*.

   c) Explain whether you think your formula is approximate or exact.

Making Connections

You worked with area in Grade 7. What shape does the diagram in step 2 resemble?

Example 1: Calculate Area From Radius

Inga is planning to add a circular skylight to her home. She measures a radius of 1.5 m for the skylight. What will the area of the skylight be? Use this formula: $A = \pi \times r^2$. Round to the nearest tenth of a square metre.

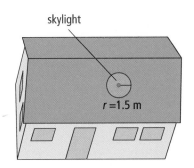

skylight

$r = 1.5$ m

Solution

$A = \pi \times r^2$

$A = \pi \times (1.5)^2$ $1.5^2 = 1.5 \times 1.5$

$A = \pi \times 2.25$

$A = 7.068\ldots$

$A \doteq 7.1$ $\boxed{c}\;\boxed{\pi}\;\boxed{\times}\;1.5\;\boxed{x^2}\;\boxed{=}\;7.068583471$

Inga's skylight will have an area of approximately 7.1 m².

Literacy Connections

Reading Squares
Read r^2 as
"r squared."
It means $r \times r$.

Example 2: Calculate Area From Diameter

Lac a l'Eau Claire is formed by two craters that are roughly circular.
Each crater measures about 3600 m across.
How much area does each crater cover?
a) in square metres?
b) in square kilometres?

Solution

a) The diameter is 3600 m. The radius is half the diameter.

$r = 3600 \div 2$

$r = 1800$

Apply the area formula.

$A = \pi \times r^2$

$A = \pi \times 1800^2$

$A = \pi \times 3\,240\,000$ Estimate: $3 \times 3\,240\,000 \doteq 10\,000\,000$

$A = 10\,178\,760.2$

$A \doteq 10\,000\,000$

Each crater covers approximately 10 000 000 m².

Literacy Connections

Reading Large Numbers
Read 10 000 000 as
"ten million."

b) The radius is 1800 m. Convert the radius to kilometres.

1800 m = 1.8 km

Apply the area formula.

$A = \pi \times r^2$

$A = \pi \times (1.8)^2$

$A = \pi \times 3.24$

$A \doteq 10.2$

Each crater covers approximately 10.2 km².

I am converting from metres to kilometres. I know 1000 m equals 1 km. So, I divide by 1000.

Key Ideas

- The area of a circle is about 3 times the square of its radius. Use this value to estimate the area of a circle before calculating it.

- To calculate the area of a circle, use the formula $A = \pi \times r^2$.

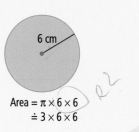

$$\text{Area} = \pi \times 6 \times 6$$
$$\doteq 3 \times 6 \times 6$$

Communicate the Ideas

1. a) What kind of units are used to measure area?
   b) Why are these units used?

2. Explain how you can calculate the area of this circle.

3. What value should you get if you divide the area of any circle by the square of its radius? Explain.

4 cm

Check Your Understanding

Practise

For help with questions 4 to 6, refer to Example 1.

4. Find the area of each circle. Round to the nearest square millimetre.

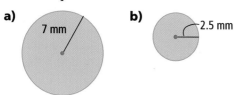

   a) 7 mm   b) 2.5 mm

5. A circular skylight has a radius of 0.8 m. What is the area of the skylight? Round to the nearest tenth of a square metre.

6. A circular porthole has a radius of 15 cm. What is the area of the porthole? Round to the nearest square centimetre.

For help with questions 7 to 9, refer to Example 2.

7. The Manicougan Crater in northern Québec is roughly circular. It measures 100 km across. How much area does it cover, in square kilometres?

8. Brent Crater in Algonquin Park, Ontario, is roughly circular. It measures approximately 4100 m across. How much area does it cover

   a) in square metres?
   b) in square kilometres?

Did You Know?

The Canadian Shield is 500 million years old. It is made of Earth's oldest surface rock. That makes Canada one of the best places on Earth to find ancient craters.

9. Find the area of each circle. Round to the nearest tenth of a square centimetre.

a)

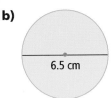

4 cm

b)

6.5 cm

10. Find the area of each circle. Round to the nearest square unit.

a)

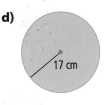

3 cm

b)

11 mm

c)

7 m

d)

17 cm

Apply

11. A circular skating rink has a diameter of 28 m. How much ice area is available for skaters?

Chapter Problem

12. This midway ride lies flat when it is not in operation.

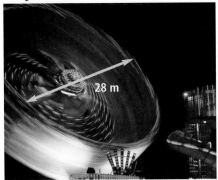

28 m

Suppose you need to make a rain cover for this ride. How big should the cover be? Use numbers, words, and pictures.

13. Nadia is playing golf. She estimates the diameter of a circular golf green at about 25 m. What is the area of the green? Round to the nearest square metre.

25 m

Try This!

14. a) Draw a circle on centimetre grid paper. Use the grid squares to estimate the area of the circle.

b) Measure the radius of the circle. Calculate the area of the circle, using the radius-area formula.

c) Compare your answers to parts a) and b). How close were they?

d) How could you improve your estimate from part a)?

Extend

15. The distance from the centre of the bulls-eye to the outer ring of a dart board is 17 cm. You can score points for any dart landing inside the outer ring.

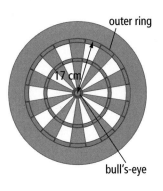

outer ring

17 cm

bull's-eye

a) How large is the scoring area? Round to the nearest square centimetre.

b) In one type of dart game, you must "double-in" to start collecting points. This means that your dart must land within a narrow band called the "double ring." How large is the area of the double-ring section?

double ring

17 cm 16 cm

c) Describe your method for part b). Can you think of another method? Explain.

Draw Circles Using a Set of Compasses

Circles are found in many places and often have many different meanings. They can be used to represent life cycles, seasons, and orbits. Some cultures use circles in their rituals and dances. How have you seen circles used in

• games and sports?
• artistic designs?

The photo shows a fabric design containing circles. How do you think the artist might have constructed the circles?

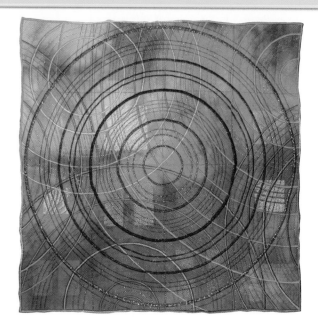

Discover the Math

How do you construct a circle using a set of compasses?

Example 1: Construct a Circle Given the Centre and the Radius

Draw a circle with a radius of 3 cm.

Solution

Draw a line segment 3 cm in length.

Choose one endpoint and let it be the centre of the circle.

Set the point of your compasses.   Construct the circle.

Example 2: Construct a Circle Given the Centre and a Point on the Circle

Draw a circle with centre A and passing through point B.

•
A

•
B

Solution

Copy the points A and B onto a sheet of paper.

Set the point of your compasses at the centre A. Adjust the compasses so that the circle will pass through point B.

Construct the circle.

- To construct a circle, given the centre and the radius,
  - set compasses to the measure of the radius
  - centre the compasses at the given centre
  - construct the circle

- To construct a circle, given the centre and one point on the circle,
  - centre the compasses at the given centre
  - set the compasses so that the circle will pass through the point
  - construct the circle

Communicate the Ideas

1. Use a set of labelled diagrams to show how to draw a circle with a radius of 4 cm.

2. Describe how you would construct a circle with centre C and passing through point P.

• P

• C

Check Your Understanding

Practise

For help with questions 3 and 4, refer to Example 1.

3. Draw a circle with each radius.

   a) 5 cm
   b) 30 mm
   c) 4 cm

4. Construct a circle with each radius.

   a) ———————
   b) ————————————
   c) ——————————————————

For help with questions 5 and 6, refer to Example 2.

5. Copy points A and B. Draw a circle with centre A passing through point B.

   a) • A   • B

   b) • B

      • A

6. Copy points C and D. Draw a circle with centre C passing through point D.

a)
   •   •
   D   C

b)
   •
   C
       •
       D

Apply

7. a) Copy this diagram on centimetre grid paper.

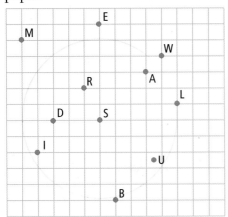

b) Construct a circle of radius 5 square widths. Centre it on point S.

c) Which points fall inside the circle? What word do they spell?

8. a) Copy this diagram on centimetre grid paper.

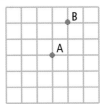

b) Construct a circle with centre A. The circle should pass through point B.

9. a) Draw a circle with a radius of 3 cm.

b) Find the circumference of this circle. Round to the nearest centimetre.

c) Find the area of this circle. Round to the nearest square centimetre.

10. a) Copy this diagram on centimetre grid paper.

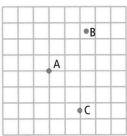

b) Construct all the circles you can, using pairs of points for centres and edge points. Describe any patterns you see.

11. Create a design using only circles with radii of 4 cm, 5 cm, and 7 cm. Colour your design.

Try This!

12. a) Draw a circle with a radius of 2.5 cm.

b) Find the circumference and the area of the circle.

c) Predict what happens to the circumference and the area of the circle if you double the radius.

d) Draw the new circle.

e) Find the circumference and the area of the new circle.

f) Were your predictions correct? Explain.

Construct Circles From Given Data

Many parks have a children's play area. How can you use math to find the best place to locate it?

Making Connections

Types of Data

Data are any kind of mathematical information. Geometric data can tell about the location or shape of something. You will learn about other kinds of data in Chapters 9 and 10.

Materials

• compasses

Recommended:
• centimetre grid paper

Optional:
• BLM 1.5A Construct Perpendicular Bisectors to Centre a Circle

Discover the Math

How do you construct a circle to fit geometric data?

Laurie, an environmental engineer, is working on some projects for a provincial park. One of her tasks is to locate a children's playground. Her planning team agrees that the playground should be the same distance from each of three camping areas, shown on the map.

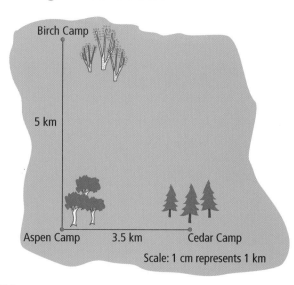

1. a) Make a copy of the map on a sheet of paper. Draw strongly enough that you can see your drawing through the back of your paper.

b) Estimate where the playground should be. Lightly mark the location on your map.

2. Laurie determines that the playground should be the centre of a circle that passes through the three campgrounds. Why is this true?

3. a) Fold your map so that Aspen Camp and Birch Camp exactly line up. Make a good crease.

   b) Unfold your map. Repeat step a) for Aspen Camp and Cedar Camp.

   c) Unfold your map. Mark the playground site where the creases cross each other. How close is this to your estimated position?

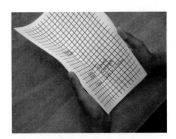

4. You need to check that the playground site you constructed is correct.

   a) Set the point of your compasses on the playground site.

   b) Adjust the pencil so that it passes through Aspen Camp.

   c) Complete the circle. How close does it come to the other two camps?

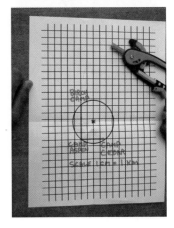

5. Reflect For steps 1 to 4, describe

   a) the geometric data you were given

   b) how you used the data to construct a circle

Key Ideas

- To construct a circle, given three points on the circle,
  - fold the paper so that one pair of points line up, and crease the fold
  - unfold the paper and repeat with a different pair of points
  - unfold the paper and centre the compasses at the constructed centre
  - set the compasses so that the circle will pass through any of the points
  - construct the circle, checking that it goes through all three points

Communicate the Ideas

1. Explain how you can find the centre of a circle if you know three points around the circumference.

2. After finding the centre of a circle using paper folding, Maria suggested another method. Is she correct? Explain how you know.

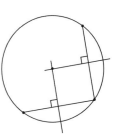

I found the centre a different way. I joined the points to form two line segments. Then, I used a ruler to measure and mark a point in the middle of each line segment. Then, I drew a line through each middle point crossing each line segment at right angles. The centre of the circle is the point where the two new lines meet.

Practise

3. Copy this diagram on centimetre grid paper.

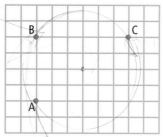

a) Find the centre of the circle that passes through points A, B, and C. Draw the circle.

b) Explain how you found the centre.

4. Copy this diagram on centimetre grid paper. Find the centre of the circle that passes through the three points shown.

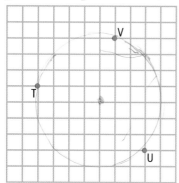

Apply

5. Stella, Mary, and Raman are writing a journal entry together about using three points to draw a circle. They can't agree what to say. Who is right, and why? Explain, using examples.

If there are three points, then there is always at least one way to draw a circle through them. **Stella**

I agree. **Mary**

You're wrong. It won't always be possible to draw a circle to join three points. **Raman**

6. a) Copy this diagram on centimetre grid paper.

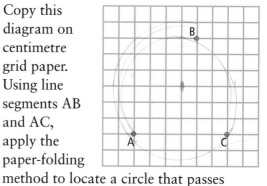

b) Using line segments AB and AC, apply the paper-folding method to locate a circle that passes through A, B, and C. Draw the circle.

c) Repeat part b) using line segments BC and AC. Describe what you notice.

7. The regional councils of three small towns decide that a water tower should be constructed at a location that is an equal distance from each town. Use the following information to draw a map that shows all three towns, and exactly where the water tower should be built.

• Elmwood is 12 km directly east of Drayden.
• Hargrove is 8 km directly south of Drayden.

Extend

8. An archaeologist has discovered the remains of an ancient wheel. Using mathematics, the archaeologist can determine the original size of the wheel.

a) Copy the diagram as accurately as possible.

b) Accurately reconstruct what the wheel looked like.

c) Find the circumference and the area of the wheel.

d) Describe your method.

Construct Circles Using *The Geometer's Sketchpad®*

Focus on...
• constructing circles

This is an alternative
to steps 3 to 5 on
page 31.

In this activity, you will use *The Geometer's Sketchpad®* to help Laurie locate the children's playground.

Part 1 Model the Park Layout

1. Open *The Geometer's Sketchpad®* and begin a new sketch.

2. From the **Edit** menu, choose **Preferences**. Set the preferences as shown.

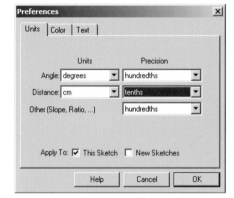

Materials

• computers
• *The Geometer's Sketchpad®* software

Alternatives:
• TECH 1.5A Construct Circles (GSP 4)
• TECH 1.5B Construct Circles (GSP 3)

3. Click on the **Point Tool**. Place a point near the bottom left corner of the screen.

4. Click on the **Text Tool**. Label this point A:
  • Click the point once to label it.
  • Click and drag the label if you want to adjust its position.

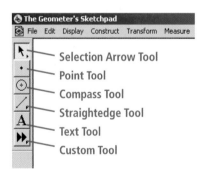

Technology Tip

• Holding the **Shift** key while dragging makes it easier to draw a vertical segment.
• Before you select a new object, make sure that you deselect first by clicking somewhere in the white space. Then, select the objects you want.

5. Click on the **Straightedge Tool**. Starting from point A, draw a vertical line segment. Label the top point as B.

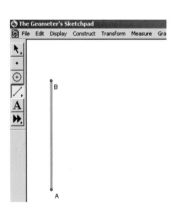

6. a) Choose the **Selection Arrow Tool**. An arrow will appear. Select points A and B by clicking on them with the arrow.

b) From the **Measure** menu, choose **Distance**.

c) Click and drag B until the distance AB equals 5.0 cm. It may be difficult to get the exact length. Try to keep AB perfectly vertical.

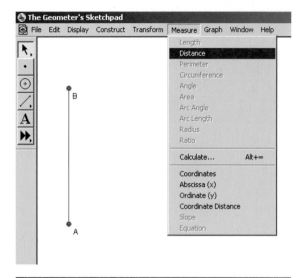

7. a) Draw a horizontal line segment from A, going right. Label point C.

b) Measure the distance AC. Click and drag C until this distance equals 3.5 cm.

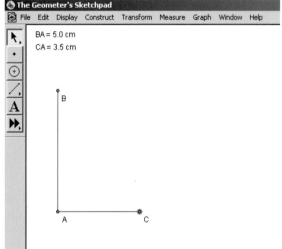

8. Suppose A, B, and C represent the three camping areas. Using the **Point Tool**, place a point D approximately where you think the playground should go.

9. Laurie determines that the playground should be the centre of a circle that passes through the three campgrounds. Why is this true?

10. a) Using the **Compass Tool**, *try* to draw a circle that passes through points A, B, and C.

b) How does this help you find the position of the playground?

c) Change your placement of point D if you want.

> **Technology Tip**
>
> • To delete an object, select it using the **Selection Arrow Tool**. Then, press the **Backspace** or **Delete** key. You can delete multiple objects at once. If you accidentally delete an object, select **Undo Delete Objects** from the **Edit** menu.

Part 2: Construct a Circle to Locate the Playground

Use your sketch from **Part 1**. Delete point D and any circles.

1. Select line segment AB. From the **Construct** menu, choose **Midpoint**. Label the midpoint D.

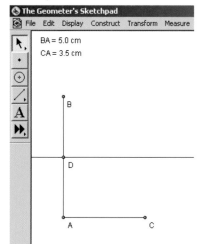

2. Select the midpoint and line segment AB. From the **Construct** menu, choose **Perpendicular Line**. A line should appear. This line divides the line segment AB exactly in half, crossing it at right angles. Deselect all these objects before you begin the next step.

Technology Tip

• Remember to deselect objects from the previous step before you begin the next one.

3. Construct the midpoint E on AC. Repeat step 2 for the midpoint and line segment AC.

4. **a)** Select the perpendicular lines from steps 2 and 3. From the **Construct** menu, choose **Intersection**. Label this point P.
   b) Why is point P important to Laurie?

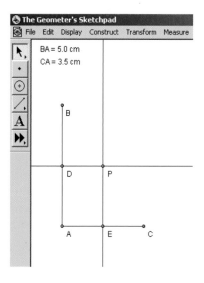

5. **a)** Select P and A, in that order. From the **Construct** menu, choose **Circle By Centre+Point**. Deselect.
   b) Describe what you notice about this circle.

6. **a)** Construct and then measure the line segments PA, PB, and PC. What do you notice?
   b) How are these distances related to the circle?
   c) Explain how these distances help Laurie place her playground.
   d) What special name can you give to PA, PB, and PC?

7. Suppose one of the campgrounds is moved. How will this change where the playground should go? Click and drag any of the points A, B, and C and describe what you notice.

Choose and Apply Circle Formulas

Focus on...
- circle formulas
- problems with circles
- systematic trial

Designs like this crop circle near Montréal, Québec, have been reported in farms all over the world. How they are created is often unknown. How could you find the diameter of this crop circle, if you knew the circumference?

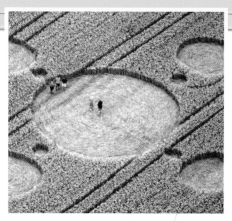

Discover the Math

Which formula do you use?

Example 1: Circumference From Radius

A child's wagon wheel has spokes 8 cm long. How far will the wagon travel in one turn of the wheels?

Solution

Each spoke connects the centre of the wheel to the rim. So, the radius is 8 cm. Apply the radius-circumference formula:

$C = 2 \times \pi \times r$
$C = 2 \times \pi \times 8$ — Estimate: $2 \times 3 \times 8 = 48$
$C = 50.265...$
$C \doteq 50$ — Round to the nearest centimetre.

The circumference is approximately 50 cm. The wagon will travel about 50 cm in one turn of the wheels.

$r = 8$ cm

I need the circumference. That's one full turn.

That's about the height of the seat of a kitchen chair.

Literacy Connections

Reading Math Problems
What data are you given? What are you being asked to find? How can the data help you?

Strategies
Make a picture or diagram

Strategies
Choose a formula

Example 2: Find the Diameter and Radius From the Circumference

The circumference of the large crop circle on the previous page is 120 m.

a) What is the crop circle's diameter, to the nearest metre?

b) What is the crop circle's radius?

Solution

a) $C = \pi \times d$.

(handwritten: 124 = 3.14 × d)

Multiply $\pi \times d$.

Use various possible values for the d variable.

Aim for an answer of about 120 m.

$\pi \times 40 = 125.663...$ **Too high.**

$\pi \times 38 = 119.380...$ **Very close.**

$\pi \times 39 = 122.522...$ **Not quite as close.**

To the nearest metre,
the closest value is $d = 38$.
The large crop circle has
a diameter of about 38 m.

The diameter should be about $\dfrac{120}{3}$ or 40. I will use 40 as my first guess.

b) The radius is half of the diameter.

$r = d \div 2$

$r = 38 \div 2$

$r = 19$

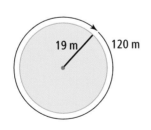

19 m   120 m

The crop circle has a
radius of about 19 m.

Example 3: The Cost of a Pathway

A circular garden has an area of 38 m². A flagstone
pathway is being built to run through the centre of the
garden. It costs about $12 per metre for the flagstones.
Determine the cost of the pathway.

38 m²

Solution

Understand

I must find the cost of the pathway. The pathway runs through
the centre of the garden. I need to find the diameter.

Plan

1. Use the area to find the radius.
2. Use the radius to calculate the diameter.
3. Determine the cost.

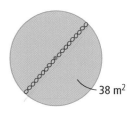

I will solve this
problem in three
steps.

Do It!

1. Use the area formula to find the radius.
Use $A = \pi \times r^2$. Try various values for r.
Keep trying until you get an answer close to 38 m².

Strategies
Choose
a formula

$\pi \times 10^2 = 314$ **Way too high.**   c π × 10 x² = 314.1592654

$\pi \times 3^2 = 28.3$ **Too low.**

$\pi \times 4^2 = 50.3$ **Too high. It's somewhere between 3 and 4.**

$\pi \times 3.5^2 = 38.48$ **Very close.**

Strategies
Use
systematic
trial

$\pi \times 3.4^2 = 36.30$ **Too low again.**

The area of a
circle is about
3.14 times the
square of its
radius.

The radius of the circle is 3.5 m.

2. Use the radius to calculate the diameter.

$d = 2 \times r$

$d = 2 \times 3.5$

$d = 7.0$

The diameter is twice
the radius.

The diameter is about 7.0 m.

3. Determine the cost.
Flagstones cost $12 per metre. Multiply by the length needed.
$12 \times 7 = 84$
The cost of the flagstones is $84.

Look Back

The area of the garden is 38 m². From the formula $A = \pi \times r^2$, r^2 is about
$38 \div 3$ or 12.7. The value 12.7 is the square of a number between 3 and 4,
so the radius is between 3 and 4. So, a diameter of about 7.0 m is
reasonable and the cost of $84 is also reasonable.

Key Ideas

- Summary of circle formulas:

Formula	Relationship
$C = 2 \times \pi \times r$	radius-circumference
$C = \pi \times d$	diameter-circumference
$A = \pi \times r^2$	radius-area

- If you are given the circumference of a circle, you can use systematic trial to find the diameter or the radius. Use the formula $C = \pi \times d$ or $C = 2 \times \pi \times r$.

- If you are given the area of a circle, you can use systematic trial to find the radius. Use the formula $A = \pi \times r^2$. Then, double the radius if you need to find the diameter.

Communicate the Ideas

1. The circumference of a bicycle wheel is 150 cm.
   a) Estimate the diameter and the radius.
   b) Explain how you found your estimates.

150 cm

2. Explain how to find the radius of a circle if you know
   a) its circumference
   b) its area

Check Your Understanding

Practise

3. Find the radius of each circle, to the nearest tenth of a unit.

   a)

   15.7 cm

   b)

   40.8 mm

4. Find the diameter of each circle, to the nearest unit.

   a)
   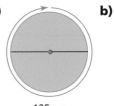

   125 cm

   b)
   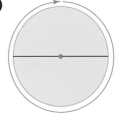

   58 m

5. Find the radius of each circle. Round to the nearest tenth of a unit.

a)

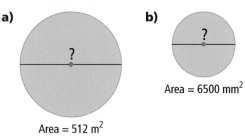

Area = 60 m²

b)

?

Area = 100 cm²

6. Find the diameter of each circle. Round to the nearest unit.

a)

?

Area = 512 m²

b)

?

Area = 6500 mm²

7. A circle has a circumference of 30 cm.

a) Find the diameter. Round to the nearest tenth of a centimetre.

b) Draw the circle. Label the diameter.

8. A circle has an area of 120 cm².

a) Find the radius. Round your answer to the nearest tenth of a centimetre.

b) Draw the circle. Label the radius.

Apply

For help with question 9, refer to Example 1.

9. A small wagon wheel has spokes 12 cm long. How far will the wagon travel in one turn of the wheels?

For help with question 10, refer to Example 2.

10. A crop circle has a circumference of 87 m.

a) What is the crop circle's diameter, to the nearest metre?

b) What is the crop circle's radius?

For help with question 11, refer to Example 3.

11. A circular garden has an area of 15 m². Cameron wants to build a flagstone pathway across the diameter of the garden. The flagstones he has chosen cost $15 per metre. What is the cost of the pathway?

12. A bicycle has spokes 16 cm long. How far will the bicycle travel in two turns of the wheels?

13. Marissa has two circular wooden tables. She wants to paint the top of each table. The radius of each table is 30 cm. What area will she need to paint?

Chapter Problem

14. A ferris wheel takes riders from ground level to a height of 20 m.

20 m

a) How far do they travel in one circle?

b) How far do they go in 10 circles?

15. A circular park has an area of 5000 m².

a) What length of fence is needed to surround the park?

b) What will it cost to build the fence if fencing costs $25 per metre?

16. A radio station claims that its signal reaches a broadcast area of 32 000 km².

   a) How far can you drive away from the transmitter before losing the signal? Round your answer to the nearest 10 km.

   b) Describe how you solved this problem.

17. To estimate the area of his circular garden, Bulwinder walks around the circumference. He walks 16 paces and estimates each pace is 1 m.

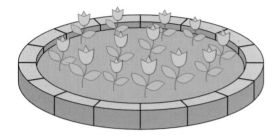

   a) What does Bulwinder's walk reveal about the size of the garden? Find as many measures as you can. Show your work.

   b) Can you find the area of Bulwinder's garden? Explain how.

18. Shi-Anne's cottage is on the shores of Circle Lake. Shi-Anne's cottage and Sonja's cottage are on opposite sides of this circular lake. It is a 2.5-km walk along the shoreline between the cottages.

   a) How far must Shi-Anne swim across the lake to get to Sonja's? Use pictures and words to show how you know.

   b) In one hour, Shi-Anne can swim 1.5 km, and walk 3 km. Which way is faster? Justify your answer.

19. Maria and her younger brother Chico are racing at a circular park with a circumference of 250 m. Because Maria can run twice as fast as Chico, they agree on these rules.

   • Maria will run once along the path around the circumference of the park.

   • Chico will run along the diameter and back.

   a) Is this fair? Justify your answer with appropriate calculations and diagrams.

   b) What method did you use to solve this problem?

   c) Describe another method you could use.

20. a) Create a circle problem involving area, circumference, radius, and/or diameter.

   b) Solve the problem.

   c) Trade with a partner and solve each other's problem.

   d) Describe how you could modify your problem to make it more challenging.

Extend

22. Bippy the hamster runs 42 m every morning on his hamster wheel. In the course of Bippy's workout, his wheel spins 75 times. Determine the circumference and radius of Bippy's hamster wheel, to the nearest tenth of a centimetre. Explain your method.

23. The second hand on a clock extends from the centre of the clock to the numerals. The tip of the second hand travels 2 cm every second.

   a) What is the length of the second hand?

   b) Explain how you solved this problem.

Key Words

Copy and complete each statement.

1. The ▨▨▨▨ of a circle can be calculated using the formula ▨ = π × r^2.

2. The ratio $\dfrac{\text{circumference}}{\text{▨▨▨▨▨▨}}$ is equal to 2 × π.

3. To calculate the ▨▨▨▨▨▨▨▨ of a circle from its area, find the ▨▨▨▨▨▨, and then multiply by 2.

1.1 Discover the Pi Relationship, pages 12–15

4. Use string and a ruler to measure the circumference and diameter of each circle.

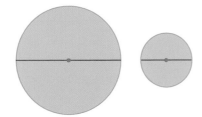

5. a) Predict the ratio $\dfrac{C}{d}$ for each circle in question 4.

   b) Calculate $\dfrac{C}{d}$ for each circle in question 4. Compare the answer with your prediction.

1.2 Circumference Relationships, pages 16–21

6. The spokes on Jesse's unicycle wheel are 0.4 m long.

   a) What is the circumference of the wheel? Round your answer to the nearest tenth of a metre.

   b) Jesse wants to travel 10.0 m. How many revolutions must he remain balanced for?

   c) Explain how you solved parts a) and b).

7. A circular swimming pool has a circumference of 50 m. How far is it to swim straight across, through the centre? Round your answer to the nearest metre.

1.3 Discover the Area of a Circle, pages 22–25

8. The Zamboni® 700 ice resurfacer has a 244-cm spinning blade. How much area does the blade shave each time it spins?

9. Ryan is buying a pool cover for his swimming pool. What area needs to be covered? Round your answer to the nearest square metre.

1.4 Draw Circles Using a Set of Compasses, pages 26–29

10. Draw a circle with each radius.

   a) 5.5 cm

   b) 37 mm

11. Construct a circle with each radius.

   a) ——————————

   b) ————————————

12. Copy this diagram on centimetre grid paper. Construct a circle with centre A and a radius of 4 square widths. Does point B lie inside or outside the circle?

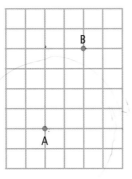

1.5 Construct Circles From Given Data, pages 30–32

13. Copy this diagram on centimetre grid paper.

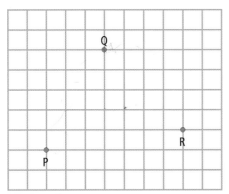

a) Find the centre of the circle that passes through points P, Q, and R. Draw the circle.

b) Explain how you found the centre.

14. Three towns are located as shown on the grid. Suppose you would like to build a gas station that is an equal distance from each town.

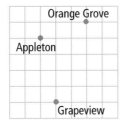

a) Copy the diagram on a sheet of grid paper.

b) Find the location for the gas station.

c) Explain why this point is at the centre of a circle that passes through all three towns.

1.6 Choose and Apply Circle Formulas, pages 36–41

15. A sprinkler can spray water a maximum distance of 8 m in all directions. What area of lawn can this sprinkler water? Round your answer to the nearest square metre.

16. A pathway around a circular garden is 28 m long. Sketch a diagram. Find the diameter, radius, and area of this garden. Round each measure to the nearest unit. Label all measures on your diagram.

17. In pottery class, Marcus plans to make a circular plate with a minimum area of 200 cm^2. He wonders what diameter he should plan for.

a) Determine the minimum diameter of the plate. Round your answer to the nearest centimetre.

b) Describe each stage of your problem-solving approach to this question.

18. A new "mega-size" pizza costs $29.99. The pizza company wants to get $0.02 per square centimetre of pizza.

a) How much area should the pizza cover?

b) What should be the pizza's diameter, to the nearest centimetre?

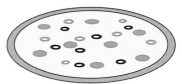

Practice Test

Strand	NSN	MEA	GSS	PA	DMP
Questions	4–7, 12, 13	1–7, 12, 13	8–11		

Multiple Choice

For questions 1 to 4, choose the best answer.

1. The circumference of the circle is

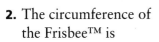

A 20 cm

B 31 cm

C 63 cm

D 314 cm

2. The circumference of the Frisbee™ is

A 38 cm

B 56 cm

C 62 cm

D 75 cm

3. The ratio $\dfrac{\text{circumference}}{\text{diameter}}$ is equal to

A π

B 2 × π

C π × d

D 2 × π × r

4. A circular pen is constructed to hold cattle. The radius of the pen is 18 m. What area do the cattle have?

A 57 m²

B 113 m²

C 324 m²

D 1018 m²

Short Answer

5. A decorative lunch plate has a diameter of 36 cm. What is its area? Round your answer to the nearest square centimetre.

6. A circular window has a diameter of 3 m.

a) Trim costs $6.50 per metre. What will it cost to put a trim around the window?

b) Glass costs $20 per square metre. What will it cost to replace the glass in the window?

7. Bim the cat likes to chase a piece of tinfoil attached to a piece of string. Bim trains his pet human to swing the tinfoil in a circular path with a radius of 1.0 m.

a) How far does Bim run each lap?

b) How many laps must Bim run in order to complete his 50-m workout?

c) What area must Bim have his pet human keep clear of obstacles? Round your answer to the nearest tenth.

8. Draw a circle with this radius.

_____

9. A circle is centred on A and passes through B. What would happen to the circle if

a) B moved away from A?

b) A moved toward B?

10. a) Describe how you can construct a circle that passes through three given points.

b) Think of an example. Use it to show how your method works.

11. Draw a circle with each radius.

a) 42 mm

b) 7.5 cm

12. a) What is the radius of a circular swimming pool that has an area of 64 m²? Show your answer to the nearest metre.

b) How far will you swim if you go across the pool and back once?

Extended Response

13. At a marine-wildlife park, dolphins play in a circular pool with a surface area of 119 m². You can also go downstairs and watch the dolphins through a glass wall.

a) What length of glass is needed to surround the pool? Round your answer to the nearest metre.

b) If the viewing windows are 2 m high, what is the total area of glass required? Round your answer to the nearest square metre.

c) Describe how you solved parts a) and b).

Chapter Problem Wrap-Up

Report on a circular midway ride of your choice.

For information about midway rides, go to **www.mcgrawhill.ca/links/math8** and follow the links.

1. Decide and explain what the ride does.

2. Calculate all the circular measures of the ride.

3. Compare your ride to the other rides discussed in this chapter. Describe any similarities and differences.

Geometry and Spatial Sense
• Investigate, explain, and apply the Pythagorean relationship.

Number Sense and Numeration
• Understand that the square roots of non-perfect squares are approximations.

• Estimate square roots without a calculator.

• Find approximate square roots using a calculator.

• Use estimation to justify the reasonableness of calculations.

Measurement
• Interpret and evaluate the use of measurement formulas.

Patterning and Algebra
• Solve first degree equations in one variable by inspection or systematic trial.

Key Words

Pythagorean relationship

hypotenuse

legs (of a right triangle)

perfect square

estimate

approximate

non-perfect square

Two-Dimensional Geometry

Geometry is an essential part of any construction project. Triangles are used in construction because they provide strength and stability. Right triangles are particularly important in building houses. Builders use a special property of their sides to ensure that walls meet at right angles.

In this chapter, you will explore how the sides of a right triangle are related. You will apply this relationship to solve problems.

Chapter Problem

You are given a piece of wood 100 cm in length. You are allowed to cut the stick of wood once, to make two pieces. How can you use the two pieces of wood to build a kite? If you glue a sheet of kite paper on one side of your frame, what will the perimeter of the kite paper be? What will its area be?

In this chapter, you will explore different possible kites.

Get Ready

Classify Triangles

Triangles can be classified according to the lengths of their sides as well as the types of angles they contain.

equilateral triangle
- three equal sides

isosceles triangle
- two equal sides

scalene triangle
- no equal sides

acute triangle
- three acute angles

right triangle
- one right angle

obtuse triangle
- one obtuse angle

1. Classify each triangle in two ways: by its sides and by its angles.

a)

b)

2. How are these two triangles alike? How do they differ?

Squares and Square Roots

The **square** of a number is calculated by multiplying the number by itself.

The square of 3 is 3^2. Its value is 3×3 or 9. Reversing the process, the **square root** of 9 is 3. This is written as $\sqrt{9} = 3$.

3. What is the value of each square?

a) 5^2 b) 7^2
c) 2^2 d) 8^2

4. What is the value of each square root?

a) $\sqrt{4}$ b) $\sqrt{25}$
c) $\sqrt{49}$ d) $\sqrt{100}$

Perimeter and Area of a Square and of a Triangle

The **perimeter** of a shape is the distance around the outside. The **area** is the number of square units of space covered.

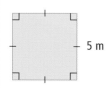

5 m

$P = 5 + 5 + 5 + 5$ or $P = 4 \times 5$
$P = 20$

The perimeter of the square is 20 m.

$A = l \times w$ or $A = s^2$
$A = 5 \times 5$ $A = 5^2$
$A = 25$

The area of the square is 25 m².

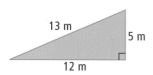

13 m   5 m

12 m

$P = 5 + 12 + 13$
$P = 30$

The perimeter of the triangle is 30 m.

$A = b \times h \div 2$
$A = 12 \times 5 \div 2$
$A = 60 \div 2$
$A = 30$

The area of the triangle is 30 m².

5. Find the perimeter and the area of each square.

a)

b)

7 m

11 cm

6. Find the perimeter and the area of each triangle.

a)

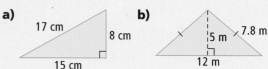

17 cm   8 cm

15 cm

b)

5 m   7.8 m

12 m

Solve Equations

Solve for x.

     a) $x + 7 = 12$ **By inspection, 5 + 7 = 12.**
        $x = 5$

     b) $25 = 16 + x$ **By inspection, 25 = 16 + 9.**
        $x = 9$

7. Solve for x.
   a) $x + 10 = 18$ b) $x + 15 = 24$
   c) $4 + x = 16$ d) $12 + x = 25$

8. Solve for x.
   a) $20 = 9 + x$ b) $36 = x + 20$
   c) $32 = x + 16$ d) $81 = x + 49$

Discover the Pythagorean Relationship

Literacy Connections

In music, a chord is a combination of three or more notes sounded together in harmony. The notes sound pleasing when played together.

Pythagoras (about 580–500 B.C.E.) was the leader of a group of people called the Pythagoreans. They believed that patterns in whole numbers could be used to explain the universe. They searched to find such patterns in geometry, astronomy, and music.

Pythagoras and this guitarist have something in common. Pythagoras experimented with stringed instruments, looking for ratios of lengths that would produce pleasing sounds when played together. He discovered the octave, and the perfect fourth and fifth chords. These chords are widely used in popular music.

Discover the Math

Materials
- ruler
- protractor
- centimetre grid paper
- scissors
- tape

Optional:
- BLM 2.1A Pythagorean Relationship Recording Sheet

What is the Pythagorean relationship?

1. Draw and cut out each set of squares from centimetre grid paper. Write the area, in square centimetres, on each square piece.
- 3 cm by 3 cm, 4 cm by 4 cm, and 5 cm by 5 cm
- 5 cm by 5 cm, 12 cm by 12 cm, and 13 cm by 13 cm
- 6 cm by 6 cm, 8 cm by 8 cm, and 10 cm by 10 cm
- 4 cm by 4 cm, 5 cm by 5 cm, and 6 cm by 6 cm
- 4 cm by 4 cm, 12 cm by 12 cm, and 14 cm by 14 cm

2. Make a triangle with each set of three squares. Arrange the three squares so that one side of each square forms a side of the triangle. Tape each arrangement onto a piece of paper.

3. Use a protractor, or the corner of a piece of paper, to determine whether or not any of the triangles contain a right angle.

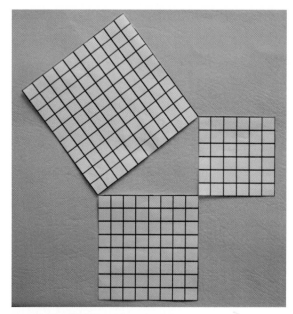

4. Copy and complete the table based on your observations of the five triangles.

Triangle Sides (cm)			Areas of Squares on Sides (cm²)			Type of Triangle (right, acute, or obtuse)
3	4	5				
5	12	13				
6	8	10				
4	5	6				
4	12	14				

5. Reflect Look for a pattern in your results.

a) Consider the first three triangles. Compare the areas of the squares on the sides of each triangle. Write a sentence to describe the relationship among them.

b) Now, examine the last two triangles. Does the relationship for the first three triangles hold for these two? How are these triangles different from the first three?

You have explored what is called the **Pythagorean relationship** . The sum of the areas of the squares on the two shorter sides, or **legs** , of a right triangle is equal to the area of the square on the **hypotenuse** .

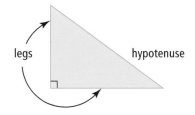

legs
• the two shorter sides of a right triangle
• legs meet at 90°

hypotenuse
• longest side of a right triangle
• opposite the right angle

Example 1: Find the Area of the Square on the Hypotenuse

A square is drawn on each side of $\triangle ABC$. Find the area of the square on side AC.

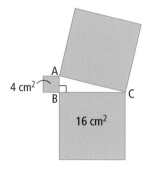

AC is the longest side. It is the hypotenuse. I can use the Pythagorean relationship.

Solution

$AB^2 + BC^2 = AC^2$

$4 + 16 = AC^2$

$20 = AC^2$

The area of the square on side AC is 20 cm².

Example 2: Find the Area of the Square on a Leg of a Right Triangle

A square is drawn on each side of $\triangle PQR$. Find the area of the square on side PQ.

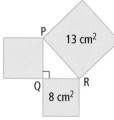

Solution

$QR^2 + PQ^2 = PR^2$ **Write the Pythagorean relationship.**

$8 + PQ^2 = 13$

$PQ^2 = 5$ **By inspection, 8 + 5 = 13.**

The area of the square on side PQ is 5 cm².

Strategies
How can you use systematic trial to solve the equation?

Key Ideas

- The Pythagorean relationship relates the areas of the squares on the three sides of a right triangle.

- The sum of the areas of the squares on the two legs of a right triangle is equal to the area of the square on the hypotenuse.

  $BC^2 + CA^2 = BA^2$

Communicate the Ideas

1. What property must a triangle have in order for the Pythagorean relationship to be true? Explain how you came to this conclusion.

2. Does the size of the right triangle affect whether the Pythagorean relationship holds true?

3. Three squares are placed together as shown. Marsha says "Triangle ABC looks like a right triangle to me." Explain how you know that △ABC is not a right triangle. Use your knowledge of the Pythagorean relationship.

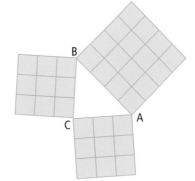

Check Your Understanding

Practise

For help with questions 4 and 5, refer to Example 1.

4. What is the area of the square on the hypotenuse of each triangle?

a)

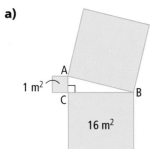

b)

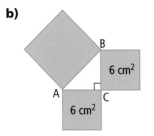

5. Find the area of the square on the hypotenuse of each triangle.

a)

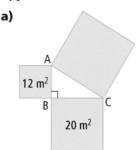

b)

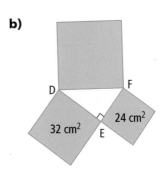

For help with questions 6 and 7, refer to Example 2.

6. What is the area of the square on the third side of each triangle?

a)

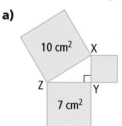

b)

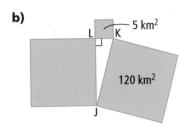

7. Find the area of the square on the third side of each triangle.

a)   **b)**

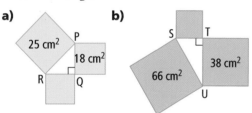

8. In each figure,
- identify the hypotenuse
- use the Pythagorean relationship to find the missing area

a)   **b)**

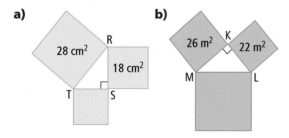

9. In a right triangle, what is the area of the square on the hypotenuse if the areas of the squares on the legs are as follows?

a) 11 cm² and 15 cm²
b) 10 m² and 4 m²
c) 7 cm² and 21 cm²
d) 26 km² and 13 km²

Apply

10. For which of the following sets of three squares does the Pythagorean relationship hold? Show your work.

a) 10 cm², 4 cm², 14 cm²
b) 3 cm², 12 cm², 16 cm²
c) 5 cm², 27 cm², 22 cm²
d) 21 cm², 2 cm², 19 cm²

11. The square on the hypotenuse of a right triangle has an area of 34 cm². The square on one of the other sides has an area of 17 cm².

a) What is the area of the square on the remaining side?
b) What other way can you classify this right triangle?

12. Does the Pythagorean relationship hold true for a right triangle with side lengths that are not all whole numbers? Give your reasoning and provide examples to illustrate your answer.

13. Larry drew a triangle with side lengths of 5 cm, 7 cm, and 9 cm. Find the areas of the squares on the three sides of the triangle. Is the triangle a right triangle? Explain why or why not.

14. The areas of the squares on two sides of a right triangle are 26 cm² and 40 cm². What are the possible areas for the square on the third side? Draw sketches to support your answers.

15. Kara has several square stickers of four different sizes, as shown.

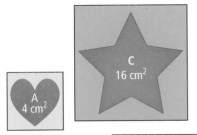

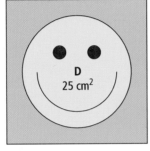

Kara is curious whether she can place any three of her stickers together to form a right triangle. Solve this problem for her. Use diagrams to show your answer.

Extend

16. Does the Pythagorean relationship work with a shape, other than a square, drawn on the sides of a right triangle? Investigate this question with either paper and pencil or *The Geometer's Sketchpad®*.

17. The Pythagorean relationship is named after the Greek mathematician, Pythagoras, but it is likely that the Babylonians and ancient Chinese knew the relationship hundreds of years earlier. Research the history of the Pythagorean relationship. Why was Pythagoras given the credit for the relationship?

18. Several Web sites provide proofs of the Pythagorean relationship. Go to **www.mcgrawhill.ca/links/math8** and follow the links to find some of the proofs.

Internet Connect

Making Connections

A concept map is a graphic representation of properties or relationships that help you organize and clarify information. To create a concept map, you must think about the concepts and how they are related to each other.

Copy and complete this concept map by replacing each ■ with the appropriate number.

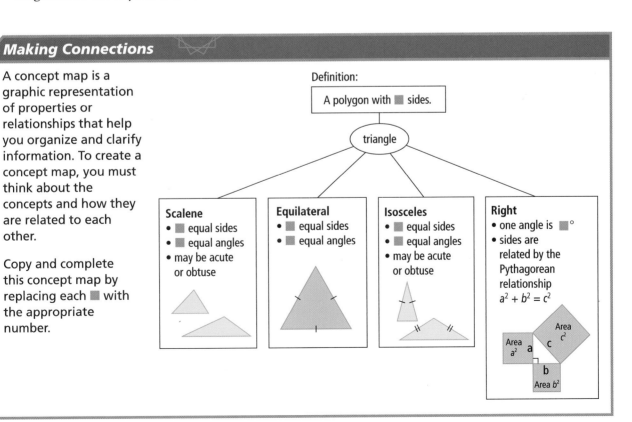

Definition:

A polygon with ■ sides.

triangle

Scalene
- ■ equal sides
- ■ equal angles
- may be acute or obtuse

Equilateral
- ■ equal sides
- ■ equal angles

Isosceles
- ■ equal sides
- ■ equal angles
- may be acute or obtuse

Right
- one angle is ■°
- sides are related by the Pythagorean relationship $a^2 + b^2 = c^2$

Explore the Pythagorean Relationship Using *The Geometer's Sketchpad®*

1. Open *The Geometer's Sketchpad®* and begin a new sketch.

2. Construct a right triangle.

    a) Use the **Straightedge** tool to create a horizontal line segment. Select the line segment and one endpoint. From the **Construct** menu, choose **Perpendicular Line**. Select the new line. From the Construct menu choose **Point on Perpendicular Line**. If the point is below the vertical line, move it up above. Select the perpendicular vertical line.

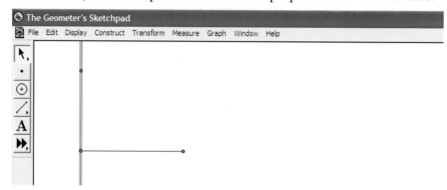

Materials

• computers
• *The Geometer's Sketchpad®* software

Alternatives:

• TECH 2.1A Explore the Pythagorean Relationship (GSP 4)
• TECH 2.1B Explore the Pythagorean Relationship (GSP 3)

    b) From the **Display** menu, choose **Hide Perpendicular Line**. Select the three points. From the **Construct** menu, choose **Segments**.

3. Use the **Selection Arrow** to select all three line segments and all three points. From the **Display** menu, choose **Show Label**. Use the text tool to change the labels to read *a*, *b*, and *c*, as shown.

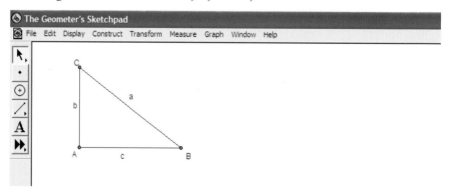

Technology Tip

• Before you select a new object, make sure that you deselect first by clicking somewhere in the white space.

Look for a relationship between the three sides.

4. Use the **Selection Arrow** to point and click on line segment *a*. From the **Measure** menu, choose **Length**. The length of *a* is displayed on the screen. Similarly, find the lengths of the other two sides, *b* and *c*.

5. a) Use the **Selection Arrow** to point and click on the measure of line segment *a*. From the **Measure** menu, choose **Calculate**. A calculator window appears.

b) Under **Values**, click on *a*. Click on the multiplication symbol, *. Click on *a* again. Then, click **OK**. The computer calculates and displays the value for $a \times a$, or the square of the length of line segment *a*.

Repeat for line segments *b* and *c*.

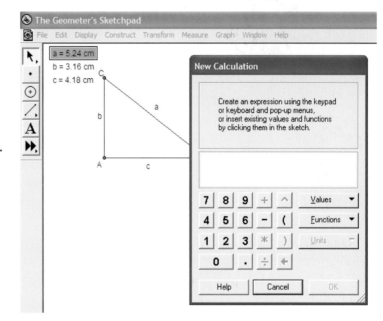

6. Compare the values for the squares of the three line segments. What relationship can you find?

7. Use the **Selection Arrow** to point, click, and drag the vertex of one of the acute angles to change the triangle. Does the triangle remain a right triangle? Notice how the measures and calculations displayed for the three line segments change as you drag the vertex. Does the relationship you discovered in step 6 still hold true?

8. Reflect Write a conclusion about how the side lengths of a right triangle are related.

Find Approximate Values of Square Roots

Focus on...
- perfect squares
- square roots
- estimation
- approximation

The fortress of Alhambra is in Granada, Spain. Its inner palaces and courts show fine architecture in their design and decorations. The site is famous for the intricate patterns of square tiles used on its floors and walls. Many mathematical properties have been found in the tile patterns.

Discover the Math

Materials
- centimetre grid paper

Optional:
- BLM 2.2A Find Approximate Square Roots

How can you find approximate square roots?

1. a) On centimetre grid paper, draw four nested squares, as shown.

b) Copy and complete the table for the four squares.

Side Length (cm)	1	2		4
Area (cm²)	1		9	

c) How is the area of each square related to its side length? How is the side length of each square related to its area?

perfect square
- a number whose square root is a whole number
- 4 is a perfect square: $\sqrt{4} = 2$

2. Now, try to find the value of $\sqrt{11}$.

a) Consider a square with area 11 cm². Between which two **perfect squares** will it fit in the nested diagram?

b) Which is it closer to, the smaller or the larger perfect square? Sketch in the square with area 11 cm².

c) Estimate the side length of a square with area 11 cm². What is the value of $\sqrt{11}$ to one decimal place? Compare your estimate with those of other students. How can you test that you have the best approximation, to one decimal place?

3. Reflect What type of numbers have exact square roots? What type of numbers can you only give an approximate square root for? Give examples of each.

Example 1: Find Exact Square Roots

Evaluate.

a) $\sqrt{49}$ **b)** $\sqrt{900}$ **c)** $\sqrt{1.21}$

Solution

a) $7 \times 7 = 49$, so $\sqrt{49} = 7$.
b) $30 \times 30 = 900$, so $\sqrt{900} = 30$.
c) $1.1 \times 1.1 = 1.21$, so $\sqrt{1.21} = 1.1$.

Example 2: Find Approximate Square Roots

a) **Estimate** $\sqrt{86}$, to one decimal place.

b) Use a calculator to find the **approximate** value of $\sqrt{86}$. Round to two decimal places.

Solution

a)

> 86 is a **non-perfect square**. 81 and 100 are the two perfect squares closest to 86. I know that $9^2 = 81$ and $10^2 = 100$. So, $\sqrt{86}$ is between 9 and 10.

> I can use a number line to help me decide which perfect square 86 is closer to. 86 is about one quarter of the way between 81 and 100.

$$\sqrt{81} \quad \overset{\sqrt{86}}{\downarrow} \quad \sqrt{100}$$

```
8     9      10    11
```

An estimate for $\sqrt{86}$ is 9.3.

b) ⓒ 86 √ 9.273618495
The value of $\sqrt{86}$, to two decimal places, is 9.27.

---

estimate

• a reasonable guess
• an answer found mentally, often using rounded numbers

approximate

• given to a certain number of decimal places
• an approximate answer can be found using a calculator or by systematic trial

non-perfect square

• a number that cannot be written as the square of a whole number

Technology Tip

• Calculator key sequences vary. You may need to enter ⓒ √ 86 = or ⓒ 86 √ =.

Key Ideas

- Perfect squares have exact square roots.
- The square root of a non-perfect square can be estimated by comparing with nearby perfect squares.

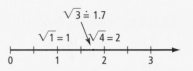

- The approximate value of the square root of a non-perfect square can be found by systematic trial or using a calculator.

Communicate the Ideas

1. Which one of the following numbers does not have an exact square root? Explain why.

   36, 16, 144, 49, 10, 225

2. Ravi was trying to estimate $\sqrt{67}$ but did not know where to start. Liz told him to list the perfect squares. Explain what Liz meant by this and how it could help Ravi.

Check Your Understanding

Practise

For help with questions 3 to 5, refer to Example 1.

3. Give the value of each square root.
   a) $\sqrt{121}$ b) $\sqrt{100}$
   c) $\sqrt{1}$ d) $\sqrt{81}$

4. Give the value of each square root.
   a) $\sqrt{25}$ b) $\sqrt{2500}$ c) $\sqrt{0.25}$

5. Give the value of each square root.
   a) $\sqrt{64}$ b) $\sqrt{6400}$ c) $\sqrt{0.64}$

For help with questions 6 to 10, refer to Example 2.

6. Explain why $\sqrt{25}$ has an exact value while for $\sqrt{30}$ you can only give an approximate answer.

7. Which of the following statements are true? Explain how you came to your answer. Correct the ones that are false.
   a) The value of $\sqrt{30}$ is between 5 and 6.
   b) The value of $\sqrt{48}$ is between 6 and 7.
   c) The value of $\sqrt{10}$ is between 4 and 5.
   d) The value of $\sqrt{75}$ is between 8 and 9.

8. Using perfect square numbers, explain how to make a reasonable estimate of $\sqrt{13}$, to one decimal place.

9. Explore how the ☑ function works on your calculator. Test it using the number 25. You know what answer to expect for $\sqrt{25}$. Practise by finding $\sqrt{36}$, $\sqrt{100}$, or the square root of other small perfect squares.

10. Estimate each square root to one decimal place. Use a calculator to find the approximate value of each square root. Round to two decimal places.

a) $\sqrt{10}$ **b)** $\sqrt{40}$
c) $\sqrt{72}$ **d)** $\sqrt{55}$
c) $\sqrt{93}$ **d)** $\sqrt{105}$
g) $\sqrt{88}$ **h)** $\sqrt{21}$

Apply

11. Is each statement always true, sometimes true, or always false? Give reasons to support your answer.

a) The square of an odd number is odd.

b) The square root of a number is greater than the square of the number.

c) The square root of a perfect square is even.

d) Square roots only exist for whole numbers.

e) Perfect squares can only exist between 1 and 10 000.

12. Tom wants to thank his art teacher by giving her one of his paintings. The painting is square with an area of 900 cm^2. Tom wants the painting to fit exactly into a gift box. What dimensions should the box have?

13. Write the following numbers in increasing order. Draw a number line and mark the approximate position of each value.

6, $\sqrt{30}$, $\sqrt{25}$, 5.8, $\sqrt{28}$

Chapter Problem

14. Brian has a square piece of kite paper with an area of 1200 cm^2. If he uses the entire piece of paper without cutting it, what is the approximate side length of his kite, to the nearest centimetre?

15. Kayla wants to build a fence around the backyard for her dogs to play in. Her backyard is square and has an area of 42 m^2.

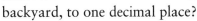
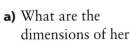

a) What are the dimensions of her backyard, to one decimal place?

b) How much will the fence cost if fencing material costs $40 per metre?

Extend

16. The label on a bag of grass seed says it will cover an area of 80 m^2. Answer the following, to two decimal places.

a) If the grass seed is spread over a square of ground, what is the side length of the square?

b) If the grass seed is spread over a circle of ground, what is the radius of the circle?

17. a) The number 4 is two times the number 2. Does this mean that 4^2 is two times the value of 2^2?

b) Consider 8 and 2. Is the value of 8^2 four times the value of 2^2? If not, what is the relationship?

c) Consider 10 and 2. Is 10^2 five times 2^2? If not, what is the relationship?

d) Look for a pattern in your results. Propose a relationship between the squares of two numbers, when one number is a multiple of the other. Test your relationship on at least three other pairs of numbers.

18. Graph the area of a square versus its side length, for side lengths from 0 to 10. Describe how you could use the completed graph to estimate roots of non-perfect squares, such as $\sqrt{30}$.

Apply the Pythagorean Relationship

Focus on...
- finding the length of the hypotenuse
- checking if a triangle is a right triangle

Fizal found a geometric way of approximating some square roots. He drew a right triangle with base 3 cm and height 3 cm. He claims that by measuring the hypotenuse of the triangle he can find $\sqrt{18}$ to one decimal place. Why does this work?

Discover the Math

How can you find the approximate length of a hypotenuse?

1. On centimetre grid paper, draw a right triangle with leg lengths 3 cm and 3 cm.

2. Draw a square attached to the triangle, using the hypotenuse as one of its sides.

3. Determine the area of this square. You can do this by finding the number of grid squares contained within it.

4. Measure the length of the hypotenuse, to the nearest tenth of a centimetre. How is this measurement related to the area of the square?

5. **Reflect** How are the Pythagorean relationship and finding square roots related?

The Pythagorean relationship can be expressed by the equation $c^2 = a^2 + b^2$. c represents the length of the hypotenuse, and a and b represent the lengths of the legs. Using this relationship and your skills with square roots, you can find the length of the hypotenuse if you know the lengths of the legs.

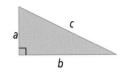

Example 1: Find the Length of the Hypotenuse

The outdoor pool at Marc's apartment building is 12 m long and 5 m wide. If Marc swims diagonally across the pool, how far does he swim?

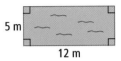

Solution

The diagonal of the pool is the hypotenuse of a right triangle. The two legs are given.
Let c represent the length of the diagonal.

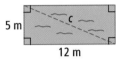

$c^2 = a^2 + b^2$ **From the diagram, $a = 5$, and $b = 12$.**
$c^2 = 5^2 + 12^2$
$c^2 = 25 + 144$
$c^2 = 169$
$c = \sqrt{169}$
$c = 13$

Marc swims 13 m diagonally across the pool.

Example 2: Test for a Right Triangle

Rita is helping to build scenery for the school play. She has built the rectangular frame for a side panel using two 6.0-m lengths and two 4.5-m widths. She wants to make sure that she has right angles at the corners. She measures one diagonal and finds that it is 7.5 m. Is the frame built correctly?

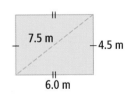

Solution

A triangle is formed by two sides of the frame, 6.0 m and 4.5 m, and the diagonal, 7.5 m. If there is a right angle in the corner, this is a right triangle.

If the diagonal and two sides of the rectangle form a right triangle, then the Pythagorean relationship will hold. The diagonal, 7.5 m, will be the hypotenuse.

$7.5^2 = 56.25$ $6.0^2 + 4.5^2$
                     $= 36 + 20.25$
                     $= 56.25$

Look Back

The square of the diagonal length does equal the sum of the squares of the other two side lengths. So, the triangle is a right triangle. Rita has built the frame correctly.

Example 3: Apply the Pythagorean Relationship

A baseball diamond is actually a square with sides 27.0 m in length. How far does the player at first base have to throw the ball to get a runner out at third base? Round your answer to the nearest tenth.

Solution

Understand

Draw a diagram of the baseball diamond. Join the diagonal from first to third base.

Let d represent the diagonal distance.

Strategies
Make a picture or diagram

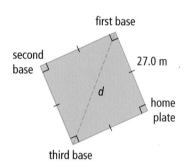

Plan

The distance from first base to third base is the hypotenuse of the right triangle. The lengths of the legs of the right triangle are both 27.0 m. Apply the Pythagorean relationship to find the hypotenuse.

Do It!

$$d^2 = 27^2 + 27^2$$
$$d^2 = 729 + 729$$
$$d^2 = 1458$$

Estimate: $\sqrt{1600} = 40$, so $\sqrt{1458}$ is a bit less than 40.

$$d = \sqrt{1458}$$

c 1458 √ 38.18376618

$$d \doteq 38.2$$

Look Back

The approximate answer checks with the estimate. The answer is reasonable for the given side lengths of the baseball diamond.

The player at first base must throw the ball 38.2 m to get a runner out at third base.

Literacy Connections

To learn about different problem solving strategies, refer to the Problem Solving section on pages xii to xix. The orange banner will help you find these pages. Refer to these pages whenever you need help deciding on a strategy to use to solve a problem.

Key Ideas

- In any right triangle, the square of the hypotenuse equals the sum of the squares of the legs.
$$c^2 = a^2 + b^2$$

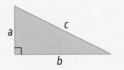

- You can test whether a triangle is a right triangle by using the Pythagorean equation. In right triangles, $c^2 = a^2 + b^2$.

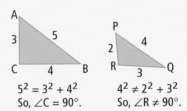

$5^2 = 3^2 + 4^2$
So, $\angle C = 90°$.

$4^2 \neq 2^2 + 3^2$
So, $\angle R \neq 90°$.

Communicate the Ideas

1. Describe the steps you would use to find the length of each hypotenuse. How does the answer for c differ from the answer for d?

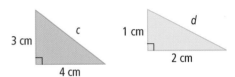

2. A rope with knots marking 12 equal parts has been used since ancient times for checking that corners are square. Explain how this rope can be used to confirm a right angle.

3. If you know the lengths of the legs of a right triangle, you can use the Pythagorean equation to find the length of the hypotenuse. Describe how you would explain the steps to a student who missed this class.

Check Your Understanding

For help with questions 4 to 7, refer to Example 1.

4. Find the length of the hypotenuse of each triangle.

a)

b)

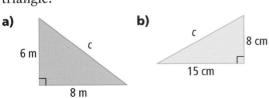

5. Find the length of the hypotenuse of each triangle.

a)

b)

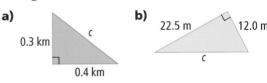

6. Find the length of the hypotenuse of each triangle. Round your answers to the nearest tenth.

a)

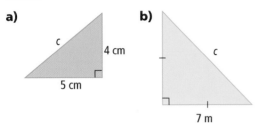

b)

7. Find the length of the hypotenuse of each triangle. Round your answers to the nearest tenth.

a)

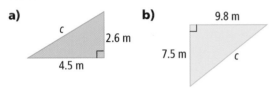

b)

For help with question 8, refer to Example 2.

8. Which of the following could be the side lengths of a right triangle? Explain how you came to your conclusions.

a) 2 cm, 4 cm, 5 cm
b) 6 cm, 8 cm, 10 cm
c) 9 cm, 15 cm, 12 cm
d) 12 cm, 8 cm, 7 cm

9. For each triangle, estimate the length of the hypotenuse. Then, use a calculator to find the approximate length to the nearest tenth.

a)

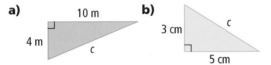

b)

Did You Know?

In construction, a 3-4-5 right triangle is often used to check that an angle is 90° or "square." For example, measurements of 3 m and 4 m away from a corner are taken and marked. If the marks are 5 m apart, then the corner is square.

Apply

10. Ahmed delivers newspapers. He starts from home and goes down his street a distance of 120 m. Then, he turns left at the corner and goes another 100 m to the last house on his route. Ahmed has a walkie-talkie with a range of 150 m. Can he call his brother, who is at home, from the farthest point on his route?

11. Simon wants to make a right-triangular brace for a picture frame to lean on. He wants the horizontal and vertical parts to measure 5 cm and 10 cm, respectively. What length of material is required to make the slant of the brace?

12. Tia is making a handrail for a staircase. The staircase rises 3.6 m over a horizontal distance of 3.2 m. How long should the handrail be, to the nearest tenth of a metre?

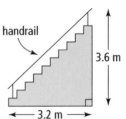

13. On his way to the cinema, Tony needs to cross a rectangular parking lot. The lot measures 80 m by 85 m. How many metres fewer will Tony walk if he goes diagonally across the lot rather than walking the length and width? Round your answer to the nearest metre.

Chapter Problem

14. Katie and Tim are building a kite. They use two wooden sticks, one measuring 30 cm and the other measuring 60 cm, to form the frame. The centre point of the shorter stick is attached to a point one third of the way from the end of the longer stick.

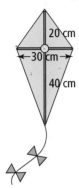

a) To the nearest tenth of a centimetre, how much ribbon will they need to glue around the four outer edges of the kite paper?

b) What area of kite paper do they need to cover one side of the frame?

15. A square tablecloth has an area of 1 m².

a) What is the length of each side of the tablecloth, in centimetres?

b) What is the diagonal distance across the tablecloth, to the nearest centimetre?

16. Cynthia wants to press some flowers between the pages of a large book. The book measures 25 cm by 35 cm. What is the length of the longest flower that she can place entirely between two pages in this book?

17. Jessie is preparing a gymnastics routine for an upcoming competition. Each of her cartwheels uses a distance of 2.5 m to complete. How many cartwheels can she perform along the diagonal of an 8 m by 8 m gymnasium mat?

18. A doorway is 0.78 m wide and 2.00 m high. Will a round tabletop with a diameter of 2.50 m fit through the doorway?

a) Draw and label a diagram to model the problem.

b) Use numbers and words to justify your answer.

Extend

19. A square peg fits snugly inside a round hole, as shown. What is the perimeter of the square, to the nearest millimetre?

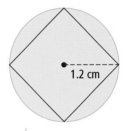

20. What is the length of the shortest path from point A to point B?

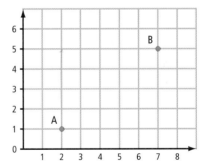

21. A fishing boat leaves St. John's, Newfoundland and Labrador, and travels due north at 7.2 km/h for 2 h. Then, the boat turns due east and continues its journey, at the same speed, for another half an hour. How far is the ship from St. John's after the $2\frac{1}{2}$ h at sea?

Use the Pythagorean Relationship

The Leaning Tower of Pisa in Italy is a beautiful bell tower, famous around the world for its tilt. Construction of the 58.5-m tower began in 1173 and was completed in 1370. Even before it was completed, the tower began to lean to one side when the marshy ground beneath it shifted under the weight of the structure.

The tower was closed in 1990 to allow for major work to try to stop the shifting. At that time, the edge of the top was approximately 4.5 m outside the edge of the foundation. After almost 12 years of repair, the Leaning Tower of Pisa was reopened to the public on December 15, 2001.

Discover the Math

How can you find the measure of any side of a right triangle?

Example 1: Find an Unknown Height

Calculate the vertical distance from the edge of the top of the Leaning Tower of Pisa to the ground, in 1990. Round your answer to the nearest tenth.

58.5 m h

4.5 m

Solution

Let h represent the vertical distance
to the ground.

$$h^2 + 4.5^2 = 58.5^2$$
$$h^2 + 20.25 = 3422.25$$
$$h^2 = 3402$$
$$h = \sqrt{3402}$$
$$h \doteq 58.3 \quad \boxed{\text{c}}\,\mathbf{3402}\ \boxed{\sqrt{\ }}\,58.32666629$$

Two side lengths are given, so I can use the Pythagorean relationship to find the missing side length.

What do I need to add to 20.25 to get 3422.25?

$60^2 = 3600$, so $\sqrt{3402}$ is a bit less than 60. The estimate confirms that the calculated square root is reasonable.

In 1990, the vertical distance from the top of the Leaning Tower
of Pisa to the ground was approximately 58.3 m.

Example 2: Find an Unknown Side Length

The gable end of a house is an isosceles triangle that has a height
of 3 m. The sloping sides measure 7 m from the peak to the eaves.
a) Find the width of the roof, to the nearest tenth of a metre.
b) What is the area of the gable end?

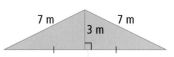

Solution

a) Let x represent the missing side length.

Use the Pythagorean relationship.
$$x^2 + 3^2 = 7^2$$
$$x^2 + 9 = 49$$
$$x^2 = 40$$
$$x = \sqrt{40}$$
$$x \doteq 6.3 \quad \boxed{\text{c}}\,\mathbf{40}\ \boxed{\sqrt{\ }}\,6.32455532$$

Half of the gable end makes a right triangle.

$6^2 = 36$, so $\sqrt{40}$ is a bit greater than 6.

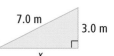

The length x is 6.3 m, to the nearest tenth.
The width of the roof is double this length. 2×6.3 m is 12.6 m.
The width of the roof is 12.6 m.

b) $A = b \times h \div 2$
$A = 12.6 \times 3 \div 2$
$A = 37.8 \div 2$
$A = 18.9$

Strategies
Choose a formula

The area of the gable end is 18.9 m^2.

Key Ideas

- The Pythagorean relationship connects the three sides of any right triangle.

- The Pythagorean equation can be used to find the length of one of the sides of a right triangle if the other two sides are known.

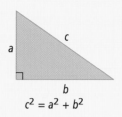

$c^2 = a^2 + b^2$

Communicate the Ideas

1. **a)** Describe the steps you would use to find the length x.
   b) Estimate the value of x. Between which two whole numbers is it?

2. To find the length b, Crystal wrote

   $$b^2 = 10^2 + 8^2$$

   Is her method correct? If not, explain what she did wrong.

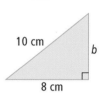

3. Darian wants to find the height, h, of this triangle. His method is to enter $\sqrt{81 - 49}$ into his calculator. Will his answer be correct? Explain why or why not.

Check Your Understanding

Practise

For help with questions 4 to 7, refer to Examples 1 and 2.

4. Find the length of the missing side in each triangle.

   a)

   x   15 cm   9 cm

   b)

   x   15 cm   17 cm

5. Find the length of the missing side in each triangle.

   a)

   x   2.5 m   1.5 m

   b)

   3.5 m   *x*   2.8 m

6. Find the length of the missing side in each triangle. Round your answers to the nearest tenth.

   a)

   x   5 cm   8 cm

   b)

   5.5 km   9.5 km   *x*

Apply

7. A wheelchair ramp is 9.6 m long. The horizontal distance it spans is 9.5 m. What vertical height does the ramp let a person rise? Round your answer to the nearest tenth.

8. Dev plans to build a toy boat for his younger brother. The side view of his plan is shown. What length of wood will he need to cut to make the top deck of the boat?

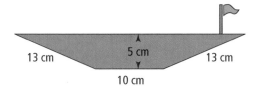

9. A square park has diagonal paths that are each 48 m long.

a) What is the perimeter of the park, to the nearest metre?

b) What is the area of the park?

10. Max was preparing to install a new pane of glass in the living room window. It measured 1.3 m by 1.5 m. He noticed a scratch that stretched across half the diagonal of the glass. Approximately how long was the scratch?

11. Many steel cables are used to support a suspension bridge. In the diagram, three of the cables are shown.

a) Cable TB is 50 m long. Find the height of the tower, TA.

b) Find the length of cables TC and TD.

c) How much longer is cable TC than cable TB? Can you add this amount to the length of TC to find the length of TD? Explain.

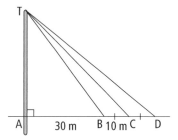

Extend

12. Find the shortest distance from A to B if the larger square has a perimeter of 36 cm and the smaller square has an area of 9 cm².

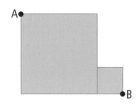

13. A ramp 3.5 m long is used to load furniture onto the back of a truck. One end of the ramp rests on a porch, which is 0.5 m off the ground. The other end of the ramp, leading into the back of the truck, is 1.0 m above the ground. What is the horizontal distance from the back of the truck to the edge of the porch, to the nearest tenth?

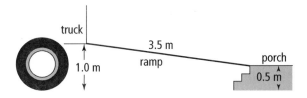

Key Words

1. A right triangle is shown.

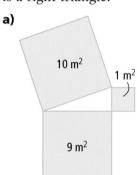

a) Which side is the hypotenuse?

b) Name one leg of the triangle.

c) How are the sides related by the Pythagorean relationship?

d) Which side length is a perfect square? Explain.

2. Which student is estimating? Which student is approximating? Explain.

I think the value of $\sqrt{40}$ is about 6.4. The number 40 is between 36 and 49 and is a bit closer to 36.

According to my calculator, $\sqrt{40}$ is 6.324 555 32. I would give its value as 6.32.

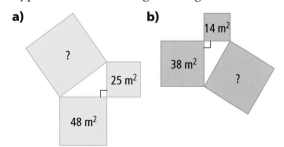

2.1 Discover the Pythagorean Relationship, pages 50–55

3. State the Pythagorean relationship. Explain why it is useful.

4. Find the area of the square on the hypotenuse of each right triangle.

a)

?
25 m²
48 m²

b)

14 m²
38 m²
?

5. Three squares are placed together to form a triangle. Determine whether each triangle is a right triangle.

a)

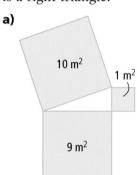

10 m²
1 m²
9 m²

b)

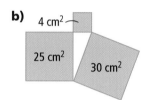

4 cm²
25 cm²
30 cm²

2.2 Find Approximate Values of Square Roots, pages 58–61

6. Give the value of each square root.

a) $\sqrt{0.01}$ **b)** $\sqrt{196}$

c) $\sqrt{400}$ **d)** $\sqrt{0.49}$

7. Estimate each value to one decimal place. Then, use a calculator to find the approximate value, to two decimal places.

a) $\sqrt{5}$ **b)** $\sqrt{41}$ **c)** $\sqrt{75}$

8. A can of spray paint says it will cover an area of 12 m². Answer the following to the nearest tenth.

a) If the can is empty after spraying a square area, what is the length of each side of the square?

b) If three cans are needed to paint a square area, what is the length of each side of this square?

2.3 Apply the Pythagorean Relationship, pages 62–67

9. Draw a diagram of a right triangle and label its sides x, y, and z. Write the Pythagorean equation for this triangle.

10. Find the length of the hypotenuse in each.

a)
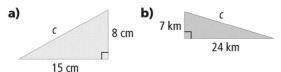

b)

11. Ria used a large cardboard box to build a maze for her pet mouse to run around in. There are only two openings located across the diagonal from each other. The route travelled by the mouse is shown in the diagram.

a) Find the length and the width of the box.

b) Find the length of the diagonal of the box.

c) How much farther did the mouse run compared to a straight path from opening to opening?

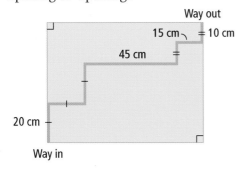

2.4 Use the Pythagorean Relationship, pages 68–71

12. Find the missing side length. Round to the nearest tenth, if necessary.

a)
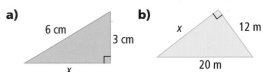

b)

c)
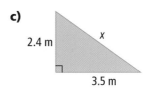

13. Avi uses a 3.5-m ladder to climb up to his tree house. The foot of the ladder is 0.8 m from the tree. How far up the tree does the ladder reach?

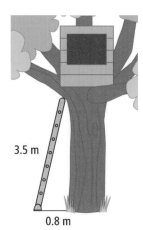

14. On a chessboard, each of the 64 small squares measures 3.2 cm by 3.2 cm.

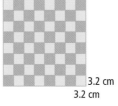

a) What is the length of the diagonal across the chessboard?

b) Solve part a) in another way.

Strand	NSN	MEA	GSS	PA	DMP
Questions	2–7, 9, 10	6, 7, 10	1, 4–10	1, 4–7, 9, 10	

Multiple Choice

For questions 1 to 4, select the best answer.

1. The area of the square on side YZ is

   A 3 cm²

   B 9 cm²

   C 27 cm²

   D 45 cm²

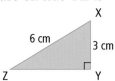

2. Which number is not a perfect square?

   A 1

   B 22

   C 81

   D 169

3. The value of $\sqrt{72}$ is closest to

   A 8

   B 8.1

   C 8.5

   D 9

4. The missing side length is

   A 8 m

   B 16 m

   C 18 m

   D 32 m

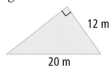

Short Answer

5. Tim made a tuna sandwich using bread that measured 9 cm by 12 cm. He cut the sandwich in half along a diagonal. What is the length of the diagonal cut that he made?

6. Calculate the perimeter and the area of the triangular plot of land shown.

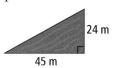

7. A lifeguard watches as people arrive at the beach. A family is setting up an umbrella and chairs 25 m away, down near the shoreline. Directly in front of the family, in the water, is a surfer approximately 60 m away. Suddenly the surfer disappears under the waves and does not resurface. What is the shortest distance the lifeguard needs to swim to reach the surfer?

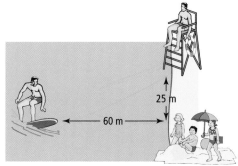

8. Explain why the following statement describing the Pythagorean relationship is incorrect.

"The area of the square on the longest side of a triangle is equal to the sum of the areas of the squares on the two shorter sides."

Use diagrams to support your reasoning.

Extended Response

9. You have two square sheets of construction paper with areas of 9 cm² and 36 cm². Describe how you can use these to find the approximate value of $\sqrt{45}$. What measurement tool will you need?

10. Jennifer wants to store her boots during the summer. Design a box that will hold the boots when they are laid on their sides.

   a) Draw a top view of the box with the boots placed inside toe to heel to save space.
   b) What is the minimum height of the box?
   c) What are the length and width of the smallest box that will hold the boots?
   d) Calculate the diagonal length across the bottom of the box.

Chapter Problem Wrap-Up

You are given a piece of wood 100 cm in length and are allowed to cut it once to make two pieces. With the two pieces of wood, you will build the cross frame for a kite.

1. Draw sketches of two possible kite designs, labelling the lengths of the two pieces of wood.

2. What area of kite paper is needed for each design?

3. How much ribbon is needed to go around the perimeter of each kite?

4. How should the stick be cut to make a kite with the greatest area? Explain.

Game Boards

All over the world, since ancient times, games have been played on square boards. The simplest is Xs and Os, played on a 3 by 3 grid.

One of the more complex is Go (Chinese Wei-Qi) in which tiles are used to capture regions of the 18 by 18 grid.

Variations of games have developed over time in different parts of the world.

North American checkers, played on an 8 by 8 grid, is essentially the same as Polish draughts, which is played on a 10 by 10 grid.

North American chess uses an 8 by 8 grid. The Japanese have three variations: Shogi uses a 9 by 9 grid, Chu Shogi uses a 12 by 12 grid, and Tai Shogi is played on 25 by 25 grid.

Snakes and Ladders is played on a 10 by 10 grid, and Scrabble® on a 13 by 13 grid.

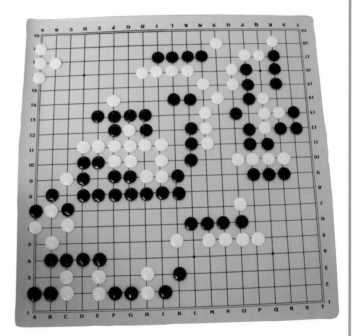

1. What is the diagonal distance across a Go board if each of its small squares has a side length of 2 cm?

2. Research to find other games that are played on square boards. Write a brief description of each game for display on a bulletin board.

What's math got to do with drain access covers?

Have you ever thought about why the metal covers on drains are round? Why are none of them square or rectangular?

Pythagoras can help provide the answer. If the cover were square or rectangular, then the diagonal length across the hole would be longer than the sides. A worker could accidentally drop the cover through the hole. A circular cover cannot fall through.

Write a paragraph, or prepare a demonstration with visual aids, to explain this to a younger student.

Design a Playground With A Wading Pool

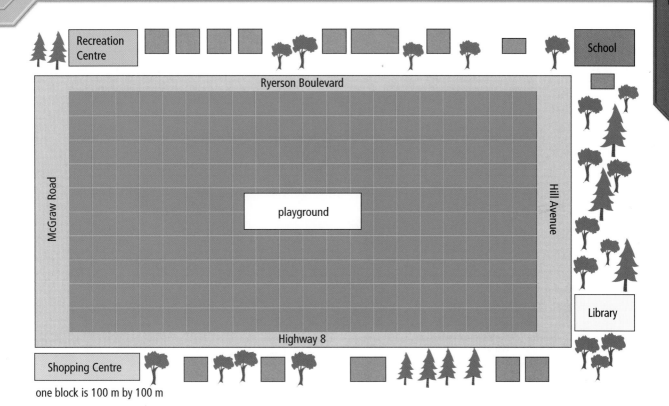

one block is 100 m by 100 m

WANTED

Innovative design for playground with circular wading pool.

Requirements:
- to be located in the green space
- can cover no more than one quarter of the area of the green space
- wading pool to cover no more than one quarter the area of the playground
- must be 100 m from any road
- must be accessible by a diagonal path to at least two streets

The map shows a large green space in a community.

The town has advertised for a design for a circular wading pool to be placed in a playground in this green space. The newspaper advertisement shows the requirements.

Choose a location and size for the playground and wading pool. Then develop a design for presentation to the town council. Include all measurements. Write a report that explains how your design meets all of the requirements.

Number Sense and Numeration

- Represent composite numbers as products of prime factors.

- Demonstrate an understanding of and proficiency in adding, subtracting, multiplying, and dividing simple fractions.

- Understand the order of operations with brackets and apply the order of operations in evaluating expressions that involve fractions.

- Ask "what if" questions, pose problems, and investigate solutions.

- Justify the choice of method for calculations and use estimation to assess reasonableness.

- Explain the process and conclusions in solving problems.

- Reflect on learning and evaluate mathematical issues using mathematical language.

Key Words

lowest common
  multiple (LCM)

lowest common
  denominator (LCD)

composite number

prime number

factor tree

reciprocal

order of operations

CHAPTER 3

Fraction Operations

Cities, towns, and tourist attractions often create beautiful flower gardens that are open for public viewing. These gardens may contain many different colours and types of flowers. One colour and type of flower may occupy only a fraction of the whole garden.

What fractions can you use to describe this garden at Dow's Lake Tulip Beds in Ottawa?

In this chapter, you will add, subtract, multiply, and divide fractions. You will find common denominators and reciprocals. You will apply the order of operations to solve problems involving operations with proper fractions, improper fractions, and mixed numbers.

Chapter Problem

Gardens often contain sections with different colours or types of flowers or vegetables. Think about a garden you have seen recently or a garden you would like to plant.

- Describe the different colours in the garden.
- What fraction of the garden is each colour?
- What fraction of the garden is each type of flower or vegetable?

Multiples and Factors

The first four **multiples** of 2 are 2, 4, 6, and 8.

Each multiple is the product of 2 and a natural number.

$1 \times 2 = 2 \qquad 2 \times 2 = 4 \qquad 3 \times 2 = 6 \qquad 4 \times 2 = 8$

The **factors** of 8 are 1, 2, 4, and 8. Each of these factors divides evenly into 8.

1. List the first four multiples of each number.

a) 6   **b)** 3   **c)** 5   **d)** 10

2. List the factors of each number, from least to greatest.

a) 12   **b)** 20   **c)** 36   **d)** 50

Represent Fractions

Let one hexagon represent one whole.

 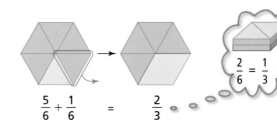

$\dfrac{1}{2} + \dfrac{1}{3} = \dfrac{5}{6}$

$\dfrac{5}{6} + \dfrac{1}{6} = \dfrac{2}{3}$

$\dfrac{2}{6} = \dfrac{1}{3}$

3. Use pattern blocks or diagrams to represent each addition.

a) $\dfrac{1}{6} + \dfrac{4}{6}$ **b)** $\dfrac{1}{3} + \dfrac{1}{6}$ **c)** $\dfrac{1}{2} + \dfrac{1}{6}$

4. Use pattern blocks or diagrams to represent each subtraction.

a) $\dfrac{5}{6} - \dfrac{1}{3}$ **b)** $\dfrac{1}{2} - \dfrac{1}{3}$ **c)** $\dfrac{2}{3} - \dfrac{1}{2}$

Compare and Order Fractions

A number line can help you compare and order fractions.

$\dfrac{1}{4}, \dfrac{1}{2}, 1, \dfrac{3}{2}, 1\dfrac{3}{4}$ are ordered from least to greatest.

5. Use a number line to show which fraction is greater.

a) $\dfrac{5}{8}$ or $\dfrac{3}{4}$ **b)** $\dfrac{5}{4}$ or $1\dfrac{1}{2}$

6. Order $\dfrac{3}{4}, \dfrac{1}{2}, \dfrac{7}{4}, 2,$ and $1\dfrac{1}{4}$ on a number line.

Write Fractions in Lowest Terms

A fraction is in **lowest terms** when the numerator and denominator have no common factors other than 1. A fraction can be written in lowest terms by dividing the numerator and the denominator by the **greatest common factor (GCF)**. The value of the fraction does not change.

To write $\frac{12}{18}$ in lowest terms, find the greatest common factor of 12 and 18.

The factors of 12 are 1, 2, 3, 4, ⑥, and 12.

The factors of 18 are 1, 2, 3, ⑥, 9, and 18.

The greatest common factor is 6.

$$\frac{12}{18} = \frac{12 \div 6}{18 \div 6}$$
$$= \frac{2}{3}$$

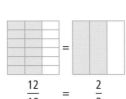

$\frac{12}{18} = \frac{2}{3}$

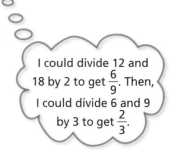

I could divide 12 and 18 by 2 to get $\frac{6}{9}$. Then, I could divide 6 and 9 by 3 to get $\frac{2}{3}$.

7. Write each fraction in lowest terms.

a) $\frac{15}{20}$ **b)** $\frac{21}{30}$ **c)** $\frac{20}{36}$

8. Write each fraction in lowest terms. Then, order the fractions from least to greatest.

$$\frac{3}{15}, \frac{5}{20}, \frac{6}{12}, \frac{6}{18}$$

Order of Operations

In grade 7, you used BODMAS to remember the order of operations.

$3 \times (7 + 5) \div 4$ **Brackets.**

$= 3 \times 12 \div 4$ **Multiply and divide in order from left to right.**

$= 36 \div 4$

$= 9$

B Brackets
O Order
D ⎫ Division and
M ⎭ Multiplication, in order from *left* to *right*
A ⎫ Addition and
S ⎭ Subtraction, in order from *left* to *right*

9. Evaluate.

a) $11 - 8 + 4$
b) $5 \times 3 + 7$
c) $9 + 8 \div 2$
d) $5 \times (4 + 2) - 10$

10. Copy each equation. Insert one set of brackets to make it true.

a) $(30 - 10) \div 2 + 3 = 13$
b) $30 - (10 \div 2) + 3 = 22$
c) $30 - 10 \div 2 + 3 = 28$

3.1 Add and Subtract Fractions

Focus on...

- estimating the size of fractions
- adding and subtracting fractions
- assessing the reasonableness of estimates

The red trapezoid is one quarter of the double hexagon. What other pattern block relationships are there? How many different ways can you make one whole from these pattern blocks?

Discover the Math

How do you add and subtract fractions?

Example 1: Add Fractions

Add $\dfrac{3}{4} + \dfrac{1}{6}$.

Solution

Method 1: Use Concrete Materials

$$\dfrac{3}{4} + \dfrac{1}{6} = \dfrac{11}{12}$$

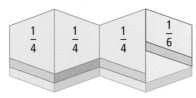 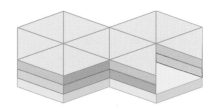

Method 2: Use Multiples to Find the Lowest Common Denominator

The denominator of $\dfrac{3}{4}$ is 4. Multiples of 4 are 4, 8, ⑫, 16, 20, ㉔, ...

The denominator of $\dfrac{1}{6}$ is 6. Multiples of 6 are 6, ⑫, 18, ㉔, ...

12 and 24 are common multiples of 4 and 6.
12 is the first multiple common to both lists.
This is the **lowest common multiple (LCM)** .

lowest common multiple (LCM)

- the lowest multiple that two or more numbers have in common
- the LCM of 4 and 5 is 20

The **lowest common denominator (LCD)** for $\frac{3}{4}$ and $\frac{1}{6}$ is 12.

$$\frac{3}{4} = \frac{3 \times 3}{4 \times 3}$$
$$= \frac{9}{12}$$

$$\frac{1}{6} = \frac{1 \times 2}{6 \times 2}$$
$$= \frac{2}{12}$$

To find equivalent fractions, multiply the numerator and denominator by the same number.

$$\frac{3}{4} + \frac{1}{6} = \frac{9}{12} + \frac{2}{12}$$
$$= \frac{11}{12}$$

Add the numerators.

If I add $\frac{1}{4}$ to $\frac{3}{4}$, I get $\frac{4}{4}$ or 1. Since $\frac{1}{6}$ is less than $\frac{1}{4}$, the answer will be less than 1.

Method 3: Use Factor Trees to Find the LCD

The denominator of $\frac{3}{4}$ is 4. The denominator of $\frac{1}{6}$ is 6.

Each denominator is a **composite number**.

You can write each composite number as a product of **prime numbers**.

These prime numbers are called prime factors.

You can use a **factor tree** to find the prime factors.

$$4 = 2 \times 2 \qquad 6 = 2 \times 3$$

Calculate the least number with all the prime factors of each denominator.

$$4 = 2 \times 2$$
$$6 = 2 \qquad \times 3$$
$$\downarrow \quad \downarrow \quad \downarrow$$
$$2 \times 2 \times 3 = 12$$

Both 4 and 6 have 2 as a prime factor. I only need two 2s and one 3 to be able to make both 4 and 6.

The LCD is 12.

$$\frac{3 \times 3}{4 \times 3} = \frac{9}{12} \qquad \frac{1 \times 2}{6 \times 2} = \frac{2}{12}$$

To find equivalent fractions, multiply the numerator and denominator by the same number.

$$\frac{3}{4} + \frac{1}{6} = \frac{9}{12} + \frac{2}{12}$$
$$= \frac{11}{12}$$

Add the numerators.

Example 2: Subtract Fractions

Subtract $\dfrac{5}{6} - \dfrac{3}{8}$.

Solution

Method 1: Use Multiples to Find the LCD

The denominator of $\dfrac{5}{6}$ is 6. Multiples of 6 are 6, 12, 18, (24), ...

The denominator of $\dfrac{3}{8}$ is 8. Multiples of 8 are 8, 16, (24), 32, 40, ...

The LCD for $\dfrac{5}{6}$ and $\dfrac{3}{4}$ is 24.

$$\dfrac{5 \times 4}{6 \times 4} = \dfrac{20}{24} \qquad \dfrac{3 \times 3}{8 \times 3} = \dfrac{9}{24}$$

$$\dfrac{5}{6} - \dfrac{3}{8} = \dfrac{20}{24} - \dfrac{9}{24}$$

$$= \dfrac{11}{24}$$

Subtract the numerators.

$\dfrac{5}{6}$ is close to 1. $\dfrac{3}{8}$ is close to $\dfrac{1}{2}$.

The answer should be close to $1 - \dfrac{1}{2} = \dfrac{1}{2}$.

$\dfrac{11}{24}$ is close to $\dfrac{1}{2}$.

The answer is reasonable.

Method 2: Use Factor Trees to Find the LCD

Use a factor tree to write each denominator as a product of its prime factors.

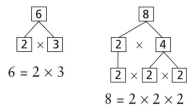

$6 = 2 \times 3$

$8 = 2 \times 2 \times 2$

To find the LCD, calculate the least number with all the prime factors of each denominator.

$6 = 2 \qquad\quad \times 3$

$8 = 2 \times 2 \times 2$

$\downarrow \quad \downarrow \quad \downarrow \quad \downarrow$

$2 \times 2 \times 2 \times 3 = 24$

The LCD is 24.

$$\dfrac{5 \times 4}{6 \times 4} = \dfrac{20}{24} \qquad\qquad \dfrac{3}{8} = \dfrac{3 \times 3}{8 \times 3} = \dfrac{9}{24}$$

$$\dfrac{5}{6} - \dfrac{3}{8} = \dfrac{20}{24} - \dfrac{9}{24}$$

$$= \dfrac{11}{24}$$

Subtract the numerators.

Key Ideas

- To add or subtract fractions, use a common denominator.

- The lowest common denominator (LCD) is the lowest common multiple (LCM) of the denominators of two or more fractions. You can find the LCD using multiples or prime factors.

  The LCD of $\dfrac{1}{4}$ and $\dfrac{1}{10}$ is 20.

- Use equivalent fractions to write each fraction with the LCD.

  $\dfrac{1 \times 5}{4 \times 5} = \dfrac{5}{20}$ $\qquad\qquad$ $\dfrac{1 \times 2}{10 \times 2} = \dfrac{2}{20}$

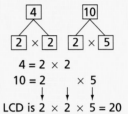

$4 = 2 \times 2$

$10 = 2 \qquad \times 5$

LCD is $2 \times 2 \times 5 = 20$

Communicate the Ideas

1. Show how many different ways you can find the LCD for $\dfrac{5}{6}$ and $\dfrac{1}{2}$.

2. Explain the error in Matt's thinking.

$\dfrac{4}{9} + \dfrac{1}{9} = \dfrac{5}{18}$.

3. What is one advantage of using the LCD when adding or subtracting fractions? Use examples to justify your answer.

Check Your Understanding

Practise

Express all answers in lowest terms.

4. Write an addition sentence to represent the fraction of each figure shaded.

a) 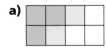 **b)**

5. Write a subtraction sentence to represent the fraction of each figure that remains.

a)

b)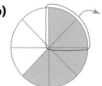

For help with questions 6 to 10, refer to Example 1.

6. Let one double hexagon represent one whole. Use pattern blocks to represent each addition. State the total fraction covered.

   a) $\dfrac{1}{2} + \dfrac{1}{4}$　　b) $\dfrac{5}{12} + \dfrac{1}{2}$

   c) $\dfrac{1}{2} + \dfrac{1}{6}$　　d) $\dfrac{3}{4} + \dfrac{1}{12}$

7. Use prime factors to find the LCD for each set of fractions.

   a) $\dfrac{2}{3}$ and $\dfrac{7}{15}$　　b) $\dfrac{5}{12}$ and $\dfrac{11}{18}$

8. Use multiples to find the LCD. Add.

   a) $\dfrac{1}{2} + \dfrac{1}{3}$　　b) $\dfrac{3}{4} + \dfrac{1}{5}$

   c) $\dfrac{1}{12} + \dfrac{1}{2}$　　d) $\dfrac{2}{3} + \dfrac{1}{10}$

9. Use factor trees to find the LCD. Add.

   a) $\dfrac{1}{4} + \dfrac{1}{6}$　　b) $\dfrac{1}{6} + \dfrac{3}{8}$

   c) $\dfrac{1}{10} + \dfrac{2}{15}$　　d) $\dfrac{5}{12} + \dfrac{1}{9}$

10. Add.

   a) $\dfrac{1}{4} + \dfrac{3}{5}$　　b) $\dfrac{3}{8} + \dfrac{1}{3}$

   c) $\dfrac{1}{2} + \dfrac{1}{5}$　　d) $\dfrac{7}{10} + \dfrac{1}{6}$

For help with questions 11 to 13, refer to Example 2.

11. Use multiples to find the LCD. Subtract.

   a) $\dfrac{2}{3} - \dfrac{1}{4}$　　b) $\dfrac{7}{8} - \dfrac{1}{2}$

   c) $\dfrac{5}{6} - \dfrac{1}{5}$　　d) $\dfrac{3}{4} - \dfrac{7}{10}$

12. Use factor trees to find the LCD. Subtract.

   a) $\dfrac{5}{8} - \dfrac{1}{6}$　　b) $\dfrac{9}{10} - \dfrac{3}{4}$

   c) $\dfrac{8}{9} - \dfrac{1}{12}$　　d) $\dfrac{9}{10} - \dfrac{2}{15}$

13. Subtract.

   a) $\dfrac{1}{2} - \dfrac{3}{8}$　　b) $\dfrac{3}{5} - \dfrac{1}{4}$

   c) $\dfrac{7}{10} - \dfrac{1}{2}$　　d) $\dfrac{7}{8} - \dfrac{1}{3}$

Apply

14. a) Which pairs of these fractions add to $\dfrac{3}{4}$? Show how you know.

   $\dfrac{1}{2}, \dfrac{3}{8}, \dfrac{1}{4}, \dfrac{1}{8}, \dfrac{5}{8}$

   b) Name two other pairs of fractions that add to $\dfrac{3}{4}$.

15. Which is greater, $\dfrac{1}{2} + \dfrac{1}{3}$ or $\dfrac{1}{2} + \dfrac{2}{5}$?

16. Which is greater, $\dfrac{3}{4} - \dfrac{1}{5}$ or $\dfrac{3}{4} - \dfrac{3}{10}$?

17. Kathy and Matan each solved $\dfrac{1}{6} + \dfrac{3}{4}$. Matan used the LCD and got

   $$\dfrac{1}{6} + \dfrac{3}{4} = \dfrac{2}{12} + \dfrac{9}{12}$$
   $$= \dfrac{11}{12}$$

   Kathy solved the same problem and got

   $$\dfrac{1}{6} + \dfrac{3}{4} = \dfrac{4}{24} + \dfrac{18}{24}$$
   $$= \dfrac{22}{24}$$

   Who is correct? Explain the difference between the solutions.

18. Irene bought flowers to plant on her balcony. She planted $\frac{1}{6}$ of the flowers before lunch and $\frac{2}{5}$ of the flowers after lunch.

a) What fraction of the flowers did she plant by the end of the afternoon?

b) She wants to finish planting the rest of the flowers in the evening. What fraction of the flowers does she still have to plant?

19. The class recycling bin was $\frac{1}{8}$ full at the beginning of the week. The bin was filled another $\frac{5}{12}$ by mid-week. By the end of the week, the bin was $\frac{5}{6}$ full.

a) How much was added to the bin in the first half of the week?

b) How much was added to the bin in the last half of the week?

c) What fraction of the bin was empty at the end of the week?

d) What fraction of the bin was empty by mid-week?

20. A tangram is a square geometric puzzle that is divided into seven geometric shapes. There are two large triangles, one medium triangle, two small triangles, one parallelogram, and one square.

Try This!

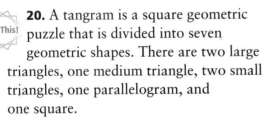

- large triangle
- parallelogram
- square
- medium triangle
- small triangle

a) Name two different combinations of shapes that cover $\frac{1}{2}$ of the tangram.

b) What fraction of the whole tangram does each tangram shape represent?

c) If you remove one large triangle, what combinations of shapes can replace it? Write an addition statement to represent each combination.

21. An Olympic swimming pool measures 50 m in length, 25 m in width, and a minimum of 2 m in depth. There are eight competing lanes that are each 2.5 m wide. There are two spaces outside lanes 1 and 8, which are also 2.5 m wide.

During practice, three of the competing lanes are used for front crawl, and half of the competing lanes are used for the butterfly stroke.

a) Write an expression for the total fraction of competing lanes used during practice.

b) Find the number of competing lanes used during practice.

c) If $\frac{5}{8}$ of the pool is used during a race, what fraction of the pool is not used?

Extend

22. Add or subtract.

a) $\frac{1}{6} + \frac{1}{4} + \frac{1}{2}$ **b)** $\frac{8}{9} - \frac{2}{3} - \frac{1}{6}$

23. Geraldine ran for $\frac{1}{2}$ h on Monday, $\frac{5}{6}$ h on Wednesday, $\frac{2}{3}$ h on Friday, and $\frac{3}{4}$ h on Saturday.

a) Estimate and then calculate how many hours she ran altogether.

b) For how many more minutes did she run on Wednesday than on Saturday?

c) Geraldine follows this schedule every week during February. Explain how you would find the total number of hours she runs that month.

3.2 Investigate Multiplying Fractions

Focus on...
- representing fractions using concrete materials
- using concrete materials to multiply fractions
- multiplying fractions

During a track and field competition, the field events take place in the field inside the track. Suppose $\frac{2}{3}$ of this area is used for field events. One-quarter of this part is used for long jump. What fraction of the field is used for long jump?

Discover the Math

How can you represent multiplying fractions?

Materials
- sheet of paper
- pencil crayons

Strategies
What strategy is being used?

1. Fold a rectangular piece of paper one way into thirds to represent the field.
   Open it up and colour $\frac{2}{3}$ to show the amount of the field that is used for field events.

2. Now, fold the paper into fourths the other way. Open up the paper. Using a different colour pencil crayon, colour $\frac{1}{4}$ to show the amount of the field that is used for long jump.

3. **a)** How many sections are there altogether?
   b) How many coloured sections overlap?
   c) How does this represent the fraction of the field that is used for long jump?
   d) What fraction of the field is used for long jump?

4. **Reflect** How can you use paper folding to model multiplying fractions?

Example: Multiply Fractions

Evaluate.

a) $\dfrac{3}{4} \times \dfrac{2}{3}$

b) $\dfrac{2}{5}$ of 5

Literacy Connections

The word "of" in math means multiplied by.

For example, $\dfrac{1}{2}$ of 4 means $\dfrac{1}{2} \times 4$.

Solution

a) *Method 1: Use a Diagram*

Draw a diagram to show $\dfrac{2}{3}$.

Divide the shaded portion into quarters.

Circle $\dfrac{3}{4}$ of this region.

The circled area shows the product $\dfrac{3}{4} \times \dfrac{2}{3} = \dfrac{1}{2}$.

I circled $\dfrac{3}{4}$ of the shaded part. I have circled $\dfrac{6}{12}$ of the diagram. That's $\dfrac{1}{2}$.

Method 2: Multiply the Numerators and Denominators

$$\dfrac{3}{4} \times \dfrac{2}{3} = \dfrac{3 \times 2}{4 \times 3}$$
$$= \dfrac{6}{12}$$
$$= \dfrac{1}{2}$$

That's the number of circled parts in the diagram.

That's the number of parts in the whole.

$\dfrac{6}{12}$ can be written in lowest terms as $\dfrac{1}{2}$.

b) $\dfrac{2}{5}$ of 5 means the same as $\dfrac{2}{5} \times 5$.

The whole number 5 can be written as the fraction $\dfrac{5}{1}$.

$$\dfrac{2}{5} \times \dfrac{5}{1} = \dfrac{2 \times 5}{5 \times 1}$$
$$= \dfrac{10}{5}$$
$$= \dfrac{2}{1} \text{ or } 2$$

Multiply the numerators. Multiply the denominators.

If I shade $\dfrac{2}{5}$ of 5 circles, I shade 2 circles.

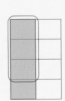

Key Ideas

- The word "of" in math means multiplied by. $\dfrac{1}{3}$ of 3 means the same as $\dfrac{1}{3} \times 3$.

- To multiply fractions, multiply the numerators and multiply the denominators.

$$\dfrac{3}{4} \times \dfrac{1}{2} = \dfrac{3 \times 1}{4 \times 2}$$
$$= \dfrac{3}{8}$$

Communicate the Ideas

1. Jared was absent the day the class learned about multiplying fractions. How would you describe how to multiply $\frac{3}{4} \times \frac{2}{3}$ to Jared? Use pictures and words.

2. Is $\frac{1}{4}$ of $\frac{1}{2}$ the same as $\frac{1}{2}$ of $\frac{1}{4}$? Explain why or why not.

Check Your Understanding

Practise

Express all answers in lowest terms.

3. Rewrite each statement using a multiplication sign.

   a) $\frac{1}{4}$ of 4   b) $\frac{1}{5}$ of 10

   c) $\frac{1}{2}$ of $\frac{1}{5}$ d) $\frac{1}{3}$ of $\frac{3}{8}$

For help with questions 4 to 6, refer to the Example.

4. Use diagrams or paper folding to find each product.

   a) $\frac{1}{2} \times \frac{1}{3}$ b) $\frac{1}{6} \times \frac{1}{4}$

   c) $\frac{3}{4} \times \frac{1}{3}$ d) $\frac{2}{3} \times \frac{5}{8}$

5. Multiply.

   a) $\frac{4}{5} \times \frac{1}{2}$ b) $\frac{2}{3} \times \frac{3}{7}$

   c) $\frac{5}{6} \times \frac{3}{4}$ d) $\frac{3}{5} \times \frac{5}{6}$

6. Calculate.

   a) $\frac{1}{4} \times 4$ b) $\frac{5}{6} \times 6$

   c) $\frac{1}{2} \times 16$ d) $\frac{2}{3} \times 6$

Apply

7. Find each amount.

   a) $\frac{4}{7}$ of $21   b) $\frac{2}{3}$ of $15

8. Evaluate.

   a) $8 \times \frac{3}{4}$ b) $12 \times \frac{5}{6}$

9. a) $\frac{2}{3}$ of the students in a class have brown eyes. $\frac{1}{2}$ of these students have brown hair. What fraction of the students have brown eyes and brown hair?

   b) $\frac{2}{5}$ of the students in a class wear glasses. $\frac{1}{4}$ of these students are boys. What fraction of the students are boys who wear glasses?

10. Write two different multiplication sentences that have a product of $\frac{4}{9}$.

11. Elena and her friends order a 24-slice party pizza. She and her friends eat $\frac{2}{3}$ of the pizza.
   a) How many slices do they eat altogether?
   b) Her brother Marcus eats $\frac{1}{2}$ of what is left. What fraction of the pizza does Marcus eat?

12. Adina had $\frac{3}{5}$ of a pizza. She gave Richard $\frac{3}{4}$ of her portion of the pizza.

  a) Did Richard receive more or less than one entire pizza? Explain how you know.

  b) Did Richard receive more or less than $\frac{3}{10}$ of the original pizza? Explain how you know.

13. Every year the school participates in a read-a-thon. About $\frac{4}{7}$ of the class collected pledge money for the event. Close to $\frac{3}{8}$ of these students raised over $50 each.

  a) What fraction of the class raised over $50 each?

  b) What fraction of the class raised less than $50?

  c) There are 28 students in the class. Estimate how many students raised over $50.

  d) There are 28 students in the class. How would you find the minimum amount of money raised?

Try This!

14. a) Find the product of 4×3 and of $\frac{2}{3} \times \frac{1}{2}$.

  b) Is the product of two whole numbers always larger, or always smaller, than each of the factors? Use pictures, numbers, or words to justify your answer.

  c) Is the product of two fractions always larger, or always smaller, than each of the factors? Use pictures, numbers, or words to justify your answer.

Extend

15. Find each product.

  a) $\frac{4}{5} \times \frac{2}{3} \times \frac{1}{2}$ **b)** $\frac{3}{4} \times \frac{1}{2} \times \frac{1}{3}$

16. a) Use diagrams to explain why $2 \times \frac{1}{2} = 1$, $3 \times \frac{1}{3} = 1$, $4 \times \frac{1}{4} = 1$, $5 \times \frac{1}{5} = 1$, and so on.

  b) What fraction multiplied by $\frac{3}{2}$ has a product equal to 1?

  c) The fraction you found in part b) is called the *reciprocal* of $\frac{3}{2}$. Explain what you think the word "reciprocal" means.

Making Connections

Math Tip: Reducing Fractions

When you multiply fractions, it can be helpful to simplify the fractions before evaluating.

For example, multiply $\frac{3}{4} \times \frac{8}{9}$.

$$\frac{\overset{1}{\cancel{3}}}{\underset{1}{\cancel{4}}} \times \frac{\overset{2}{\cancel{8}}}{\underset{3}{\cancel{9}}}$$

Since 3 is a factor of 3 and 9, I can divide both 3 and 9 by 3.
Since 4 is a factor of 4 and 8, I can divide both 4 and 8 by 4.

$$= \frac{1 \times 2}{1 \times 3}$$

$$= \frac{2}{3}$$

If I don't simplify first, I get

$$\frac{3}{4} \times \frac{8}{9} = \frac{24}{36}$$

$$= \frac{24 \div 12}{36 \div 12}$$

$$= \frac{2}{3}$$

When you reduce fractions before multiplying, the answer will already be in lowest terms.

3.3 Investigate Dividing Fractions

Focus on...
- representing fractions using concrete materials
- using concrete materials to divide fractions
- dividing fractions

To plant the school garden, each grade gets six full flats of flowers. The grade 8 classes are split into groups and each group gets $\frac{1}{4}$ of a flat of flowers to plant. How many groups are the grade 8 classes divided into?

Discover the Math

Materials
- at least six sheets of paper
- scissors

How can you divide fractions?

1. Use six sheets of paper to represent the six flats of flowers. Cut each piece of paper into quarters.

   a) Write a division statement to represent this situation.
   b) How many pieces of paper do you have?
   c) Write a related multiplication statement that has the same answer.

Strategies
What strategy is being used?

2. Use paper cutting to show each division. Copy and complete the table.

3. How does each division statement compare with its related multiplication statement?

Division Statement	Total Number of Pieces of Paper	Related Multiplication Statement
$3 \div \frac{1}{2}$		
$3 \div \frac{1}{4}$		
$3 \div \frac{1}{3}$		

4. Predict the value of

a) $3 \div \dfrac{1}{5}$ **b)** $3 \div \dfrac{3}{4}$

5. Reflect

a) Use the results of steps 2 and 3 to write a rule for dividing fractions.

b) Use your rule to check your predictions in step 4.

Example: Divide Fractions

Find each quotient.

a) $6 \div \dfrac{1}{2}$ **b)** $\dfrac{1}{2} \div 6$ **c)** $\dfrac{1}{2} \div \dfrac{1}{3}$

Solution

a) *Method 1: Use a Diagram*

How many groups of $\dfrac{1}{2}$ can be made from 6?

Draw a diagram.
Divide each circle in half.
There are 12 half circles.

$6 \div \dfrac{1}{2} = 12$

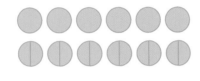

So, 12 groups of $\dfrac{1}{2}$ can be made from 6.

> This is the same as $6 \times 2 = 12$.

Method 2: Multiply by the Reciprocal

To divide fractions, you can multiply by the **reciprocal** .
To do this, invert, or flip, the divisor and multiply.

$6 \div \dfrac{1}{2} = 6 \times \dfrac{2}{1}$
$\qquad = 6 \times 2$
$\qquad = 12$

> The reciprocal of $\dfrac{1}{2}$ is $\dfrac{2}{1}$.
> The fraction $\dfrac{2}{1}$ is the same as the whole number 2.

b) $\dfrac{1}{2} \div 6 = \dfrac{1}{2} \times \dfrac{1}{6}$
$\qquad = \dfrac{1 \times 1}{2 \times 6}$
$\qquad = \dfrac{1}{12}$

> Multiply by the reciprocal. The whole number 6 is the same as the fraction $\dfrac{6}{1}$. The reciprocal of $\dfrac{6}{1}$ is $\dfrac{1}{6}$.

c) $\dfrac{1}{2} \div \dfrac{1}{3} = \dfrac{1}{2} \times \dfrac{3}{1}$
$\qquad = \dfrac{1 \times 3}{2 \times 1}$
$\qquad = \dfrac{3}{2}$ or $1\dfrac{1}{2}$

> Multiply by the reciprocal.

reciprocals
- two numbers that have a product of 1
- $\dfrac{3}{4}$ and $\dfrac{4}{3}$ are reciprocals since
  $\dfrac{3}{4} \times \dfrac{4}{3} = \dfrac{3 \times 4}{4 \times 3}$
  $\qquad = \dfrac{12}{12}$
  $\qquad = 1$

● Reciprocals are two numbers that have a product of 1.

The fraction $\frac{6}{5}$ is the reciprocal of the fraction $\frac{5}{6}$.

$$\frac{6}{5} \times \frac{5}{6} = \frac{30}{30}$$
$$= 1$$

● To divide fractions, write the reciprocal of the divisor (invert) and multiply.

$4 \div \frac{1}{3}$

$$4 \div \frac{1}{3} = \frac{4}{1} \times \frac{3}{1}$$
$$= 12$$

You can remember how to divide fractions using the phrase "invert and multiply."

Communicate the Ideas

1. Use pictures, numbers, and words to show $5 \div \frac{1}{4}$.

2. Explain how a fraction division question can be thought of as a multiplication question. Use pictures, numbers, and words to explain.

3. Explain the error in Leanne's thinking.

$$\frac{3}{4} \div \frac{2}{3} = \frac{4}{3} \times \frac{2}{3}$$
$$= \frac{8}{9}$$

Check Your Understanding

Practise

Express all answers in lowest terms.

4. Write the reciprocal of each number.

a) $\frac{2}{3}$ **b)** $\frac{5}{4}$

c) 7   **d)** $\frac{1}{8}$

For help with questions 5 to 8, refer to the Example.

5. Use diagrams to find each quotient.

a) $6 \div \frac{1}{3}$ **b)** $5 \div \frac{1}{2}$ **c)** $4 \div \frac{1}{4}$

6. Divide.

a) $\frac{1}{2} \div 3$ **b)** $\frac{3}{5} \div 4$ **c)** $\frac{4}{3} \div 7$

7. Divide.

a) $\dfrac{3}{4} \div \dfrac{1}{2}$ b) $\dfrac{3}{4} \div \dfrac{3}{8}$ c) $\dfrac{4}{7} \div \dfrac{5}{7}$

8. Divide.

a) $\dfrac{5}{6} \div \dfrac{2}{3}$ b) $\dfrac{3}{8} \div \dfrac{1}{5}$ c) $\dfrac{3}{5} \div \dfrac{9}{10}$

Apply

9. Copy each equation. Replace each ■ to make the equation true.

a) $\dfrac{2}{3} \times$ ■ $= \dfrac{2}{9}$

b) ■ $\times \dfrac{3}{5} = \dfrac{6}{15}$

c) $\dfrac{1}{2} \div$ ■ $= 2$

d) $\dfrac{3}{4} \div$ ■ $= \dfrac{9}{20}$

10. Jonah found $\dfrac{2}{3}$ of a bag of cookies in the cupboard. He and his friends each ate $\dfrac{1}{6}$ of the bag of cookies for a snack. How many people ate cookies?

Cookies

11. A theatre presentation consists of a series of short plays. Each play lasts $\dfrac{3}{10}$ h. The entire presentation lasts for exactly 2 h with one intermission.

a) Estimate the number of plays that are performed.

b) How many plays are performed?

c) How reasonable was your estimate? Explain.

d) How long is the intermission?

 12. For a camping trip, Albert bought 6 bags of trail mix that he wants to split into portions that are $\dfrac{3}{7}$ of the whole.

a) Draw a diagram to represent this situation.

b) Estimate how many portions he can make.

c) Find how many portions he can make.

d) Predict why Albert wants to divide the trail mix into $\dfrac{3}{7}$ portions.

Extend

13. Maria told her friend Alisa of another way to divide fractions.

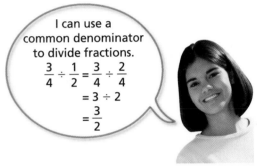

I can use a common denominator to divide fractions.
$$\dfrac{3}{4} \div \dfrac{1}{2} = \dfrac{3}{4} \div \dfrac{2}{4}$$
$$= 3 \div 2$$
$$= \dfrac{3}{2}$$

Use diagrams or words to explain why this method works.

14. Use the method from question 13 to find each quotient.

a) $\dfrac{3}{8} \div \dfrac{7}{8}$

b) $\dfrac{1}{4} \div \dfrac{5}{8}$

c) $\dfrac{4}{5} \div \dfrac{1}{2}$

d) $\dfrac{2}{5} \div \dfrac{3}{4}$

15. Explain why the quotient of $\dfrac{5}{8} \div \dfrac{3}{4}$ is larger than either fraction.

3.4 Order of Operations With Fractions

Focus on...
- BEDMAS
- applying the order of operations to fractions
- solving multi-step fraction problems
- explaining multi-step fraction problems

You often have to correctly answer a skill-testing question to win a contest. Which student will win the contest?

order of operations

- correct sequence of calculations for evaluating an expression

  B Brackets
  E Exponents
  D ⎫ Division and
  M ⎭ Multiplication, in order from *left* to *right*
  A ⎫ Addition and
  S ⎭ Subtraction, in order from *left* to *right*

Making Connections

You will learn more about the order of operations with exponents in Chapter 7.

Discover the Math

How do you choose the order in which to apply operations when evaluating an expression?

Example 1: Evaluate Expressions With Fractions

Use the order of operations to evaluate $\dfrac{5}{6} - \dfrac{1}{2} \times \dfrac{1}{3}$.

Solution

$$\dfrac{5}{6} - \dfrac{1}{2} \times \dfrac{1}{3} \qquad \textbf{Multiply.}$$

$$= \dfrac{5}{6} - \dfrac{1 \times 1}{2 \times 3}$$

$$= \dfrac{5}{6} - \dfrac{1}{6} \qquad \textbf{Subtract.}$$

$$= \dfrac{4}{6}$$

$$= \dfrac{2}{3}$$

$\dfrac{2}{3}$ is equivalent to $\dfrac{4}{6}$.

$\dfrac{2}{3}$ is in lowest terms.

Example 2: Evaluate Expressions With Fractions and Brackets

Use the order of operations to evaluate $\left(\dfrac{5}{6} - \dfrac{1}{2}\right) \times \dfrac{1}{3}$.

Solution

$\left(\dfrac{5}{6} - \dfrac{1}{2}\right) \times \dfrac{1}{3}$ **Brackets.**

The lowest common denominator (LCD) for $\dfrac{5}{6}$ and $\dfrac{1}{2}$ is 6.

$= \left(\dfrac{5}{6} - \dfrac{3}{6}\right) \times \dfrac{1}{3}$

$= \dfrac{2}{6} \times \dfrac{1}{3}$ **Multiply.**

Multiply the numerators.
Multiply the denominators.

$= \dfrac{2}{18}$

$= \dfrac{1}{9}$ $\dfrac{2}{18}$ can be written in lowest terms as $\dfrac{1}{9}$.

Key Ideas

- To evaluate expressions with fractions, follow the order of operations.
  Use BEDMAS to help you remember the order.

B	Brackets
E	Exponents
D }	Division and Multiplication, from *left* to *right*
M	
A }	Addition and Subtraction, from *left* to *right*
S	

Communicate the Ideas

1. Amy and Michael each got a different answer to the skill-testing question $\dfrac{2}{3} - \dfrac{1}{4} \times \dfrac{1}{2}$.

I got $\dfrac{13}{24}$.

I got $\dfrac{5}{24}$.

Explain how Amy and Michael found their answers. Who is correct?
What mistake did the other person make?

2. Which student won the contest at the top of page 96? Justify your response.

Practise

Express all answers in lowest terms.

3. Copy each expression in your notebook. Underline the step you would do first to evaluate the expression.

   a) $\dfrac{1}{2} - \dfrac{1}{4} \div \dfrac{1}{2}$

   b) $\dfrac{3}{4} \times 2 \div \dfrac{1}{2}$

   c) $\dfrac{9}{10} - \dfrac{1}{2} + \dfrac{1}{3}$

   d) $\left(\dfrac{3}{8} + \dfrac{1}{4} \right) \div \dfrac{2}{3}$

For help with questions 4 and 5, refer to Example 1.

4. Evaluate. Show your steps.

   a) $\dfrac{2}{3} + \dfrac{1}{4} - \dfrac{1}{6}$

   b) $\dfrac{4}{5} - \dfrac{1}{2} + \dfrac{7}{10}$

5. Evaluate. Show your steps.

   a) $\dfrac{2}{3} \times \dfrac{3}{8} - \dfrac{1}{12}$

   b) $\dfrac{9}{12} - \dfrac{3}{4} \times \dfrac{2}{5}$

For help with questions 6 and 7, refer to Example 2.

6. Evaluate.

   a) $\left(\dfrac{4}{5} + \dfrac{2}{3} \right) \times \dfrac{5}{2}$

   b) $\dfrac{2}{5} \times \left(\dfrac{7}{8} + \dfrac{3}{4} \right)$

7. Evaluate.

   a) $\left(\dfrac{3}{4} - \dfrac{1}{2} \right) \div \dfrac{1}{8}$

   b) $\dfrac{7}{8} \div \left(\dfrac{1}{2} + \dfrac{1}{4} \right)$

8. Evaluate.

   a) $\dfrac{2}{3} \times \left(\dfrac{5}{8} + \dfrac{1}{4} \right) \div \dfrac{7}{6}$

   b) $\dfrac{5}{9} + \left(\dfrac{5}{6} - \dfrac{1}{3} \right) \div \dfrac{1}{4}$

   c) $5 - \left(\dfrac{2}{9} + \dfrac{1}{6} \right) \div \dfrac{7}{6}$

   d) $3 + \left(\dfrac{8}{9} - \dfrac{2}{3} \right) \div \dfrac{2}{3}$

Apply

9. A car starts with a full tank of gas. After a drive around the city, $\dfrac{1}{7}$ of the gas has been used. With the rest of the gas in the car, the car can travel to and from Ottawa three times. What fraction of a tank of gas does each complete trip to and from Ottawa use?

10. Nathalie has one large bowl of popcorn. She invites three friends over to watch a movie. Her brother takes $\dfrac{1}{5}$ of the popcorn for himself. Nathalie must share the rest of the popcorn equally with her three friends. How much of the bowl of popcorn does each person get?

11. Copy each equation. Use brackets where necessary to make the equation true. Show how you got your answer.

a) $12 \times \dfrac{1}{3} + \dfrac{1}{2} = 10$

b) $\dfrac{1}{4} \times \dfrac{4}{7} \div \dfrac{6}{7} = \dfrac{1}{6}$

c) $\dfrac{3}{4} \div \dfrac{5}{6} - \dfrac{3}{4} \times \dfrac{2}{3} = 6$

d) $\dfrac{5}{6} \times \dfrac{3}{5} + \dfrac{3}{4} - \dfrac{1}{3} = \dfrac{11}{12}$

Chapter Problem

12. Talia's backyard has a vegetable garden in one back corner and a flower garden in the other back corner. Each garden takes up $\dfrac{1}{6}$ of the space in her yard. In $\dfrac{1}{4}$ of the vegetable garden, she grows carrots. In $\dfrac{1}{2}$ of the flower garden, she grows roses.

a) Draw a diagram to represent Talia's backyard.

b) Write an expression to calculate the amount of her backyard that Talia uses to grow carrots and roses.

c) How much of her backyard does Talia use to grow carrots and roses?

d) How would your expression change if you wanted to find out how much more of her backyard Talia uses for roses than for carrots?

13. Jerry tells his friend Mark that the answer to $\dfrac{1}{2} \times \dfrac{1}{3} \div \dfrac{1}{4}$ is the same as the answer to $\dfrac{1}{2} \div \dfrac{1}{3} \times \dfrac{1}{4}$. Is Jerry correct? Explain.

Try This!

14. a) Make up a skill-testing question that involves fractions and up to three operations. Make sure you can answer your question.

b) How many different questions can you make using the same fractions in order and adding or removing brackets? Describe them.

Did You Know?

There is a reason why contest winners have to answer a skill-testing question. It is a Canadian law! According to Canada's Criminal Code, giving away prizes based only on chance is illegal. A contest must involve a skill, such as answering a question. Then, the contest is not considered a game of chance.

Extend

15. Copy each expression. Then, find as many different solutions to each one as you can by adding brackets.

a) $\dfrac{2}{3} \times \dfrac{1}{2} + \dfrac{3}{8} \div \dfrac{1}{4}$

b) $\dfrac{7}{9} + \dfrac{5}{6} \div \dfrac{3}{4} - \dfrac{2}{3} \times \dfrac{5}{12}$

3.5 Operations With Mixed Numbers

Focus on...
- operations with fractions
- solving multi-step problems

In a school relay race, teams run $3\frac{1}{2}$ laps of the track. Each team has four members. How many laps does each team member run?

Discover the Math

How do you perform operations with mixed numbers?

Example 1: Add and Subtract Mixed Numbers

During swim practice, Jay swam $4\frac{3}{4}$ lengths of front crawl and $1\frac{7}{8}$ lengths of butterfly stroke.

a) Show each fraction as an improper fraction.
b) How many lengths did Jay swim in total?
c) The next day, Jay swam $2\frac{7}{8}$ fewer lengths altogether. How many lengths did he swim?

Solution

a)

$$4\frac{3}{4} = \frac{19}{4}$$

> Multiply the whole number by the denominator of the fraction part and add the numerator.
> $$4\frac{3}{4} = \frac{4 \times 4 + 3}{4}$$

$$1\frac{7}{8} = \frac{15}{8}$$

> $$1\frac{7}{8} = \frac{1 \times 8 + 7}{8}$$

b) Add the lengths.

$$4\frac{3}{4} + 1\frac{7}{8} = \frac{19}{4} + \frac{15}{8}$$

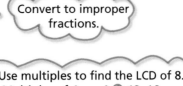 Convert to improper fractions.

$$= \frac{38}{8} + \frac{15}{8}$$

$4\frac{1}{2} + 2$. The answer should be about $6\frac{1}{2}$.

Use multiples to find the LCD of 8.
Multiples of 4 are 4, 8, 12, 16, ...
Multiples of 8 are 8, 16, 24, 32, ...

$$= \frac{53}{8}$$

$$= 6\frac{5}{8}$$

Jay swam $6\frac{5}{8}$ lengths in total.

Change $\frac{53}{8}$ to a mixed number by dividing 8 into 13.

$$53 \div 8 = 6\frac{5}{8}$$

c) Subtract $2\frac{7}{8}$ from the total number of lengths.

Method 1: Use Improper Fractions

$$6\frac{5}{8} - 2\frac{7}{8} = \frac{53}{8} - \frac{23}{8}$$

Convert to improper fractions.

$$= \frac{30}{8}$$

$$= 3\frac{6}{8} \text{ or } 3\frac{3}{4}$$

Convert to a mixed number.

Jay swam $3\frac{3}{4}$ lengths on the second day.

Method 2: Use Mixed Numbers

$$6\frac{5}{8} - 2\frac{7}{8} = 5\frac{13}{8} - 2\frac{7}{8}$$

$$= 3\frac{6}{8} \text{ or } 3\frac{3}{4}$$

I can't subtract $\frac{7}{8}$ from $\frac{5}{8}$. I need to borrow one whole from the 6.

$$6\frac{5}{8} = 5 + \frac{8}{8} + \frac{5}{8}$$

$$= 5\frac{13}{8}$$

Jay swam $3\frac{3}{4}$ lengths on the second day.

Subtract the whole numbers. Subtract the fractions.

Example 2: Multiply and Divide Mixed Numbers

At a fundraising car wash, Katrina worked for $1\frac{1}{2}$ h and washed six cars. Her friend Monique worked $2\frac{1}{4}$ times longer.

a) How long did Katrina spend washing each car?
b) How many hours did Monique spend washing cars?

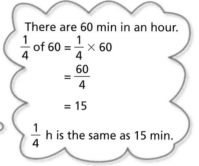

I know she washed 6 cars in $1\frac{1}{2}$ h. I need to divide $1\frac{1}{2}$ by 6 to find how long it took to wash one car.

Solution

a) $1\frac{1}{2} \div 6 = \frac{3}{2} \div 6$

> Change mixed numbers to improper fractions.

$$= \frac{3}{2} \times \frac{1}{6}$$

> To divide fractions, invert and multiply.

$$= \frac{3 \times 1}{2 \times 6}$$

$$= \frac{3}{12}$$

$$= \frac{1}{4}$$

> There are 60 min in an hour.
> $\frac{1}{4}$ of 60 $= \frac{1}{4} \times 60$
> $= \frac{60}{4}$
> $= 15$
> $\frac{1}{4}$ h is the same as 15 min.

Katrina spent $\frac{1}{4}$ h or 15 min washing each car.

b) Monique worked $2\frac{1}{4}$ times longer.

Multiply to find how many hours Monique spent washing cars.

$$1\frac{1}{2} \times 2\frac{1}{4} = \frac{3}{2} \times \frac{9}{4}$$

> Change mixed numbers to improper fractions.

$$= \frac{3 \times 9}{2 \times 4}$$

$$= \frac{27}{8}$$

$$= 3\frac{3}{8}$$

> Convert to a mixed number.

$2\frac{1}{4}$ is about 2. So, I estimate the answer to be about $1\frac{1}{2} \times 2$, or 3.

Monique worked for $3\frac{3}{8}$ h.

> This is close to the estimate of 3 h.

■ To add or subtract mixed numbers, you can change the mixed numbers to improper fractions first or you can use the mixed numbers to solve.

$$1\frac{1}{2} + 2\frac{2}{3} = \frac{3}{2} + \frac{8}{3}$$
$$= \frac{9}{6} + \frac{16}{6}$$
$$= \frac{25}{6}$$
$$= 4\frac{1}{6}$$

$$1\frac{1}{2} + 2\frac{2}{3} = 1\frac{3}{6} + 2\frac{4}{6}$$
$$= 3\frac{7}{6}$$
$$= 4\frac{1}{6}$$

$$2\frac{1}{3} - 1\frac{3}{4} = \frac{7}{3} - \frac{7}{4}$$
$$= \frac{28}{12} - \frac{21}{12}$$
$$= \frac{7}{12}$$

$$2\frac{1}{3} - 1\frac{3}{4} = 2\overset{1}{\underset{\ }{\cancel{4}}}\overset{+12}{\frac{4}{12}} - 1\frac{9}{12}$$
$$= 1\frac{16}{12} - \frac{19}{12}$$
$$= \frac{7}{12}$$

■ To multiply or divide mixed numbers, change the mixed numbers to improper fractions before solving.

$$1\frac{1}{3} \times 2\frac{3}{4} = \frac{4}{3} \times \frac{11}{4}$$
$$= \frac{44}{12}$$
$$= 3\frac{8}{12} \text{ or } 3\frac{2}{3}$$

$$1\frac{1}{3} \div 2\frac{3}{4} = \frac{4}{3} \div \frac{11}{4}$$
$$= \frac{4}{3} \times \frac{4}{11}$$
$$= \frac{16}{33}$$

Communicate the Ideas

1. Use diagrams to show that $5\frac{2}{3} = 4\frac{5}{3}$.

2. Judah and Chenile each found different answers to the question $4\frac{1}{2} + 2\frac{3}{4}$.

   Judah solved the question using mixed numbers and he got $7\frac{1}{4}$.

   Chenile solved the question using improper fractions and she got $\frac{29}{4}$.

   Which student is correct? Show how you know using pictures, numbers, and words.

3. a) Evaluate $1\frac{1}{3} - \frac{11}{15}$ in two ways.

   b) Which method do you prefer? Why?

Practise

Express all answers in lowest terms.

For help with questions 4 to 7, refer to Example 1.

4. Change each mixed number to an improper fraction.

a) $5\frac{1}{2}$ **b)** $3\frac{2}{5}$

c) $4\frac{3}{8}$ **d)** $8\frac{5}{6}$

5. Change each improper fraction to a mixed number.

a) $\frac{11}{3}$ **b)** $\frac{18}{5}$

c) $\frac{67}{10}$ **d)** $\frac{37}{4}$

6. Evaluate.

a) $6 + 1\frac{2}{3}$

b) $7\frac{2}{5} + \frac{4}{5}$

c) $5\frac{2}{3} + 2\frac{1}{6}$

d) $6\frac{1}{2} + 2\frac{1}{3}$

7. Evaluate.

a) $4 - 1\frac{3}{4}$

b) $6\frac{5}{8} - 2\frac{3}{8}$

c) $3\frac{4}{5} - 1\frac{1}{2}$

d) $7\frac{1}{2} - 3\frac{3}{4}$

For help with questions 8 and 9, refer to Example 2.

8. Evaluate.

a) $5 \times 2\frac{1}{4}$

b) $3\frac{1}{2} \times 4$

c) $2\frac{1}{4} \times 3\frac{1}{3}$

d) $3\frac{2}{3} \times 1\frac{4}{5}$

9. Evaluate.

a) $8 \div 2\frac{1}{3}$

b) $3\frac{1}{5} \div 4$

c) $3\frac{1}{2} \div 1\frac{1}{8}$

d) $4\frac{2}{3} \div 1\frac{1}{4}$

Apply

10. Kathy-Anne usually reads $7\frac{1}{2}$ pages of the newspaper while eating breakfast. Today she is running late and only has time to read $3\frac{1}{8}$ pages. She decides to read the rest of the $7\frac{1}{2}$ pages on the bus. How many pages does she read on the bus?

11. Craig spent $2\frac{2}{3}$ h cleaning his bedroom one weekend. The next weekend he spent $\frac{1}{2}$ as long cleaning his bedroom. How long did he spend cleaning his room the second weekend?

Chapter Problem

12. Jared's neighbour gave him $4\frac{1}{2}$ packages of bean seeds and 3 packages of peas to plant in his vegetable garden.

a) If he planted the beans in three rows, what fraction of a package of seeds did he plant in each row?

b) If he planted $\frac{3}{4}$ of a package of peas in a row, how many rows of peas did he plant?

c) If he planted the beans and peas evenly in eight rows, what fraction of a package of seeds did he plant in each row?

13. Nora is making lemonade to share with her friends. She has enough lemonade to fill $6\frac{3}{4}$ large glasses. She needs eight glasses of lemonade. If she pours equal amounts in all eight glasses, how much of a large glass of lemonade does each person get?

Try This!
14. Daria cuts lawns for her neighbours to earn extra money. One day, she cuts $2\frac{3}{4}$ lawns before lunch and $1\frac{2}{5}$ lawns before her afternoon break.

a) Draw a diagram to represent each number of lawns.

b) How many lawns does she cut altogether before her afternoon break?

c) She needs to cut six lawns before stopping for the day. How many lawns does she have left to cut after her break?

d) Suppose each lawn takes $\frac{2}{3}$ h to cut. If she starts work at 10:00 A.M., at what time does she eat lunch?

Extend

15. Use the order of operations to evaluate.

a) $2\frac{1}{4} \times \left(\frac{4}{5} - \frac{1}{2} \right) \div \frac{2}{3}$

b) $3\frac{1}{2} - \left(\frac{1}{3} + \frac{1}{6} \right) \div \frac{1}{6}$

16. One of these quotients has a proper fraction as a result, and one has an improper fraction. Determine which is which. Explain why they differ.

$3\frac{3}{5} \div 2\frac{1}{2}$

$2\frac{1}{2} \div 3\frac{3}{5}$

17. José wants to cut a triangular piece of wood from the rectangular board shown. The height of the triangle is $\frac{5}{3}$ the length of the base. The base of the triangle is 6 cm.

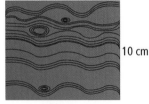
10 cm

12 cm

a) Write an equation to determine the area of the triangle.

b) What is the area of the triangle?

c) How many triangles will José be able to cut from the rectangular board?

Key Words

Unscramble each set of letters. Use the clues to help you solve the puzzles.

1. R M I P E

   a number with exactly two different factors, 1 and itself

2. O E P S M C T O I

   a number that has factors other than 1 and itself

3. T F R R C E A O E T

   a diagram used to divide a number into its prime factors (2 words)

4. E R F R D O N I E A R P O T O S O

   the correct sequence of calculations for evaluating an expression (3 words)

5. A C L S R O E R I C P

   two numbers that have a product of 1

Express all answers in lowest terms.

3.1 Add and Subtract Fractions, pages 82–87

6. Find the LCD for each set of fractions.

   a) $\frac{1}{4}$ and $\frac{5}{6}$

   b) $\frac{3}{8}$ and $\frac{5}{12}$

7. Add.

   a) $\frac{1}{2} + \frac{2}{3}$

   b) $\frac{3}{4} + \frac{1}{10}$

   c) $\frac{5}{8} + \frac{1}{6}$

   d) $\frac{7}{12} + \frac{1}{4}$

8. Subtract.

   a) $\frac{2}{3} - \frac{1}{6}$

   b) $\frac{9}{10} - \frac{1}{2}$

   c) $\frac{5}{6} - \frac{1}{10}$

   d) $\frac{7}{8} - \frac{2}{3}$

9. A bag contains green, red, and blue marbles. $\frac{2}{5}$ of the marbles are green. $\frac{1}{4}$ of the marbles are red. The rest are blue.

   a) What fraction of the marbles are green or red?

   b) What fraction of the marbles are blue?

3.2 Investigate Multiplying Fractions, pages 88–91

10. Multiply.

    a) $\frac{3}{8} \times \frac{4}{5}$

    b) $\frac{4}{9} \times \frac{1}{2}$

    c) $6 \times \frac{1}{3}$

    d) $\frac{3}{4} \times \frac{5}{6}$

11. Estimate, then evaluate.

    a) $\frac{4}{5}$ of 15

    b) $\frac{3}{10}$ of 20

    c) $\frac{2}{3}$ of 18

12. $\frac{4}{5}$ of the students in a class are right-handed. $\frac{2}{3}$ of these students have brown hair. What fraction of the students are right-handed and have brown hair?

3.3 Investigate Dividing Fractions, pages 92–95

13. Divide.

a) $\dfrac{2}{3} \div \dfrac{4}{5}$

b) $\dfrac{3}{10} \div \dfrac{2}{5}$

c) $\dfrac{5}{8} \div \dfrac{2}{3}$

d) $\dfrac{1}{3} \div \dfrac{5}{6}$

14. Copy each equation. Fill in the ■ to make it true.

a) $\blacksquare \times \dfrac{3}{4} = \dfrac{1}{4}$

b) $\dfrac{3}{10} \div \blacksquare = \dfrac{3}{4}$

15. Omar and his friends like to eat peanuts during baseball games. Omar has five bags of peanuts. It takes $\dfrac{5}{7}$ of a bag to fill a container.

a) Will Omar be able to divide the peanuts equally into full containers? Explain how you know.

b) How many full containers can Omar make?

3.4 Order of Operations With Fractions, pages 96–99

16. Evaluate. Write each answer in lowest terms.

a) $\dfrac{1}{4} + \dfrac{2}{3} - \dfrac{5}{6}$

b) $\left(\dfrac{5}{6} + \dfrac{3}{4} \right) \div \dfrac{3}{4}$

17. Copy each equation. Add brackets to make it true.

a) $\dfrac{5}{6} \times \dfrac{1}{2} + \dfrac{3}{5} - \dfrac{11}{12} = 0$

b) $\dfrac{1}{4} + \dfrac{2}{5} - \dfrac{3}{10} \times 2 = \dfrac{7}{10}$

3.5 Operations With Mixed Numbers, pages 100–105

18. Convert each fraction to either a mixed number or an improper fraction.

a) $3\dfrac{3}{5}$

b) $\dfrac{43}{6}$

c) $6\dfrac{3}{7}$

d) $\dfrac{32}{3}$

19. Estimate, then evaluate. How close was your estimate?

a) $2\dfrac{1}{3} + 5$

b) $5\dfrac{3}{4} \div 1\dfrac{2}{3}$

c) $5 \times 4\dfrac{1}{8}$

d) $3\dfrac{5}{6} - \dfrac{3}{4}$

20. It snowed for $4\dfrac{1}{6}$ h on Saturday and for $5\dfrac{1}{4}$ h on Sunday.

a) For how many hours did it snow altogether?

b) On which day did it snow longer? By how much?

Multiple Choice

For questions 1 to 5, select the correct answer.

1. What are the prime factors of 24?

   A 1, 2, 4, 3
   B 2, 2, 6
   C 2, 2, 3, 3
   D 2, 2, 2, 3

2. $\frac{3}{4} + \frac{1}{10}$ in lowest terms is

   A $\frac{2}{10}$ **B** $\frac{17}{20}$
   C $\frac{4}{14}$ **D** $\frac{2}{7}$

3. $\frac{3}{8} \times \frac{2}{3}$ in lowest terms is

   A $\frac{6}{24}$ **B** $\frac{9}{16}$
   C $\frac{1}{4}$ **D** $\frac{25}{24}$

4. $\frac{3}{10} \div \frac{4}{5}$ in lowest terms is

   A $\frac{15}{40}$ **B** $\frac{12}{50}$
   C $\frac{6}{25}$ **D** $\frac{3}{8}$

5. $3\frac{1}{4} - 2\frac{1}{12}$ in lowest terms is

   A $\frac{14}{12}$ **B** $5\frac{4}{12}$
   C $\frac{7}{6}$ **D** $5\frac{1}{3}$

Short Answer

Express all answers in lowest terms.

6. Construct a factor tree for 36.

7. **a)** Explain how the prime factors of 6 and 8 can be used to find the LCD of $\frac{1}{6}$ and $\frac{1}{8}$. Use diagrams and words.

   b) Explain why the product of prime numbers is always a composite number.

8. Evaluate $\left(\frac{1}{5} + \frac{3}{4} \right) \times \frac{1}{2}$.

9. Add brackets to make the equation true.

   $$\frac{1}{6} \times \frac{3}{4} + \frac{2}{3} \div \frac{1}{3} = \frac{17}{24}$$

10. Deirdre usually sleeps for $8\frac{1}{2}$ h. Last night it took her $3\frac{1}{6}$ h more than usual to fall asleep.
    a) How many hours did she sleep?
    b) How many minutes is this?

11. During November, the precipitation often changes from snow to rain. One Friday in November, there was $3\frac{1}{2}$ h of precipitation. It rained for $\frac{6}{7}$ of the time.
    a) How many hours did it rain?
    b) How many hours did it snow?

Extended Response

12. When Shanroy painted his bedroom, he used $1\frac{1}{2}$ cans of paint for the ceiling and trim and $2\frac{1}{3}$ cans of paint for the two coats on the walls.

a) How many cans of paint did Shanroy use to paint his bedroom?

b) Suppose he only uses one coat of paint on the walls. Will he use more or less paint for the walls than for the ceiling and trim? How much more or less?

13. The school's yearbook committee raises money by selling advertisements in the yearbook. One year, they sell six advertisements of $\frac{1}{8}$ page each, five advertisements of $\frac{1}{4}$ page each, and two advertisements of $\frac{1}{2}$ page each.

a) How many pages of advertisements do they sell altogether?

b) If they want all the advertisements to fit on two pages, how should they change the sizes of the advertisements?

Chapter Problem Wrap-Up

1. The grade 8 classes are asked to suggest a design for the school flower garden.

Your class is responsible for $\frac{1}{4}$ of the entire garden. This portion must contain four different colours of flowers.

a) Create a design for the part of the garden your class is responsible for.

b) What fraction of the entire garden is each colour you used? Show how you know.

2. Create a design for your own garden. Use at least four different types of flowers or vegetables. Describe as many fraction relations as you can about your garden. Use each of the four operations ($+, -, \times, \div$) at least once in the relations you describe. Use pictures, words, and numbers in your report.

Data Management and Probability

- Use probability to describe everyday events.

- Identify favourable outcomes and state probabilities.

- Identify 0 to 1 as a range from "impossible" to "certain" when investigating probability.

- List outcomes and calculate probabilities using tree diagrams, modelling, and lists.

- Compare predicted and experimental probability.

- Apply knowledge of probability in sports and games, weather predictions, and political polling.

Key Words

outcome

favourable outcome

probability

experimental probability

predicted probability

simulation

CHAPTER 4

Probability

Fishing can be a fun and relaxing hobby that you can participate in as a family, with friends, or by yourself. You can make it into a game. The winner can be the person who catches the biggest fish or the first fish. Does each person have an equal chance of winning?

By the end of this chapter, you will develop your own version of a fishing game. You will be able to use probability to help you select the best starting position. How will you make your game fair?

Chapter Problem

Play the game *Into the Pond* with a classmate. Here is how you play.

- Each player places his or her set of fish anywhere on the number line.
- Take turns spinning the spinner.
- If you have a fish on the number line at the number spun, put it into the pond.
- You can only put *one* fish into the pond at a time.
- The winner is the first player with all of his or her fish in the pond.

You have six fish. Where will you put them on the number line?

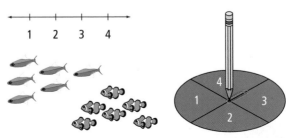

Equivalent Fractions

Fraction strips can be used to show that $\dfrac{8}{12}$ and $\dfrac{2}{3}$ are equivalent.

1. Draw fraction strips for each pair of fractions. State which pairs are equivalent.

a) $\dfrac{4}{16}$ and $\dfrac{1}{4}$ **b)** $\dfrac{6}{10}$ and $\dfrac{4}{5}$

c) $\dfrac{3}{4}$ and $\dfrac{9}{11}$ **d)** $\dfrac{3}{8}$ and $\dfrac{12}{32}$

2. Write an equivalent fraction for each.

a) $\dfrac{1}{2}$ **b)** $\dfrac{2}{3}$ **c)** $\dfrac{5}{6}$

d) $\dfrac{7}{28}$ **e)** $\dfrac{8}{12}$ **f)** $\dfrac{12}{30}$

Compare and Order Fractions

Fractions can be compared and ordered by writing them with a common denominator.

Compare $\dfrac{5}{8}$ and $\dfrac{3}{4}$. List the multiples of 8 and 4 to find the common denominator.

The multiples of 8 are ⑧, 16, 24, ...

The multiples of 4 are 4, ⑧, 12, ...

$\dfrac{3}{4}$ is greater than $\dfrac{5}{8}$.

$$\dfrac{5}{8}$$

$$\dfrac{3 \times 2}{4 \times 2} = \dfrac{6}{8}$$

> Multiply the numerator and denominator by the same number to get an equivalent fraction.

Fractions can also be compared and ordered by converting to decimals.

$\dfrac{5}{8} = 0.625$ Ⓒ 5 ÷ 8 = 0.625 $\dfrac{3}{4} = 0.75$ Ⓒ 3 ÷ 4 = 0.75

Since 0.75 is greater than 0.625, $\dfrac{3}{4}$ is the greater fraction.

3. Write the fractions in each pair with a common denominator. Which fraction is greater?

a) $\dfrac{2}{5}$ or $\dfrac{3}{10}$ **b)** $\dfrac{17}{20}$ or $\dfrac{1}{4}$ **c)** $\dfrac{9}{10}$ or $\dfrac{14}{15}$

4. Write each fraction as a decimal. Then, order the fractions from least to greatest.

$$\dfrac{9}{10}, \dfrac{5}{8}, \dfrac{11}{20}, \dfrac{1}{2}, \dfrac{3}{5}$$

Tree Diagrams

A **tree diagram** is useful for organizing combined outcomes from a probability experiment. This tree diagram shows the outcomes for spinning the spinner twice.

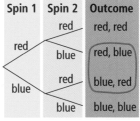

You read a tree diagram from left to right:
- The branches on the left of the tree show the outcomes for the first spin.
- The branches on the right of the tree show the outcomes for the second spin.
- The column on the far right lists the combined outcomes.

For example, there are two outcomes for spinning red and blue.

Spin 1	Spin 2	Outcome
red	red	red, red
	blue	red, blue
blue	red	blue, red
	blue	blue, blue

5. The tree diagram shows the combined outcomes for tossing three coins.

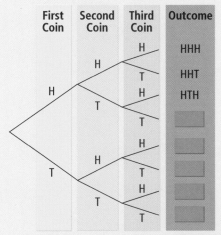

H stands for heads. T stands for tails.

a) Copy and complete the tree diagram.
b) How many outcomes are there?
c) How many of the outcomes are for tossing a combination of two heads and one tail?

6. **a)** Draw a tree diagram to show the combined outcomes for spinning the spinner and tossing a coin.

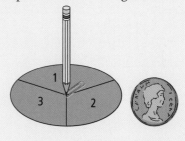

b) How many outcomes are there?
c) How many of the outcomes are for spinning a 2 and tossing heads?

7. **a)** Draw a tree diagram to show the combined outcomes for spinning the spinner two times.

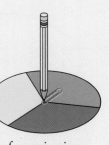

b) How many outcomes are for spinning yellow both times?
c) How many outcomes are for spinning yellow and blue in two spins?

4.1

Focus on...
- outcomes
- favourable outcomes
- probability

Explore Basic Probability

Games are played to win! The object of the game GREED is to get the most points during each round before the leader rolls a double.

How many points do you think you can get before the leader rolls a double?

Discover the Math

Materials
- two number cubes
- paper

Optional:
- BLM 4.1A GREED

How can you increase your chances of winning at the game GREED?

1. Write the word GREED at the top of a piece of paper as shown.

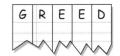

2. Play GREED.

Instructions for GREED

- Stand up.
- The leader rolls two number cubes.
- Record the sum of the numbers rolled in the appropriate column. For example, the sums for round 1 are recorded in the G column.
- Choose to remain standing or sit down until the next round.
- Continue to record the sum of the numbers rolled until you choose to sit down.
- The round is finished when a double is rolled. If you are standing when a double is rolled, then you get 0 points for that letter. Otherwise, your score is the sum of all the numbers for that letter.
- The game has five rounds, one for each letter in the title.
- The person with the most points at the end wins.

---

3. Reflect

a) Explain why you think rolling a double is an important **outcome**.

b) Do you think that a certain number of rolls will happen before a double? Explain.

c) If you played the game again, how would you change your strategy to increase your chances of winning? Explain.

outcome

• one possible result of a probability experiment

Example 1: Spinner Probabilities

Alicia is celebrating her birthday at her favourite restaurant. The server spins the spinner to determine what prize Alicia will get.

a) How many possible outcomes are there?

b) Alicia is hoping for the T-shirt. How many **favourable outcomes** are there?

c) What is the **probability** of the spinner landing on T-shirt?

d) For 100 guests, how many T-shirts should the restaurant buy?

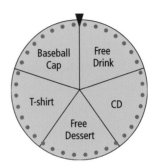

favourable outcome

• an outcome that counts for the probability being calculated

probability

• the chance that something will happen
• often expressed as a proper fraction, a percent, or a decimal between 0 and 1

Solution

a) The spinner is divided into five equal sections. So, there are five possible outcomes.

b) One section of the spinner is labelled T-shirt, so there is one favourable outcome.

c) Probability(T-shirt) = $\dfrac{\text{favourable outcomes}}{\text{all outcomes}}$

$$= \frac{\text{T-shirt}}{\text{spinner}}$$

$$= \frac{1}{5}$$

The probability of the spinner landing on T-shirt is $\frac{1}{5}$. So, for 100 spins, multiply by 100.

Strategies
How else could you find the answer?

d) $\dfrac{1}{5} \times 100 = 20$

The spinner should land on T-shirt about 20 times out of 100.
The restaurant should buy at least 20 T-shirts.

Example 2: Compare Probabilities

Find each probability. How likely is each probability?

a) What is the probability of spinning an even number?

b) What is the probability of spinning a 9?

c) What is the probability of spinning *any* number from 1 to 8?

d) What is the probability of spinning a factor of 24?

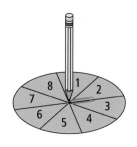

$$\text{impossible} \quad \overset{\text{equally}}{\text{likely}} \quad \text{certain}$$

0	$\frac{1}{2}$	1

Probability

| 0% | 50% | 100% |

Solution

a) Probability(even number) $= \dfrac{\text{favourable outcomes}}{\text{all outcomes}}$

$= \dfrac{\text{spinning 2, 4, 6, or 8}}{\text{spinning 1, 2, 3, 4, 5, 6, 7, or 8}}$

$= \dfrac{4}{8}$

$= \dfrac{1}{2}$

$\frac{1}{2}$ is 50%. I can use percents instead of fractions.

A probability of $\frac{1}{2}$ or 50% means there is an *equally likely* chance of spinning an even number.

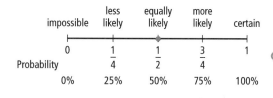

$$\text{impossible} \quad \overset{\text{less}}{\text{likely}} \quad \overset{\text{equally}}{\text{likely}} \quad \overset{\text{more}}{\text{likely}} \quad \text{certain}$$

0	$\frac{1}{4}$	$\frac{1}{2}$	$\frac{3}{4}$	1

Probability

| 0% | 25% | 50% | 75% | 100% |

b) Probability(9) $= \dfrac{\text{favourable outcomes}}{\text{all outcomes}}$

$= \dfrac{\text{spinning 9}}{\text{spinning 1, 2, 3, 4, 5, 6, 7, or 8}}$

$= \dfrac{0}{8}$

$= 0$ or 0%

There is no 9 on the spinner.

A probability of 0 or 0% means it is *impossible* to spin a 9.

c) Probability(any number from 1 to 8) $= \dfrac{\text{favourable outcomes}}{\text{all outcomes}}$

$= \dfrac{\text{spinning 1, 2, 3, 4, 5, 6, 7, or 8}}{\text{spinning 1, 2, 3, 4, 5, 6, 7, or 8}}$

$= \dfrac{8}{8}$

$= 1$ or 100%

All the numbers on the spinner are from 1 to 8.

A probability of 1 or 100% means it is *certain* that a number from 1 to 8 will be spun.

d) Probability(a factor of 24) = $\dfrac{\text{favourable outcomes}}{\text{all outcomes}}$

$$= \dfrac{\text{spinning 1, 2, 3, 4, 6, or 8}}{\text{spinning 1, 2, 3, 4, 5, 6, 7, or 8}}$$

$$= \dfrac{6}{8}$$

$$= \dfrac{3}{4} \text{ or } 75\%$$

> Each one of these numbers divides evenly into 24.

> There is also a $\dfrac{1}{4}$ or 25% (less likely) chance of spinning a number that is not a factor of 24.

> A probability of $\dfrac{3}{4}$ or 75% means that spinning a factor of 24 is *more likely*.

	impossible	less likely	equally likely	more likely	certain
Probability	0	$\dfrac{1}{4}$	$\dfrac{1}{2}$	$\dfrac{3}{4}$	1
	0%	25%	50%	75%	100%

Key Ideas

- An outcome is one possible result. For example, spinning T-shirt is one outcome on the spinner.

- Probability can be described on a number line with a scale from *impossible* to *certain*. Impossible is a probability of 0 and certain is a probability of 1.

	impossible	equally likely	certain
Probability	0	$\dfrac{1}{2}$	1
	0%	50%	100%

Probability(T-shirt) = $\dfrac{\text{favourable outcomes}}{\text{all outcomes}}$

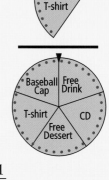

$$= \dfrac{1}{5}$$

Communicate the Ideas

1. Mary says, "The probability of spinning green is $\dfrac{1}{4}$." Madison says, "The probability is 25%." Who is right? Explain.

2. Raymond tossed a coin to decide who should go first in a soccer match. Does each team have an *equally likely* chance of winning the coin toss? Explain.

Practise

For help with questions 3 to 7, refer to Example 1.

3. In each situation, find the total number of outcomes and the number of favourable outcomes.

a) tossing heads on a nickel

b) rolling a 5 on a number cube

c) spinning blue on the spinner

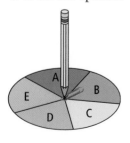

4. For each part in question 4, find the probability as a fraction.

5. In each situation, find the total number of outcomes and the number of favourable outcomes.

a) spinning an A or a C on the spinner

b) choosing a white marble from the bag

6. For each part in question 5, find the probability as a fraction.

7. A spinner has four sections numbered 1 to 4.

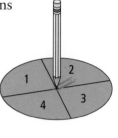

a) How many possible outcomes are there?

b) How many favourable outcomes are there for each number?

c) What is the probability of spinning a 4?

d) In 100 spins, how many times would you expect the spinner to land on 4?

For help with questions 8 to 12, refer to Example 2.

8. Match the probability of each situation with a letter on the number line.

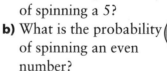

a) the sun rising tomorrow

b) a coin landing tails up

c) February having 30 days

9. Find each probability as a fraction and as a percent.

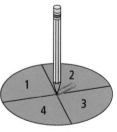

a) What is the probability of spinning a 5?

b) What is the probability of spinning an even number?

c) What is the probability of spinning *any* number from 1 to 4?

10. Use the number line to determine how likely each part of question 9 is.

Apply

11. To introduce probability to his class, Mr. Ogg wrote each letter of the word PROBABILITY on a separate card and placed the cards face down.

a) What is the probability of choosing the letter B?

b) What is the probability of choosing a consonant?

c) What is the probability of choosing a vowel?

d) Explain why the probability is different for different letters.

12. Candice challenged Melanie to determine the probability of a list of situations on a scale from 0 to 1. Locate each probability on the number line. Justify your reasoning.

| | less | equally | more | |
impossible	likely	likely	likely	certain
0	$\frac{1}{4}$	$\frac{1}{2}$	$\frac{3}{4}$	1
0%	25%	50%	75%	100%

Probability

a) an ice cream cone melting on a summer day

b) rain on December 1st

c) snow on December 31st

d) a coin sinking in a pond

13. a) List two situations that are *impossible* (probability of 0, 0%).

b) List two situations that are *equally likely* to happen (probability of $\frac{1}{2}$, 50%).

c) List two situations that are *certain* to happen (probability of 1, 100%).

14. Consider a number cube.

a) What is the probability of rolling an odd number?

b) What is the probability of rolling a 7?

c) What is the probability of rolling *any* number from 1 to 6?

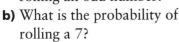

15. Consider the birthday prize spinner of free items.

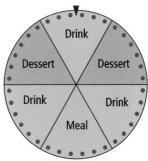

a) Do you have an equal chance of winning each prize? Explain.

b) Describe a situation that is *certain* to happen.

c) Describe a situation that is *impossible*.

d) Describe two situations that are *equally likely* to happen.

Extend

16. To play their favourite board game, Manuel and Rob record the product of the numbers on two number cubes.

a) List all the possible outcomes.

b) What is the probability of rolling a product of 20?

c) What is the probability of rolling an even product?

d) What is the probability of rolling an odd product?

e) What is the probability of rolling a product greater than 15?

f) Determine which products are most likely. Explain your reasoning.

17. Simon walked into class and was surprised to find a quiz. He had forgotten to study and had no knowledge of the content. He decided to use a coin toss to make his decisions.

a) Explain why tossing a coin would be a good way to make a decision on a true-or-false quiz.

b) Explain how Simon could use a coin to answer a multiple choice question that has 4 possible choices.

Organize Outcomes and Compare Probabilities

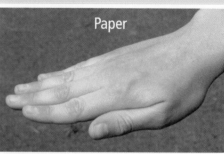

Rock

Paper

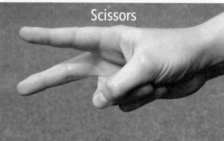

Scissors

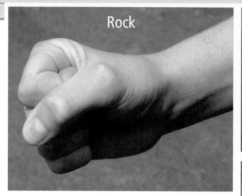

Rock, Paper, Scissors is a version of an old Japanese game known as Roe, Sham, Boe. In this game, two players use hand positions to determine a winner.

Discover the Math

How can you organize outcomes in Rock, Paper, Scissors?

Rock, Paper, Scissors is played in pairs.
- Face each other with one hand in a fist.
- Move your fists up and down and count to 3. On 3, change your fist into one of the three hand positions.
- The winner depends on the combination.
  - Rock wins over scissors. *(Rock dulls scissors.)*
  - Scissors win over paper. *(Scissors cut paper.)*
  - Paper wins over rock. *(Paper covers rock.)*

1. Create a way of organizing all the possible outcomes for this game.

2. Use your organizer from step 1 to estimate the probability of each hand position winning.

3. Play the game for about 5 min. Record your results. Use your results to find the **experimental probability** of each hand position winning.

4. Compare your experimental probabilities to the probabilities you predicted in step 1. This is known as a fair game. Explain why.

5. Reflect How well does your organizer show your results?
How else could you show your results?

Example: Probability Situations on a Spinner

You and a friend are guests on the "Oh No! Factor" television program. To play the game, you first spin the spinner to find out the "factor." Then, you toss a chip labelled "Your Team" on one side and "Opposing Team" on the other side.

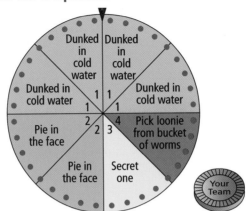

a) Use an organizer to show all the possible outcomes.

b) What is the
predicted probability of your
team having to pick a loonie from a bucket of worms.

c) Estimate how often the opposing team will get dunked in cold water out of 12 turns.

predicted probability

- the chance that something *should* happen
- $\frac{\text{favourable outcomes}}{\text{all outcomes}}$

Solution

a)

		Spinner							
		1	1	1	1	2	2	3	4
Chip	Y	Y, 1	Y, 1	Y, 1	Y, 1	Y, 2	Y, 2	Y, 3	Y, 4
	O	O, 1	O, 1	O, 1	O, 1	O, 2	O, 2	O, 3	O, 4

Strategies
What other organizers could you use? How would you use them?

b) There is only one favourable outcome, (Y, 4).

Probability(your team, pick loonie from worms) = $\dfrac{\text{favourable outcomes}}{\text{all outcomes}}$

$$= \frac{1}{16}$$

Ordered pairs can be used to represent outcomes. The letter stands for the chip outcome. The number stands for the spinner outcome. For example, (Y, 3) means your team does the secret one.

c) There are four favourable outcomes of (O, 1).

Probability(opposing team, dunk in water) = $\dfrac{\text{favourable outcomes}}{\text{all outcomes}}$

$$= \frac{4}{16} \text{ or } \frac{1}{4}$$

Multiply the probability for one turn by 12.
$$\frac{1}{4} \times 12 = 3$$

Multiply the numerator by the whole number 12.

The opposing team will get dunked in cold water in about 3 out of 12 turns.

- Results from an experiment are used to find experimental probabilities. Suppose your experimental results from Rock, Paper, Scissors are: rock wins 3 times, paper wins 4 times, and scissors win 5 times. The experimental probability of rock winning is $\frac{3}{12}$ or $\frac{1}{4}$.

- Organizers such as tree diagrams and tables show all of the possible outcomes. For example, the tree diagram here shows the outcomes from the Example.

- Outcome organizers show the predicted probability. From the tree diagram, the probability of your team getting a pie in the face is $\frac{2}{16}$ or $\frac{1}{8}$.

- Experimental probability and predicted probability are not always the same. The more you repeat an experiment, however, the closer the experimental probability should get to the predicted probability. For example, the more times you play the game Rock, Paper, Scissors, the closer the experimental probability of each hand position winning should get to $\frac{1}{3}$.

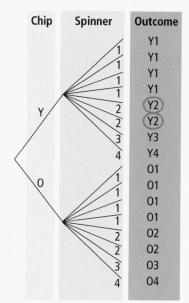

Legend	
Y = your team	
0 = opposing team	
1 = dunked in cold water	
2 = pie in the face	
3 = secret one	
4 = pick loonie from bucket of worms	

Communicate the Ideas

1. The table shows the possible outcomes from tossing a coin twice.

   Joan says the ordered pairs are written correctly. Connor says that the outcome in the bottom left corner should be (T, H). Explain why Connor is right.

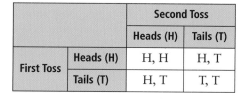

		Second Toss	
		Heads (H)	Tails (T)
First Toss	Heads (H)	H, H	H, T
	Tails (T)	H, T	T, T

2. Hasan says, "There is a 1 in 4 chance of spinning blue because there are 4 colours."

   Kuzana says, "There is a 1 in 2 chance of spinning blue because half of the spinner is blue."
   Who is right? Explain.

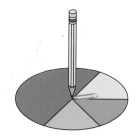

Practise

3. List all the possible outcomes for each situation.

a) Toss a coin.

b) Spin the spinner.

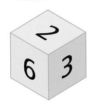

c) Roll a number cube.

4. List all the possible outcomes for each situation.

a) Pick a marble out of a bag.

b) Spin the spinner.

c) Pick a coin out of a piggy bank.

For help with questions 5 to 10, refer to the Example.

5. Draw a table or tree diagram to show all the possible outcomes for spinning both spinners.

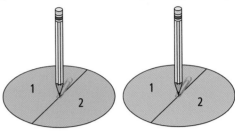

6. Draw a tree diagram to show all the possible outcomes for spinning both spinners.

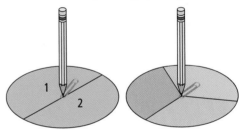

7. Use an organizer to show all the possible outcomes for spinning the spinner and tossing the coin.

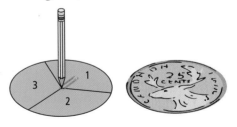

8. Use an organizer to show all the possible outcomes for spinning both spinners.

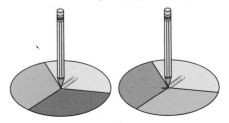

9. a) Create an organizer to show all the possible outcomes for the spinner and the coin.

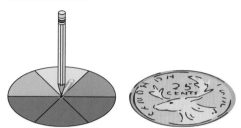

b) What is the predicted probability of spinning yellow and getting tails?

c) What is the predicted probability of spinning blue and getting heads?

10. Jai and her two sons spin a spinner to decide which television show to watch. Jai chooses if her name is spun twice in two spins. Otherwise, her sons choose.

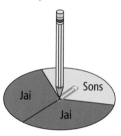

a) Create an organizer to show all the possible outcomes for spinning the spinner twice.

b) What is the predicted probability of Jai choosing the show?

c) What is the predicted probability of her sons choosing the show?

Apply

11. Two pairs compared their experimental probabilities for Rock, Paper, Scissors. Their results were different. Explain why experimental probabilities are not always the same.

12. A version of *Into the Pond* uses the sum of two spinners.

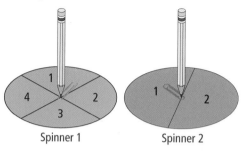

a) What are the possible sums when you add the results from these two spinners?

b) What is the predicted probability of getting each sum?

13. Two spinners are numbered as shown.

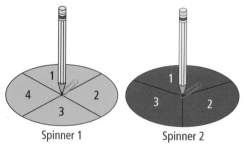

a) Draw a tree diagram to show all the possible outcomes for spinning both spinners.

b) Find the product of each outcome in your tree diagram.

c) What is the predicted probability of spinning a product of 1?

d) What is the predicted probability of spinning a product of 4?

e) What is the predicted probability of spinning a product that is an even number?

Literacy Connections

To find the product of each outcome, multiply the results from the spinners.

14. Jenna and Monique cannot agree on which movie to see. They decide to toss a coin and "best of three wins." If there are at least two heads out of three, Jenna gets to decide. Otherwise, Monique decides.

a) Create an organizer to show all the possible outcomes.

b) What is the predicted probability that Jenna gets to decide?

c) What is the predicted probability of getting at least one tail?

15. Choose numbers for your own pair of spinners.

a) What are the possible sums when you add the results from your two spinners?

b) What is the predicted probability of getting each sum?

c) Spin the spinners for 5 min. Record the results of your experiment in a tally chart.

d) Determine the experimental probability of getting each sum.

e) Compare your experimental probabilities to the predicted probabilities you found in part b).

Extend

16. Patricia and Ethan cannot decide which music CD to buy.

- Patricia suggests that they roll a number cube and spin a spinner. The spinner is divided in half. One half is labelled 1 and the other half is labelled 2. If the sum of the numbers from the cube and spinner is even, Patricia gets to decide. Otherwise, Ethan does.
- Ethan suggests that they toss a coin and roll a colour cube. Three faces of the cube are yellow and three faces are blue.

a) Draw a tree diagram to show all the possible outcomes for each person's suggestion for deciding.

b) What is the predicted probability of Ethan winning using Patricia's suggestion?

c) Explain how Ethan's suggestion could be used to give each person an equal chance of winning.

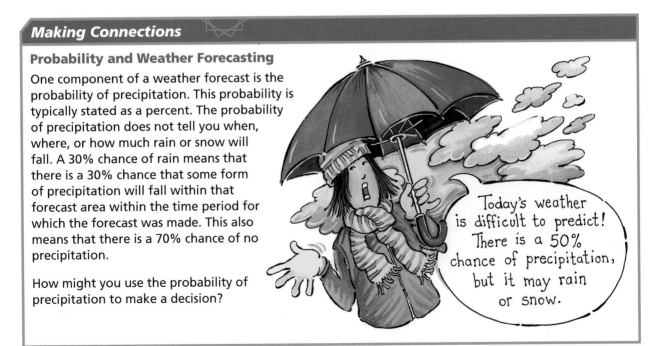

Making Connections

Probability and Weather Forecasting

One component of a weather forecast is the probability of precipitation. This probability is typically stated as a percent. The probability of precipitation does not tell you when, where, or how much rain or snow will fall. A 30% chance of rain means that there is a 30% chance that some form of precipitation will fall within that forecast area within the time period for which the forecast was made. This also means that there is a 70% chance of no precipitation.

How might you use the probability of precipitation to make a decision?

Today's weather is difficult to predict! There is a 50% chance of precipitation, but it may rain or snow.

More on Predicted Probabilities

In this game of Outdoor Olympics, you spin the Sport Spinner and then the Option Spinner. How many possible outcomes are there?

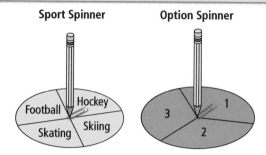

Sport Spinner   **Option Spinner**

	Option Legend		
	1	**2**	**3**
Hockey	Forward	Defence	Goalie
Skiing	Cross-country	Downhill	Snowboarding
Skating	Speed	Figure	Inline
Football	Receiver	Kicker	Quarterback

Discover the Math

How can you use outcomes to find predicted probabilities?

Example 1: Find Predicted Probability

What is the predicted probability of spinning skiing and downhill in the game Outdoor Olympics?

Solution

Method 1: Use a Table

		Option Spinner		
		1	**2**	**3**
Sport Spinner	Hockey	H, 1	H, 2	H, 3
	Skiing	S, 1	S, 2	S, 3
	Skating	K, 1	K, 2	K, 3
	Football	F, 1	F, 2	F, 3

> For the sports, I'll use H for hockey, S for skiing, K for skating, and F for football. For the options, I'll use 1, 2, and 3. The favourable outcome is (S, 2).

The probability of skiing and downhill is equal to the shaded area.

Since 1 out of 12 squares is shaded, Probability(S, 2) = $\frac{1}{12}$.

Method 2: Use a Tree Diagram

Sport	Option	Outcome
H	1	H1
	2	H2
	3	H3
S	1	S1
	2	S2
	3	S3
K	1	K1
	2	K2
	3	K3
F	1	F1
	2	F2
	3	F3

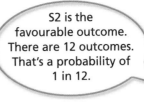

S2 is the favourable outcome. There are 12 outcomes. That's a probability of 1 in 12.

$$\text{Probability}(S2) = \frac{1}{12}$$

Example 2: State the Predicted Probability

A number cube is rolled and a coin is flipped. What is the predicted probability of rolling a 4 and tossing tails?

Solution

Number Cube	Coin	Outcome
1	H	1H
	T	1T
2	H	2H
	T	2T
3	H	3H
	T	3T
4	H	4H
	T	4T
5	H	5H
	T	5T
6	H	6H
	T	6T

Hey! The probability of rolling a 4 is $\frac{1}{6}$. The probability of tossing tails is $\frac{1}{2}$. The answer is $\frac{1}{12}$. That's the same as $\frac{1}{6} \times \frac{1}{2}$.

The favourable outcome is 4T.

$$\text{Probability}(4 \text{ and tails}) = \frac{1}{12}$$

- Outcome organizers such as tree diagrams and tables help you find predicted probabilities.

- Tables and tree diagrams show all the possible outcomes. For example, there are four possible outcomes from tossing a coin twice. The probability of each outcome is $\frac{1}{4}$.

First Toss	Second Toss	Outcome
H	H	HH
	T	HT
T	H	TH
	T	TT

- Favourable outcomes can be shaded in a table of outcomes. The shaded area represents the probability.

The probability of tossing tails and tails is $\frac{1}{4}$.

		Second Toss	
		Heads (H)	Tails (T)
First Toss	Heads (H)	H, H	H, T
	Tails (T)	T, H	T, T

Communicate the Ideas

1. What is the probability of tossing two heads if you use two pennies? Is the probability of tossing two heads the same or different if you use a quarter and a dime? Explain.

2. Charles missed today's probability lesson and asks Victoria to explain the new idea. Victoria decides to use these two spinners to teach Charles how to state the predicted probability. When stating the probability of spinning 2 and blue, Victoria uses a shaded area in a table. Write Victoria's explanation for Charles.

3. a) Is the predicted probability of spinning 2 and blue for the spinners in question 2 always the same? Explain.

   b) Is the experimental probability of spinning 2 and blue always the same? Justify your reasoning.

Check Your Understanding

Practise

4. Find the probability of each roll for a cube that is labelled A, A, B, C, D, D.

   a) rolling a B
   b) rolling an A
   c) rolling an A or a C
   d) rolling an A or a D

5. Find the probability of each selection for a piggy bank that contains 5 quarters, 7 dimes, and 12 nickels.

   a) a quarter   b) a dime
   c) a nickel   d) a penny
   e) a quarter or a dime

For help with questions 6 to 8, refer to Example 1.

Use the spinner and cards to answer questions 6 to 8.

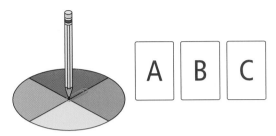

6. a) Draw a tree diagram for the spinner and cards.
b) Organize the outcomes in a table for the spinner and cards.

7. Use an organizer from question 6 to find the predicted probability for each situation.
a) blue and an A
b) yellow and a B
c) green and a C

8. Use an organizer from question 6 to find the predicted probability for each situation.
a) green, and an A or a B
b) yellow or red, and a C
c) any colour and a B
d) blue and any letter

For help with questions 9 and 10, refer to Example 2.

9. a) Draw a tree diagram for spinning the spinner twice.
b) What is the predicted probability of spinning two Cs?
c) What is the predicted probability of spinning an A and a B?

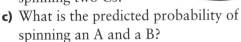

10. a) Draw a tree diagram for spinning both spinners.

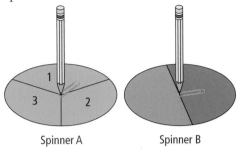

Spinner A   Spinner B

b) What is the predicted probability of spinning a 1 and red?
c) What is the predicted probability of spinning a 3 and blue?

Apply

11. Pina and Paul play a spinner game. First, Pina chooses a spinner combination. If Paul spins that combination, he gets a point. Otherwise, Pina gets the point. State each predicted probability.

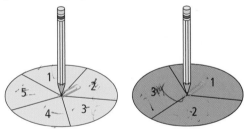

a) a 5 and a 1
b) a 2 and a 3
c) a number less than 3 and a 1
d) a prime number and a 2

12. It is Paul's turn to choose the spinner combination for the game in question 11. He chooses the sums of the spins. State each predicted probability.

a) a sum of 2
b) a sum of 7
c) a sum of 4
d) a sum greater than 5

13. Two number cubes are rolled.

  a) What is the probability of rolling a 6 on the white number cube? on the red number cube?

  b) The predicted probability of rolling a 6 on both number cubes is $\frac{1}{36}$. Show why this is correct.

Chapter Problem

14. A version of *Into the Pond* uses a number cube and a spinner. Roll the number cube. Then, spin the spinner. Multiply.

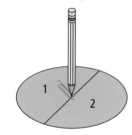

  a) What are the possible products when you multiply the results of the spinner and the number cube?

  b) What is the predicted probability of getting each product?

15. A carnival game uses a spinner. A player must spin the same number more than once to win.

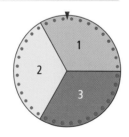

  a) What is the predicted probability of spinning the same number twice in a row?

  b) What is the predicted probability of spinning the same number three times in a row?

  c) Which option from parts a) and b) do you think the game operator would use? Explain.

16. Fred spins the spinners and creates a new colour from the result of the spins.

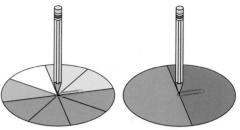

  a) What is the predicted probability that you will spin purple? Hint: Red and blue mix together to make purple.

  b) Make the spinners and carry out the experiment. What is the experimental probability of spinning purple?

  c) Explain why there is a difference between the experimental and predicted probabilities.

Extend

17. In Monopoly®, players use two number cubes. A player that rolls a double three times in a row goes to jail.

First Roll	Second Roll	Outcome
double	double	double, double
	no double	double, no double
no double	double	no double, double
	no double	no double, no double

  a) Explain why the probability of rolling a double is $\frac{1}{6}$ and the probability of not rolling a double is $\frac{5}{6}$.

  b) What is the predicted probability of rolling a double twice in two rolls?

  c) Can you develop a method for calculating the probability of rolling a double twice in two rolls without using an organizer?

  d) Use your method to find the predicted probability of rolling a double three times in a row. Check your calculation by drawing a tree diagram.

4.4

Extension: Simulations

Focus on...
- devising strategies
- simulating experiments

Yo Sep's favourite cereal company is including a free music CD in its box. There are three different CDs. Do you think this type of promotion will increase sales for the company?

Discover the Math

How can you simulate probability experiments?

Example: Simulate With a Spinner

Yo Sep found out that, for every one of CD 2 or CD 3, there are four of CD 1. He decides to run a **simulation** using a six-section spinner. Yo Sep spun the spinner and recorded his results in a tally chart. He continued to spin until he had spun all three numbers.

simulation
- a probability experiment used to model a real situation

CD	Tally
1	卌
2	‖
3		

a) How many boxes of cereal did Yo Sep have to "buy"?

b) Which number appears to have been last? Explain your reasoning.

Solution

a) Add up the tallies. Yo Sep bought eight boxes of cereal.

b) The number 3 only has one tally. This suggests that Yo Sep was waiting for a 3 to complete the simulation.

- A simulation models a real-life situation when you cannot easily predict the outcomes.

- A real-life situation can be simulated in many different ways. Ensure that the number of possible outcomes of the simulation matches the number of outcomes of the real situation.

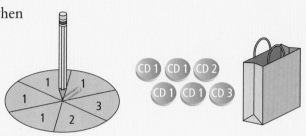

Communicate the Ideas

1. Why is a simulation helpful in a problem like Yo Sep's?

2. Yo Sep used a spinner to simulate collecting all three music CDs. What other methods might he have used?

3. Yo Sep found that he would have to "buy" eight boxes of cereal to get all three CDs. Is it fair to say that every person who purchases eight boxes of cereal will collect all three CDs? Justify your reasoning.

Check Your Understanding

Practise

For help with questions 4 and 5, refer to the Example.

4. The tally chart shows the results of a spinner simulation.

Letter	Tally
M	||
U	|||
S		
I	|||
C	|||||

a) How many spins were needed to get all five letters?

b) Which letter was last? How do you know?

5. The tally chart shows the results of a number cube simulation.

Number	Tally
1				
2					
3			
4		
5						
6		

a) How many rolls were needed to get all six numbers?

b) Which numbers could have been last? Explain your reasoning.

6. Describe an item that could be used to simulate each situation. Explain why each item is appropriate.

a) Choose one of two DVD movies.

b) Choose a sundae topping at random from eight choices.

c) Win a free music CD by collecting letters from pop bottle caps to spell C-A-P.

Apply

7. Inside the wrapper of a chocolate bar is a letter. You win if you collect W, I, and N. Explain how each spinner could be used to simulate this contest.

a)

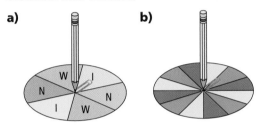

b)

c)

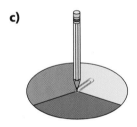

8. Describe a situation that can be simulated using each method.

a) flipping a coin

b) rolling an odd number on a number cube

c) picking a certain coloured marble from a bag of 5 green, 2 red, and 3 yellow marbles

d) picking a certain card from a deck of 52 cards

9. In the Example, Yo Sep used a six-section spinner to simulate buying cereal boxes to get three CDs. Suppose another CD is added. For every four copies of CD 1, there is one each of CD 2, CD 3, and CD 4.

a) How many boxes might he have to "buy" to get all four CDs?

b) Design and conduct a simulation for the situation.

c) Compare your prediction with the simulation. Explain your results.

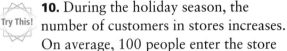

10. During the holiday season, the number of customers in stores increases. On average, 100 people enter the store every hour. 50% are women, 30% are men, and the rest are children.

a) Predict who the next 20 customers will be.

b) Design and conduct a simulation for the situation.

c) Compare your prediction with the simulation. Explain your results.

Extend

11. A letter is printed on the inside of a water bottle cap. To win the contest, participants must collect the letters to spell Y-O-U-W-I-N. One letter is twice as likely to be printed as the others.

a) Explain how you would simulate this situation.

b) Use the simulation to find how many water bottles need to be purchased to collect all six letters.

c) Explain how the probability changes depending on the likelihood of each outcome.

Apply Probability to Real Life

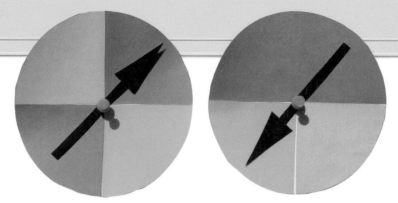

Games allow you to practise your skills in a fun way. Some games are designed to be unfair. What could be unfair about the spinners in this photograph?

Discover the Math

How can you use probability to make a game fair?

The game *Matching Spins* is played in pairs. Here is how you play.
• Players take turns spinning the spinners.
• Player 1 wins one point if the colours on the spinners match. Otherwise, Player 2 wins.
• The first player to reach 10 points wins!

1. Create two spinners with four equal-sized sections. Colour the sections of the spinners as shown in the photograph.

2. Create a tally chart to act as a score sheet.

3. Before playing the game, write two explanations:
   a) why you think Player 1 might win
   b) why you think Player 2 might win

4. Play the game for 10 min. Record who wins each game. How many times did Player 1 win? How about Player 2?

5. **Reflect**
   a) Which player has a greater chance of winning? Explain.
   b) How could you change the game to give each player an equal chance of winning?

Materials
• white cardboard
• compasses
• ruler
• pencil crayons
• 2 paper clips
• 2 pencils

Optional:
• BLM 4.5A Matching Spins Spinners

Example 1: Probability in Weather

The local forecast predicts a 70% chance of rain today.
a) What is the probability of rain as a fraction?
b) What is the probability of no rain today?

Solution

a) A 70% chance of rain means that the probability of rain is $\frac{70}{100}$ or $\frac{7}{10}$.

b) The chance that it will *not* rain is 30%. The probability that it will not rain is $\frac{30}{100}$ or $\frac{3}{10}$.

Example 2: Probability in Polling

There are three people running in the School Board election. A poll is held to determine the standings of the candidates. Of 500 people polled, 150 chose Eric, 225 chose Eliana, and 125 chose Karina.
a) Based on the poll, what is the probability of Eliana winning the election?
b) What percent of the people polled chose Eric?
c) Who is the least likely to win the election? State the probability.

Literacy Connections

Polling
Polls are used to get people's opinions. For example, people are polled to predict who will win an election.

Solution

a) Out of the 500 people polled, the greatest number chose Eliana. She is most likely to win. The probability that Eliana will win is $\frac{225}{500}$ or 45%.

b) 150 out of 500, or 30%, of the people chose Eric.

c) Karina is the least likely to win. The probability of Karina winning is $\frac{125}{500}$ or 25%.

- In some real-life games, the probability of things happening can be predicted. Predicted probability can help you make a decision in a game.

- In other real-life situations, like sports and weather, the probability of things happening is based on experimental data.

> A 20% chance of rain means that, if you stay in that location, you will get rained on 20 days out of 100.

Communicate the Ideas

1. How can probability be used to predict the winner in a game or an election?

2. Why do you think that the probability in games is predicted, while the probability in sports and weather is experimental?

> I just interviewed 20 grade 8 students chosen at random. 50% of them plan to vote for Victor in the student council elections.

Check Your Understanding

Practise

For help with questions 3 to 5, refer to Example 1.

3. The weather report says there is a 50% chance of snow.

   a) What is the probability of snow as a fraction?

   b) What is the probability of no snow?

4. The weather report says there is a 100% chance of rain.

   a) What is the probability of rain?

   b) What is the probability of no rain?

5. The weather report says there is a 0% chance of precipitation.

   a) What is the probability of precipitation?

   b) What is the probability of no precipitation?

For help with questions 6 to 8, refer to Example 2.

Three students are running for student council. 100 students are polled.

Student Council Poll Results

Student	Votes
Connor	20
Gilbert	50
Marilyn	30

Use the poll results to answer questions 6 to 8.

6. What is the probability of Connor winning the election?

7. What percent of the students polled chose Gilbert?

8. Who is least likely to win the election? State the probability.

Apply

9. Vivian's batting average is .400. This means that she has gotten a hit 40% of her times at bat.

   a) What is the probability of Vivian getting a hit on her next at-bat?

   b) What is the probability of Vivian not getting a hit on her next at-bat?

10. Four students are running for grade 8 class president. In a poll, 8 students chose Pedro, 4 chose Tristan, 6 chose Arielle, and 7 chose Brent.

    a) What fraction of the students chose Tristan?

    b) What percent of the students chose Brent?

    c) There are 150 students in grade 8. If the poll is accurate, can you determine the number of votes each student will receive in the election? Explain how.

    d) Determine the number of votes each student will receive in the election, based on the poll results.

11. Lorenzo and Wesley are playing backgammon, which uses two number cubes. A player can move two game pieces separately or move one game piece the sum of the numbers shown on the number cubes.

    a) What is the probability that the sum is 7?

    b) What is the probability that the sum is less than 5?

    c) Lorenzo needs a 10 or higher on his next roll to win. Explain how to determine the probability of rolling a 10 or higher. State the probability.

Try This!

12. Gillian and Brandon play "best of three wins" to decide who will speak first at the class assembly. Both Gillian and Brandon count to three and show a number 1 or 2 on their fingers. If the sum is odd, Gillian wins. Otherwise, Brandon wins.

    a) What is the probability of an even sum? What is the probability of an odd sum?

    b) If you were to play this game, would you call odds or evens? Explain why.

    c) This was to be a three-round game. Why did Brandon say Gillian won after only 2 rounds?

Extend

13. In his last 20 times at bat, Torrance hit 8 home runs.

    a) What is the probability of Torrance hitting a home run at his next at-bat?

    b) What is the probability of Torrance not hitting a home run?

    c) If Torrance is up to bat twice, what is the probability of him hitting a home run only on his second at-bat?

14. Three people are running for mayor in the city of Riverton. A poll is held 8 weeks before the election. Another poll is held 4 weeks before the election.

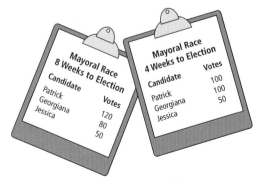

    a) How do the two polls compare?

    b) Who do you predict will win the election? Explain.

Key Words

For questions 1 to 3, copy the statement and fill in the blanks. Use some of these words:

outcomes — favourable outcomes
probability — experimental probability
simulation — predicted probability

1. Jarod spins two spinners. He uses his results to find the ▪▪▪▪▪▪▪▪◯▪◯ ▪◯▪▪▪◯▪▪▪ of each outcome.

2. Hai draws a tree diagram to show all the outcomes for spinning two spinners. She uses her organizer to find the ▪▪▪▪▪◯◯▪▪ ▪▪▪▪◯▪▪▪▪▪ of each outcome.

3. Both students need to count the ▪▪▪▪▪▪▪◯ and ▪▪▪▪▪◯▪▪▪ ▪▪▪▪▪◯▪▪ to find the probabilities.

4. Rearrange the circled letters in questions 1 to 3 to make a key word. Define the key word.

4.1 Explore Basic Probability, pages 114–119

Use this visual for questions 5 and 6.

5. Aly picks a card at random.

a) What is the probability of picking the 3 of ♥? Explain.

b) What is the probability of picking the 5 or the 8 of ♥? Explain.

6. Use the number line to determine how likely each situation is.

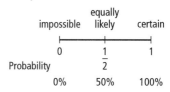

a) picking a black card
b) picking a red card
c) picking an even-numbered card

7. Consider a number cube.

a) State a situation that is *impossible* (probability of 0, 0%).

b) State a situation that is *equally likely* to happen (probability of $\frac{1}{2}$, 50%).

c) State a situation that is *certain* to happen (probability of 1, 100%).

4.2 Organize Outcomes and Compare Probabilities, pages 120–125

8. Ayani spins the spinner twice.

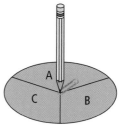

a) Draw a tree diagram showing all the possible outcomes.

b) What is the probability of spinning two As?

c) What is the probability of spinning a B and a C?

9. Paul and Laura use the sum of two number cubes to determine who gets out of doing chores. Paul chooses a sum of 11. Laura chooses a sum of 9. They take turns rolling the number cubes.

a) Use an organizer to show all the possible outcomes.

b) Who has a greater probability of getting out of doing chores? Explain.

4.3 More on Predicted Probabilities, pages 126–130

10. A number cube is rolled and the spinner is spun.

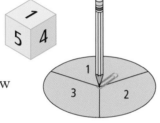

a) Use an organizer to show all the possible outcomes.

b) State each predicted probability.
- rolling a sum of 7
- rolling a sum greater than 8

11. a) State each predicted probability.
- spinning a 3 and pink
- spinning a prime number and yellow
- spinning an even number and blue

b) Explain whether the predicted probability of spinning a 3 and pink is always the same. Justify your reasoning.

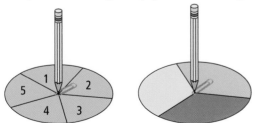

4.4 Extension: Simulations, pages 131–133

12. Leenor's bag of jellybeans has 2 red, 3 orange, 1 black, and 2 pink jellybeans. She wants to determine how many times she has to pull one jellybean at random from the bag before she gets one of each colour. She replaces the jellybean after each pick.

a) Predict how many times Leenor will have to pull a jellybean out of the bag before she gets one of each colour.

b) Design and conduct a simulation for the situation.

c) Justify why you repeated the simulation the number of times you did.

d) Compare your prediction with the simulation. Explain your results.

4.5 Apply Probability to Real Life, pages 134–137

13. The weather report says that there is a 30% chance of rain.

a) What is the probability of rain as a fraction?

b) What is the probability of no rain?

14. Greenville is having an election for mayor next month. Out of 400 people polled, 40% chose candidate A, 25% chose candidate B, and the rest chose candidate C.

a) How many people chose candidate A?

b) What is the probability of candidate C winning the election?

c) Based on the poll, who will win the election? Explain.

d) If the poll is accurate, how many votes should each candidate expect if 1000 people vote?

Practice Test

Multiple Choice

For questions 1 to 5, select the best answer.

1. What is the probability of rolling a 6 on a number cube?

A $\dfrac{5}{36}$ **B** $\dfrac{9}{36}$

C $\dfrac{1}{9}$ **D** $\dfrac{1}{6}$

Use the spinner for questions 2 and 3.

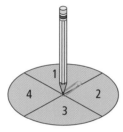

2. How likely is spinning an even number?

A certain   **B** more likely

C equally likely   **D** impossible

3. What is the probability of spinning *any* number from 1 to 4?

A 1   **B** $\dfrac{1}{2}$ **C** $\dfrac{1}{4}$ **D** 0

4. The weather report says there is a 40% chance of rain. What is the probability of no rain?

A 30%   **B** 40%   **C** 60%   **D** 70%

5. Three students are running for student council. Of the 50 students polled, 15 chose Herald, 25 chose Gina, and 10 chose Marlene. What is the probability of Marlene winning the election?

A 10%   **B** 20%

C 25%   **D** 50%

Short Answer

6. Use the number line to determine how likely each probability is.

a) rolling an odd number on a number cube

b) a rock floating in water

c) the sun setting today

7. A cube is numbered 2, 2, 3, 5, 9, 9. Find each probability.

a) rolling a 3

b) rolling a 2

c) rolling a prime number

d) rolling a multiple of 3

8. Each letter of TORONTO is printed on a separate card. The cards are shuffled and placed face down. Find each probability.

a) picking a T

b) picking a consonant

c) picking a vowel

9. a) Use an organizer to show all the possible outcomes for spinning the two spinners.

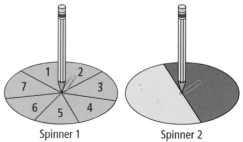

Spinner 1   Spinner 2

b) What is the predicted probability of spinning an odd number and yellow?

Extended Response

10. Shaheen has a bag with 5 red, 3 blue, and 2 yellow marbles. He picks one marble without looking.

a) Find the probability of picking each colour.

b) Are the probabilities in part a) experimental or predicted? Explain.

c) Explain how two players could use the bag of marbles in a fair game.

11. Riley is ordering an ice cream cone. She can choose one item from each category.

cone: plain or sugar

ice cream: chocolate, vanilla, or strawberry

toppings: whipped cream or cherries

a) Use a tree diagram to show Riley's possible choices.

b) If Riley randomly chooses, what is the predicted probability of her ordering a sugar cone with chocolate ice cream and cherries?

c) Describe an item that Riley could use to simulate just her ice cream choices.

Chapter Problem Wrap-Up

In question 12 on page 124, and question 14 on page 130, you used different items to play different versions of *Into the Pond*.

Develop your own version of *Into the Pond* for the number line shown.

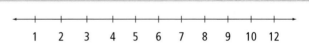
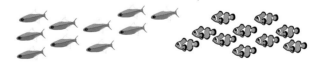

Pick two items to use for determining which fish go into the pond.

1. Where will you put your fish on the number line? Why?

2. Is your game fair for two players? Explain.

3. Test your game. Modify it if necessary.

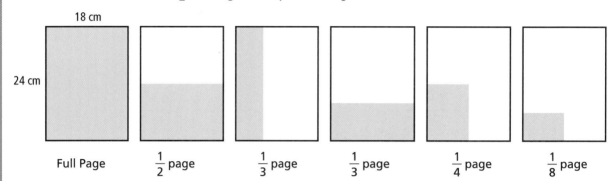

Spin the Spinner; Pick a Card

1. Copy and cut out the fraction cards and spinner.

2. Play the game for 15 minutes and record your results.

To play:
• Lay the cards, face down.
• Pick a card at random. Write down the number.
• Spin the spinner and write down the operation.
• Pick a second card and write down the number.

Example:

1st card   spinner   2nd card   solution

$\dfrac{2}{3}$ ÷ $\dfrac{3}{4}$ =

• Solve!

Player A gets a point for all answers less than one.
Player B gets a point for answers equal to or greater than one.
The player with the most points wins.

---

3. Which player has the advantage? Explain why.

4. Use your knowledge of probability and fractions to revise the game to make it fair. Use pictures, words, and diagrams to report on your new game.

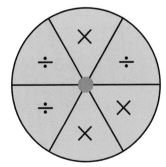

$\dfrac{1}{2}$ $\dfrac{2}{3}$ $\dfrac{3}{4}$

Chapters 1–4 Review

Chapter 1 Measurement and Number Sense

Round your answers to one decimal place if necessary.

1. A circular field has a radius of 55 m.

   a) Find the circumference of the field.
   b) Find its area.

2. A disk has a diameter of 8 cm.

   a) What is its circumference?
   b) What is its area?

3. Create a concept map showing how circumference, diameter, and radius are related.

4. a) Construct a circle with radius 4.5 cm.
   b) Construct a circle with diameter 7.8 cm.

5. Copy this diagram onto grid paper.

   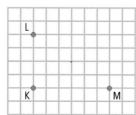

   a) Find the centre of the circle that passes through K, L, and M.
   b) Explain how you found the centre.

6. When Juliette swims across her circular pool and back, she travels a total distance of 16 m. She swims through the centre of the pool both ways. Find the area of the surface of the swimming pool.

7. Lars walks a distance of 120 m, halfway around a circular field. How much less would he walk if he walked straight across the diameter?

Chapter 2 Two-Dimensional Geometry

8. a) Which side of △ABC is the hypotenuse?
   b) What is the area of the square on side AB?

   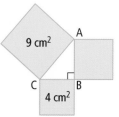

9. Write the following values in order from least to greatest. Draw a number line and label the approximate position of each value.

   $\sqrt{4}$, 0.5, $\sqrt{0.64}$, $\sqrt{1}$

10. Estimate the length of the missing side in each triangle. Then, use a calculator to find the approximate length, to the nearest tenth.

    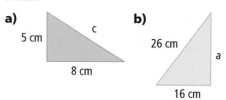

11. Renata swims diagonally across a square pool. Each side of the pool is 8 m long. How many times will she need to go diagonally across the pool to complete a distance of 100 m? Round your answer to the nearest whole number.

Chapter 3 Fraction Operations

12. Find each sum or difference. Write each answer in lowest terms.

a) $\dfrac{1}{3} + \dfrac{1}{2}$ **b)** $\dfrac{3}{4} - \dfrac{3}{5}$

c) $\dfrac{5}{6} + \dfrac{1}{3}$ **d)** $\dfrac{7}{10} - \dfrac{1}{2}$

13. One Saturday Grace spent $\dfrac{3}{4}$ h cleaning her room and $1\dfrac{1}{2}$ h cutting the grass. How long did she spend on chores that day?

14. Estimate, then evaluate.

a) $\dfrac{1}{3}$ of 20   **b)** $\dfrac{3}{4}$ of 30

15. On Ian's hockey team, $\dfrac{4}{5}$ of the players are right-handed. Of these players, $\dfrac{1}{2}$ have brown eyes. What fraction of Ian's team members are right-handed and have brown eyes?

16. What fraction of the rectangle is shaded?

17. Evaluate. Write each answer in lowest terms.

a) $\dfrac{5}{8} - \dfrac{1}{2} + \dfrac{3}{4}$ **b)** $\dfrac{1}{5} + \dfrac{5}{6} \div \dfrac{2}{3} - \dfrac{7}{10}$

18. It takes Jill $\dfrac{1}{4}$ h to type up half a page of her handwritten report. If the report is $10\dfrac{1}{2}$ pages long, how long will it take her to type up the whole report?

Chapter 4 Probability

19. A number cube is rolled.

a) What is the probability of rolling a 6?

b) What is the probability of rolling an odd number?

c) What is the probability of rolling an 8?

20. A number cube is rolled and a coin is tossed.

a) Use an organizer to show all the possible outcomes.

b) State each predicted probability.
- rolling a 3 and tossing heads
- rolling an even number and tossing tails

21. Describe an item that could be used to simulate each situation. Explain why each item is appropriate.

a) Choose a CD from a box of 6.

b) Choose a video to watch from a choice of 10 titles.

c) Choose a colour of T-shirt to wear from your drawer, which contains 5 white, 3 blue, and 2 black T-shirts.

22. The weather report says there is a 60% chance of snow tomorrow. What is the probability of no snow?

23. A poll is conducted to predict the outcome of an election. Of the 200 people polled, 36 chose Brad, 112 chose Josi, and 52 chose Aaron.

a) Based on the poll, what is the probability that Josi will win the election?

b) What percent of the people chose Aaron?

c) Who is the least likely to win the election? Find his or her probability of winning.

Number Sense and Numeration
- Apply unit rates in problem solving situations.
- Solve problems that involve converting between fractions, decimals, percents, rates, and ratios.
- Apply percents in solving problems involving discounts, sales tax, commission, and simple interest.

Measurement
- Identify and apply relationships among measurement concepts.

Patterning and Algebra
- Apply patterning strategies in problem solving situations.

Key Words

ratio

rate

proportion

speed

unit rate

unit price

discount

sales taxes

Provincial Sales Tax (PST)

Goods and Services Tax (GST)

commission

principal

simple interest

CHAPTER 5

Ratios, Rates, and Percents

In the summer of 2003, Toronto invited the Rolling Stones to play a concert. It was the largest concert in Canadian history. This historic event, designed to stimulate tourism, attracted over 450 000 rock fans of all ages. As well as international superstars such as the Stones, from England, and AC/DC, from Australia, a number of famous Canadian acts performed.

The huge size of a concert like this requires careful planning to ensure a safe and entertaining event. The skills with rates, ratios, and percents that you will learn in this chapter will allow you to solve some of the kinds of problems the concert organizers faced.

Chapter Problem

You are the organizer of a major outdoor concert event. The first band starts to set up at noon. The concert ends 10 h later.

You guarantee the bands that

Headliners	Supporting Acts
The Howlin' Cats	Moondancer
Virtual Thunder	C.U. L8er
The Crunch-Bunnies	Rap Pappy and Sonny Shine
3 Left Feet	New Girls Up the Street
	Breakdances With Woodchucks
	Flip Flop and the Clodhoppers

- headliners each get the same amount of playing time
- supporting acts each get the same amount of playing time
- a headliner gets twice as much playing time as a supporting act
- each band gets 25 min to set up before its show

How would you schedule the bands?

What fraction of the concert time is spent setting up?

Write Ratios

A **ratio** is a comparison of measures that have the same units. A ratio that compare two measures can be written in ratio form or in fraction form.

The ratio of basketballs to tennis balls is 4:6.

> I can read the ratio as "four to six" or "four as compared to six."

first term:
number of basketballs

second term:
number of tennis balls

4:6 can be written in fraction form as $\frac{4}{6}$.

In simplest form, the ratio is 2:3 or $\frac{2}{3}$.

1. Write a ratio to compare the numbers of each type of ball.

   a) basketballs to tennis balls
   b) basketballs to golf balls
   c) golf balls to the total number of balls

2. Write each ratio in question 1 in fraction form.

3. Write each ratio in question 1 in simplest form.

Equivalent Fractions

$\frac{2}{3}$ and $\frac{6}{9}$ are **equivalent fractions**.

They are two ways of naming the same fraction.

$$\frac{2}{3} = \frac{2 \times 3}{3 \times 3}$$
$$= \frac{6}{9}$$

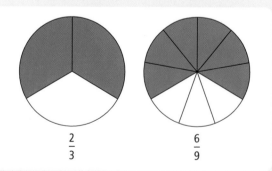

$\frac{2}{3}$ $\frac{6}{9}$

4. Find the missing value to make an equivalent fraction.

   a) $\frac{3}{4} = \frac{6}{\blacksquare}$ **b)** $\frac{5}{7} = \frac{\blacksquare}{28}$

   c) $\frac{4}{12} = \frac{8}{\blacksquare}$ **d)** $\frac{1}{20} = \frac{5}{\blacksquare}$

5. Write an equivalent fraction for each.

   a) $\frac{4}{5}$ **b)** $\frac{3}{7}$

   c) $\frac{1}{25}$ **d)** $\frac{3}{8}$

Convert Fractions to Decimals

To convert a fraction to a decimal, divide the numerator by the denominator.

$$\frac{3}{4} = 0.75 \quad 4\overline{)3.00}^{\,0.75} \qquad \frac{12}{8} = 1.5 \quad 8\overline{)12.0}^{\,1.5} \qquad \frac{2}{3} = 0.\overline{6} \quad \boxed{c}\; 2 \boxed{\div} 3 \boxed{=} \; 0.666\,666$$

6. Convert each fraction to a decimal.

   a) $\dfrac{3}{5}$ **b)** $\dfrac{3}{8}$ **c)** $\dfrac{9}{12}$

7. Convert each fraction to a decimal.

   a) $\dfrac{13}{5}$ **b)** $\dfrac{8}{6}$ **c)** $1\dfrac{1}{4}$

Convert Percents to Decimals

Percent means *for every hundred*. To convert a percent to a decimal, divide by 100 and delete the percent sign. If a percent is written as a mixed number, convert the fraction part to a decimal first.

$$8\% = \frac{8}{100} \qquad\qquad 6.2\% = \frac{6.2}{100} \qquad\qquad 4\tfrac{1}{4}\% = 4.25\%$$
$$\;\;\; = 0.08 \qquad\qquad\quad\;\; = 0.062 \qquad\qquad\qquad\; = 0.0425$$

8. Convert each percent to a decimal.

   a) 3%   **b)** 11%
   c) 9.2%   **d)** 10.5%

9. Convert each percent to a decimal.

   a) $6\dfrac{1}{2}\%$ **b)** $7\dfrac{3}{4}\%$ **c)** $5\dfrac{1}{4}\%$

Find a Percent of a Number

Find 7% of 120.

Method 1

$$7\% \text{ of } 120 = \frac{7}{100} \times 120$$
$$= \frac{840}{100}$$
$$= 8.4$$

Method 2

$$7\% \text{ of } 120 = \frac{7}{100} \times 120$$
$$= 0.07 \times 120$$
$$= 8.4$$

> Convert the percent to a decimal. Then, multiply.

10. Find each amount.

   a) 8% of 250   **b)** 12% of 50
   c) 25% of 36   **d)** 20% of 84

11. Find each amount.

   a) $5\dfrac{1}{2}\%$ of 120   **b)** 8.5% of 300

Apply Ratio and Proportion

Imagine you are choosing tiles to renovate a bathroom. You decide to combine several different-coloured square tiles to create a pattern and then repeat the pattern to cover a floor or wall. How many of each colour tile will you need?

You can use **ratios** to solve this kind of problem.

ratio

• a comparison of quantities measured in the same units

Materials

Optional:
• pattern blocks

Discover the Math

How can you use ratios to describe and extend patterns?

1. Imagine you created a border pattern using pattern blocks, as shown. Look at the steps of the pattern. Copy and complete the table to find the ratios at each step of the pattern.

Step	Number of Yellow Blocks	Number of Red Blocks	Total Number of Blocks	Yellow/Red	Yellow/Total
1					
2	2				
3					

Literacy Connections

A *part-to-part* ratio compares different parts of a group to each other.

A *part-to-whole* ratio compares one part of a group to the whole group.

2. **a)** What is the ratio of the number of yellow blocks to the number of red blocks?
   b) Why do you think this is called a *part-to-part* ratio?

3. **a)** What is the ratio of the number of yellow blocks to the total number of blocks?
   b) Why do you think this is called a *part-to-whole* ratio?

4. a) If you extend the pattern to use 8 red blocks, how many yellow blocks will you use? Explain your reasoning.

    b) How many blocks of each colour would you need to make a pattern that has a total of 30 blocks? Explain your reasoning.

5. Reflect Describe how ratios are useful in describing and extending patterns.

Making Connections

You will learn more about patterns in Chapter 6.

Example 1: Apply Ratios to Tiling

Look at the square tile pattern.
a) Compare the number of yellow tiles to the number of green tiles. Write the ratio in simplest form.
b) Compare the number of blue tiles to the total number of tiles. Write the ratio in simplest form.
c) How many of each colour tile are needed to make a two-by-two repeat of the pattern?

Literacy Connections

A ratio is in *simplest form* when its terms have no common factors. This is the same concept as expressing a fraction in *lowest terms*.

Solution

a) There are 4 yellow tiles and 16 green tiles.

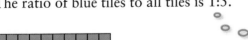

For each yellow tile, there are 4 green ones. This means that 4:16 is the same as 1:4.

4:16 = 1:4   **This kind of equation is called a proportion .**

The ratio of yellow tiles to green tiles is 1:4.

This is a part-to-part ratio.

b) There are 5 blue tiles and 25 tiles in total.

5:25 = 1:5

One out of every 5 tiles is blue. This means that 5:25 is the same as 1:5.

The ratio of blue tiles to all tiles is 1:5.

This is a part-to-whole ratio.

proportion
- a statement that says two ratios are equal
- can be written in ratio form:
  4:16 = 1:4
  or in fraction form:
  $\frac{4}{16} = \frac{1}{4}$

c)

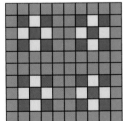

To make a two-by-two repeat of the pattern, I use four identical pattern squares. Multiply the number of each colour tile in the pattern by 4.

Blue: 4 × 5 tiles = 20 tiles
Yellow: 4 × 4 tiles = 16 tiles
Green: 4 × 16 tiles = 64 tiles

20 blue tiles, 16 yellow tiles, and 64 green tiles are needed to make a two-by-two repeat of the pattern.

Example 2: Apply Ratios to Recipes

Lena has a recipe for a fruit punch that calls for 4 cups of raspberry juice and 6 cups of orange juice.
a) How much orange juice should Lena use if she only uses 2 cups of raspberry juice?
b) Suppose Lena wants to make 50 cups of punch for a family gathering. How much of each type of juice should she use?

raspberry juice   orange juice

Solution

a)

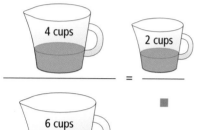 = ■

I need to compare two part-to-part ratios of the form $\dfrac{\text{raspberry juice}}{\text{orange juice}}$.

$$\frac{4}{6} = \frac{2}{\blacksquare}$$

$$\frac{4}{6} \xrightarrow{\div 2} \frac{2}{3}$$

This is like working with equivalent fractions. $4 \div 2 = 2$. So, for the denominator, I need $6 \div 2 = 3$.

Strategies
What strategy are you using to solve this problem?

Lena should mix 3 cups of orange juice with 2 cups of raspberry juice.

b)

I need to compare two part-to-whole ratios of the form $\dfrac{\text{raspberry juice}}{\text{total}}$ and $\dfrac{\text{orange juice}}{\text{total}}$.

The total amount of juice in the recipe is 4 cups + 6 cups = 10 cups.

Raspberry juice: $\dfrac{4}{10} = \dfrac{\blacksquare}{50}$

$$\frac{4}{10} \xrightarrow{\times 5} \frac{20}{50} \quad 4 \times 5 = 20$$

Lena needs to use 20 cups of raspberry juice to make 50 cups of punch.

Orange juice: $\dfrac{6}{10} = \dfrac{\blacksquare}{50}$

$$\frac{6}{10} \xrightarrow{\times 5} \frac{30}{50} \quad 6 \times 5 = 30$$

Lena needs to use 30 cups of orange juice to make 50 cups of punch.

Key Ideas

- A part-to-part ratio compares two parts of a group.
  The ratio of red beads to yellow beads is 4:3.

- A part-to-whole ratio compares a part of a group to the whole group.
  The ratio of red beads to the total number of beads is 4:7.

- A proportion is a statement that two ratios are equal.

  $4:3 = 8:6$ or $\dfrac{4}{3} = \dfrac{8}{6}$

Communicate the Ideas

1. In your class, what is the ratio of the numbers of
   a) boys to girls?
   b) girls to students?

2. Consider this classification of the days of the week.

   Bad days: Monday, Tuesday, Wednesday
   Good days: Thursday, Friday
   Excellent days: Saturday, Sunday

   a) Write a ratio to compare the number of excellent days to
   the number of bad days.
   b) Write a ratio to compare the number of excellent days to
   the number of days in a week.
   c) How can you determine the number of good days in a year?
   d) Describe some factors that might affect the way the days are classified.

Check Your Understanding

Practise

*For help with questions 3 to 5, refer to
Example 1.*

3. Look at the beads.

   Explain what each
   ratio represents.

   a) 3:4
   b) 5:4
   c) 5:12
   d) 1:3

4. Look at the bag of
marbles.

Draw a diagram to
represent each ratio.
Then, use numbers to
write each ratio in
simplest form.

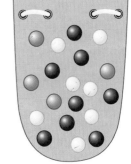

   a) blue marbles:white
   marbles
   b) black marbles:blue marbles
   c) white marbles:total number of marbles

5. Write each ratio in simplest form.

    a) 5:10   **b)** 18:6

    c) 14:35   **d)** 120:50

For help with questions 6 and 7, refer to Example 2.

6. What is the missing number in each proportion?

    a) $\dfrac{4}{7} = \dfrac{\blacksquare}{14}$ **b)** $\dfrac{\blacksquare}{5} = \dfrac{12}{15}$

    c) $\dfrac{16}{36} = \dfrac{4}{\blacksquare}$ **d)** $\dfrac{2}{3} = \dfrac{\blacksquare}{15}$

7. Find the missing number in each proportion.

    a) 1:6 = $\blacksquare$:54   **b)** 6:8 = 3:$\blacksquare$

    c) 5:20 = $\blacksquare$:4   **d)** $\blacksquare$:4 = 8:16

Apply

8. Look at the shape pattern. The pattern has 10 blocks in total.

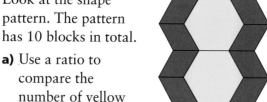

    a) Use a ratio to compare the number of yellow blocks to the total number of blocks. Write the ratio in simplest form.

    b) How are the numbers of yellow blocks and blue blocks related?

    c) Would your answer to part b) change if the pattern were repeated so it had a total of 50 blocks? Explain your reasoning.

9. Tami makes her own oil and vinegar dressing. Her recipe calls for 150 mL of olive oil and 200 mL of vinegar.

    a) Write a ratio, in simplest form, to compare the amounts of the two ingredients.

    b) What amount of vinegar is needed to mix with 270 mL of olive oil?

    c) If Tami wants to make 700 mL of the dressing, what quantity of each ingredient does she need?

10. A recipe for two-cheese lasagna calls for 200 g of ricotta and 300 g of mozzarella.

    a) Write a ratio, in simplest form, to compare the amounts of the two cheeses.

    b) What amount of mozzarella is needed to make a lasagna that contains 800 g of ricotta?

    c) What amount of each cheese is needed to make a lasagna that contains 1 kg of cheese in total?

11. A baseball team's win-loss record is 20:15.

    a) Write this ratio in simplest form. Explain what this ratio tells you.

    b) If this trend continues, how many losses would you expect the team to have once they have won 60 games?

    c) Approximately how many games would you expect the team to win over a 161-game season?

12. At a soccer tournament, one team's win-loss record was 12:8. A second team had a win-loss record of 15:5. Both teams had no ties.

    a) Express each ratio in simplest form.

    b) How many games did each team play?

    c) Explain how you solved parts a) and b).

13. Look at Example 2, part b). What other way can you calculate the amount of orange juice, once you know the amount of raspberry juice?

    a) Show your calculation.

    b) Explain why this method works.

Chapter Problem

14. The concert lasts 10 h. Each headliner plays twice as long as each supporting act. Each band gets 25 min to set up.

Headliners	Supporting Acts
The Howlin' Cats	Moondancer
Virtual Thunder	C.U. L8er
The Crunch-Bunnies	Rap Pappy and Sonny Shine
3 Left Feet	New Girls Up the Street
	Breakdances With Woodchucks
	Flip Flop and the Clodhoppers

a) What is the ratio, in simplest form, of the number of headliners to the number of supporting acts?

b) How much total time is used for
- band set-up?
- playing time?

c) Write a ratio, in simplest form, to compare total set-up time to total playing time.

d) Determine how many minutes
- each supporting act gets to play
- each headliner gets to play

15. There are 100 passengers on the train at the start of the route. The train stops at a station and 36 passengers get off. Write the ratio, in simplest form, that compares the number of passengers remaining on the train to the total number at the start.

 16. The ratio of the length to the width of the Canadian flag is 2:1.

a) The flag on the cover of a Canadian atlas is 8 cm wide. How long is it?

b) The large flag outside a Brampton school is 5 m long. How wide is it?

c) One Canadian flag has a perimeter of 2.7 m. What is its length?

Extend

17. A company finds that 9 out of 10 of its new read-write CDs pass a performance test.

a) Write ratios to compare
- the number passed to the number tested
- the number failed to the number tested
- the number passed to the number failed

b) The company makes some design improvements. Now, only half as many CDs fail the test. Write new ratios for part a).

18. The side view of a ramp is shown.

a) Express the ratio of rise to run in simplest form. This ratio describes the slope of the ramp.

b) Express the slope ratio in fraction form and as a decimal.

c) Describe the effect you think each of the following has on the slope of the ramp:
- increasing the rise
- decreasing the rise
- increasing the run
- decreasing the run

d) Test your predictions from part c) using drawings. Use *The Geometer's Sketchpad*® or pencil and paper. Write a brief report that summarizes your findings.

Did You Know?

The ratio $\frac{rise}{run}$ is called the slope. It describes how steep something is. This same ratio is used for ski slopes, roof steepness, road inclines, and ramps.

Making Connections

In high school, you will use ratios to measure slopes of lines that describe relationships in mathematics and science.

5.2

Explore Rates

At a track-and-field meet, Shaun and Raoul are competing in a 1000-m race. Suppose that, after the first few seconds of acceleration, both runners run at a constant **speed** .

speed

• comparison of distance travelled to time taken

• speed = $\dfrac{\text{distance}}{\text{time}}$

The judges recorded the following information using a stopwatch:
• After 20 s, Shaun passed the 100-m mark.
• After 25 s, Raoul passed the 150-m mark.
How can you determine the winner of the race?

Discover the Math

Materials

Optional:
• grid paper
• ruler
• manipulatives (e.g., counters)

rate

• a comparison of two quantities measured in different units

• 120 km in 2 h, $210 per week, and $2.49 for 0.5 kg are rates

How can you compare quantities measured in different units?

Speed is an example of a **rate** . Look at the given information about Shaun and Raoul. Shaun runs 100 m in 20 s. Raoul runs 150 m in 25 s. In each case, a comparison is made between the distance run and the time taken.

1. Who is running faster? Explain how you know.

2. If the runners continue at their current speeds, who will win the race? Explain how you know.

3. a) Suppose Shaun runs at the same speed throughout the race. How far will he travel in 40 s? in 5 s?
   b) How did you find the answers in part a)?

4. a) How can you write Shaun's speed with a denominator of 1? Use the equation below to help you:

$$\frac{100 \text{ m}}{20 \text{ s}} = \frac{\blacksquare}{1 \text{ s}}$$

Rates that have a denominator of 1 are called **unit rates** .
What does this unit rate mean?

b) Repeat part a) for Raoul.

5. Reflect Does writing speed as a unit rate help you compare the runners? Explain.

> **unit rate**
> • a rate in which the second term is 1
> • 60 km/h, $4.98/kg, and $30 per day are rates

Example 1: Apply Rates to Earnings

Maggie has a babysitting job for which she gets paid an hourly rate.
One evening she earned $24 for 4 h of babysitting.
a) Write a unit rate that describes how much Maggie gets paid.
b) How much will Maggie earn if she babysits for 14 h?

> **Making Connections**
>
> In high school, you will apply the concept of rate to measure the slopes of lines when you study graphs.

Solution

a) Maggie earned $24 in 4 h. Write this rate in fraction form.

$$\frac{\$24}{4 \text{ h}}$$
$$= \frac{\$6}{1 \text{ h}}$$

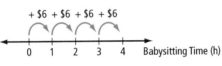

Maggie is paid $6/h.

> $24 for 4 h.
> That's the same as $6 for each hour.

> **Literacy Connections**
>
> Read $6/h as "six dollars per hour."

b) Maggie earns $6/h. To find how much she will earn in 14 h, multiply by 14.

$$\frac{\$6}{1 \text{ h}} = \frac{\blacksquare}{14 \text{ h}}$$

× 14

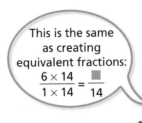

> This is the same as creating equivalent fractions:
> $$\frac{6 \times 14}{1 \times 14} = \frac{\blacksquare}{14}$$

$6 × 14 = $84
Maggie will earn $84 for 14 h of babysitting.

Example 2: Convert Rates to Unit Rates

Find the unit rate in each situation.

a) Javier ran 600 m in 2 min.

b) Gina scored 60 points in 80 games.

Solution

a) $\dfrac{600 \text{ m}}{2 \text{ min}}$

$= 300 \text{ m/min}$

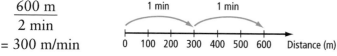

1 min   1 min

0   100 200 300 400 500 600   Distance (m)

If I write the rate in fraction form, then I can find the unit rate by dividing.

b) $\dfrac{60 \text{ points}}{80 \text{ games}}$

$= 0.75$ points per game

Example 3: Apply Rates to Shopping

Jinji went to the grocery store to buy some peanut butter. He found his two favourite brands. Assuming Jinji likes each brand equally, which is the better buy?

Nutz! 750 g

Koala Krunch 250 g

$5.49 $1.99

Solution

Method 1: Compare Unit Prices

Grocery stores often post **unit prices** to allow for easy comparison shopping. Find the unit price of each brand and compare.

Nutz!:

Unit price $= \dfrac{\$1.99}{250 \text{ g}}$ ⓒ 1.99 ÷ 250 = 0.00796

$= \$0.007\ 96/\text{g}$

Nutz! costs $0.007 96/g or 0.796¢/g.

$1 = 100¢. To convert dollars to cents, multiply by 100.

Koala Krunch:

Unit price $= \dfrac{\$5.49}{750 \text{ g}}$ ⓒ 5.49 ÷ 750 = 0.00732

$= \$0.007\ 32/\text{g}$

Koala Krunch costs $0.007 32/g or 0.732¢/g.

The unit price for Koala Krunch is less than the unit price for Nutz!. Koala Krunch is the better buy.

unit price
• a unit rate that applies to shopping

Jaffa Dates
02154   375 GR/24   001
                          15

UNIT PRICE   **1.88**
50.1¢
PER 100GR

Method 2: Use a Proportion

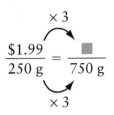

$\dfrac{\$1.99}{250 \text{ g}} = \dfrac{\blacksquare}{750 \text{ g}}$

×3 (top), ×3 (bottom)

How much would it cost for the same amount of each brand? I can find the cost for 750 g of Nutz!.

$\$1.99 \times 3 = \$5.97$

It costs \$5.97 for 750 g of Nutz!, which is more than the \$5.49 it costs for 750 g of Koala Krunch.

Koala Krunch is the better buy.

Key Ideas

- A rate is a comparison of quantities measured in different units.

- A rate can be written in fraction form. $\dfrac{\$3}{4 \text{ cans}}$

$3 for 4 cans

- A unit rate is a rate in which the second term, or denominator, is 1. $\dfrac{\$3}{4 \text{ cans}} = \dfrac{\$0.75}{1 \text{ can}}$

  You can also write this as \$0.75/can.

- Unit prices are unit rates involving prices. Unit prices make it easier to compare the cost of similar items.
  For example, $0.732¢/\text{g} < 0.796¢/\text{g}$.

Communicate the Ideas

1. **a)** How are rates similar to ratios?
   b) How are they different?

2. Last night 40 cm of snow fell in 5 h. Today 3 cm/h is falling.

   a) Which sentence uses a rate? Which uses a unit rate?
   b) What is the advantage of converting a rate to a unit rate? Explain.

3. Jo and Erin both have part-time jobs. Jo works 10 h per week and earns \$15/h. Erin is paid \$60 for a 5-h shift. She works three shifts per week.

   a) Who earns more money per hour?
   b) Who earns more money per week?
   c) Why are the answers to parts a) and b) different?

Practise

Remember to include proper units in all rates and unit rates.

For help with questions 4 and 5, refer to Example 1.

4. Vera earns $8.00/h working at a coffee shop. How much will she earn in

a) a 4-h shift?

b) a 35-h work week?

5. Don is paid $9.25/h. How much does he earn in

a) a 7-h day?   **b)** a 37-h work week?

For help with questions 6 and 7, refer to Example 2.

6. Find the unit rate in each situation.

a) Edmund rode his bicycle 60 km in 3 h.

b) Sasha earned $68 in 8 h.

c) Ron was charged $84 for a 7-h canoe rental.

7. What is the unit rate in each?

a) The road crew painted 8 km of highway lane markers in 2 days.

b) The temperature rose 12°C in 5 h.

c) The tomato plant produced 36 tomatoes in 6 weeks.

For help with questions 8 and 9, refer to Example 3.

8. Find the unit price for each item.

a) Fish costs $25.20 for 4 kg.

b) Shampoo costs $2.95 for 250 mL.

c) A can of apple juice costs $1.35 for 900 mL.

9. Kiki is shopping for ketchup. Her favourite brand is available in two sizes.

a) Estimate which is the better buy. Explain your choice.

b) Justify your choice. Show calculations to support your reasoning.

Ketchup 500 mL   Ketchup 750 mL

$1.99 $3.19

Apply

10. A plane is cruising at a steady speed of 500 km/h.

a) How far will the plane travel in 4 h?

b) How long will it take the plane to travel 3000 km?

11. Ariel has scored 96 points in 8 games so far this season.

a) What is her unit rate of scoring?

b) At this rate, how many points can Ariel expect to score during a 24-game season?

12. Pietro runs 200 m in 30 s, while his sister Wanda runs 300 m in 36 s.

a) Who is the faster runner? Explain how you can tell.

b) How far will each runner go in 2 min?

c) How long would it take for each runner to travel 1 km? State any assumptions that you must make.

13. Each week, Karla earns $420 for 35 h of work at a factory. Her friend Enzo makes $440 for 40 h of work at a store.

a) Who has the greater hourly rate of pay?

b) How much does Enzo earn in an 8-h shift?

14. It takes Famke 10 min to type one quarter of her 1000-word essay.

   a) What is Famke's average typing speed, in words per minute?

   b) At this rate, how long will it take for Famke to finish typing her essay?

15. A 500-g package of pastrami costs $6.25.

   a) Determine the unit price per 100 g.

   b) What would 750 g of pastrami cost?

   c) How much would 2 kg cost?

Chapter Problem

16. The forecast for an outdoor concert is sunny and hot. Because there is no shade for the audience, each person should drink at least one 500-mL bottle of water every 2 h.

   a) How many millilitres will each person need for a 10-h concert? How many litres is this?

   b) How many litres should you have available, if you expect 1000 people to attend?

   c) At the 2003 Rolling Stones concert in Toronto, almost 500 000 people attended. It was a hot, sunny day with no shade. If everyone stayed for the entire concert, how many litres of water were needed?

17. The makers of Purr 'n' Chew cat food want to price their cat food so that it costs just less than their main competitor, Happy Kitty.

A 5-kg bag of Happy Kitty costs $12.99.

   a) What is the maximum price that Purr 'n' Chew should charge for their 4-kg bag of cat food?

   b) Explain how you found this price.

 Try This!

18. Two brands of noodles are shown. The noodles are of the same quality.

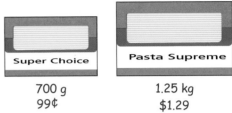

Super Choice	Pasta Supreme
700 g	1.25 kg
99¢	$1.29

   a) Without calculating, which do you think is the better buy? Explain your decision.

   b) Find the unit price per 100 g for each brand.

   c) Which is the better buy? Explain your choice. Compare it with your prediction.

   d) Explain why estimating unit costs is useful when grocery shopping.

Extend

19. Rose uses prices from a shopping flyer to prepare her grocery list. Rose has no cash left, so she stops at the bank machine to make a withdrawal. The machine only gives $10 and $20 bills.

Item	Price	Quantity
potatoes	45¢/kg	5 kg
eggs	$1.89/dozen	2 dozen
chicken	$1.29/100 g	500g
cole slaw	49¢/100 ml	750 mL

   a) Estimate the minimum amount that Rose should withdraw to pay for the groceries.

   b) Find the exact amount that Rose will need to pay.

   c) How much change will Rose receive?

20. Hans jogs at an average speed of 8 km/h.

   a) How far will he jog in 45 min?

   b) How much faster will Hans need to jog in order to run the same distance in 40 min? Explain your reasoning.

21. Refer to the running race at the start of this section. Suppose Raoul doubles his speed at the halfway point. Who will win the race? By how much time? Show how you found your answers.

5.3

Apply Percent to Sales Taxes and Discounts

Focus on...
- sales taxes
- discounts

Dieter is shopping for a new bicycle. Pop's Cycles has one he likes for $249. If Dieter is buying a bicycle in Ontario, he must pay 8% **Provincial Sales Tax (PST)** and 7% **Goods and Services Tax (GST)**. How much will Dieter have to pay, including **sales taxes**?

sales taxes
- money collected by the government on purchases
- usually written as a percent

Provincial Sales Tax (PST)
- sales tax collected by the provincial government
- rate varies by province

Goods and Services Tax (GST)
- tax on sales and services, collected by the federal government

Discover the Math

How can you find the final price, including discounts and taxes?

Example 1: Calculate PST and GST

The bicycle that Dieter likes at Pop's Cycles costs $249 plus PST and GST. How much will the bike cost, including taxes?

Solution

Method 1: Find Each Tax Separately

Provincial Sales Tax is 8% of $249.
PST = 0.08 × $249
  = $19.92
The Provincial Sales Tax is $19.92.

Goods and Services Tax is 7% of $249.
GST = 0.07 × $249
  = $17.43
The Goods and Services Tax is $17.43.

Bicycle	$249.00
PST	$19.92
GST	$17.43
TOTAL	$286.35

> I need to add both taxes to the price of the bicycle to find the total cost.

The cost of the bicycle, including taxes, is $286.35.

Method 2: Find Both Taxes Together

15% of $249
= 0.15 × $249
= $37.35

The total tax is $37.35.

Adding 8% of a number and 7% of a number is the same as adding 15% of a number.

Bicycle	$249.00
PST & GST	$37.35
TOTAL	$286.35

Add the taxes to the price of the bicycle to find the total cost.

The cost of the bicycle, including taxes, is $286.35.

Making Connections

Calculating Taxes Mentally

You can calculate 15% mentally by realizing that 15% = 10% + 5%.

10% of $250 is $25.

Add half of this (5%):
$25 + $12.50
= $37.50.

Example 2: Calculate a Discount and Taxes

The regular price of a DVD is $28.99. Now, it is on sale at a 25% **discount**.

a) Find the sale price.

b) At the store, PST and GST are calculated on the discount price. How much would you have to pay for the DVD, including taxes?

discount
• amount subtracted from a listed price to give a sale price

Solution

a) *Method 1: Find the Discount First, Then Subtract*

Discount = 25% of $28.99
= 0.25 × $28.99
$\doteq$ $7.25

Round to the nearest cent.

Estimate: 25% = $\frac{1}{4}$
$\frac{1}{4}$ of $28 is $7.

Sale price = regular price − discount
= $28.99 − $7.25
= $21.74

The sale price of the DVD is $21.74.

Method 2: Find the Sale Price Directly

Sale price = 75% of $28.99
= 0.75 × $28.99
$\doteq$ $21.74

Estimate: 75% = $\frac{3}{4}$
$\frac{3}{4}$ of $28 is $21.

The sale price of the DVD, before taxes, is $21.74.

b) Taxes on DVD = 8% PST + 7% GST
= 15% of $21.74
= 0.15 × $21.74
$\doteq$ $3.26

Estimate: 10% of $20 is $2. Add half of this for 5%. $2 + $1 = $3.

Total cost = sale price + taxes
= $21.74 + $3.26
= $25.00

The total cost of the DVD, including taxes, is $25.00.

Did You Know?

Not all items sold have PST and GST added. Some purchases, such as basic food items, are tax-free. Other items, such as books, are subject to GST only.

- Taxes are extra costs that retailers must collect on sales and send to the government.

- The two taxes added onto purchases in Ontario are the Provincial Sales Tax (PST) and the Goods and Services Tax (GST).

- A discount is an amount subtracted from the regular price of an item to give a sale price.

- To calculate the final price of an item, first subtract any discounts. Then, add the sales taxes that apply.

```
shirt    $35.99
PST       $2.88
GST       $2.52
TOTAL    $41.39
```

Communicate the Ideas

1. What is the difference between a sale price and a final price?

2. List the steps you would use to find the final price on an item that is on sale at a 20% discount.

Check Your Understanding

Practise

For help with questions 3 to 6, refer to Example 1.

3. Find the 7% GST on each item.
   a) a concert ticket that cost $20
   b) a haircut that costs $15
   c) a pen that costs $1.99

4. Find the 8% PST on each item.
   a) a hair brush that costs $10
   b) a jacket that costs $85.50
   c) a card that costs $1.99

5. Find the PST and the GST on each item.

	Item	Price
a)	CD	$18.99
b)	In-line skates	$325.00
c)	Scarf	$10.95

6. Find the total cost of each item, including PST and GST.

	Item	Price
a)	CD player	$79.00
b)	Earrings	$9.50
c)	Watch	$128.00

For help with questions 7 to 9, refer to Example 2.

7. Estimate, then calculate, each discount.

a) 25% off jeans at $48.99

b) 20% off museum admission at $32.00

c) 30% off a digital camera at $299.95

8. A clothing store has an end-of-season sale. All items are discounted by 30%. Estimate, then calculate, the sale price of each item. Then, find the final price of each item including taxes.

	Item	Price
a)	Sweater	$59.00
b)	Gloves	$8.79
c)	Coat	$209.95

9. Estimate, then calculate, the sale price of each item. Then, find the final price of each item including taxes.

	Item	Regular Price	Discount
a)	T-shirt	$9.79	50%
b)	Crayons	$4.59	10%
c)	Computer	$1199.00	30%

Apply

10. a) Find three advertisements in a flyer, magazine, or newspaper that give a regular price and a percent discount.

b) Estimate the final price of each item.

c) Calculate the discount, sale price, total taxes, and final price of each item.

d) State any assumptions you needed to make.

e) Compare your estimates to your calculated values. Are you getting any better at estimating final prices? When you go shopping, try to estimate the final price before the cashier rings it up.

11. A shirt has a regular price of $30. You notice that it is now marked at 15% off.

The final price will be $30. The discount will just cancel out the sales tax.

Is Matt correct? Show calculations to support your answer.

 12. The price of a hockey stick is $24.99. You must pay PST and GST on hockey sticks.

$24.99

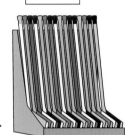

a) Find the total cost, including taxes, for one hockey stick.

b) Solve part a) using a different method.

c) The store delivers flyers with 20% discount coupons. What is the total price of two sticks with the discount?

Extend

13. When you eat at a restaurant, it is normal to leave a tip that is between 10% and 15% of the bill, depending on the quality of service.

Mixed greens salad x2	$11.00
Vegetable pizza	$6.00
Risotto	$7.00
Total	$24.00
	Thank you!

a) Suppose your food bill totals $24.00. What range of tip would be acceptable, assuming good service?

b) The GST and PST are usually shown on the bill. Describe how you can use this information to estimate the tip.

5.4 Apply Percent to Commission

Focus on...
- percent
- commission

PRODUCT
DESCRIPTION
PRICE
DOLPHIN WINDSOCK
$11.98
4 HORSE LAWN ORNAMENTS
$17.98
METAL CAT & BUTTERFLY WINDMILL
$39.95

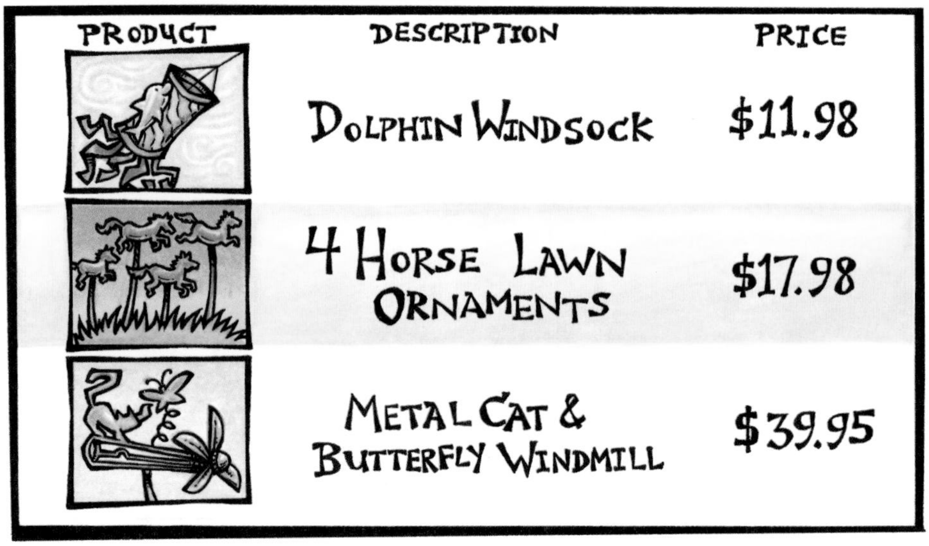

commission
- a payment earned for sales made
- usually expressed as a percent of sales

People who work in sales are often paid a **commission**. When this happens, the amount of money earned depends on the amount of sales. Suppose you sell catalogue items such as the ones shown. How can you determine your earnings?

Discover the Math

How do you calculate earnings made by commission?

Look at the items in the illustration above. The company pays a 25% commission on sales.

1. a) Estimate how much you would earn if you sold one of each item or set.
b) Explain how you found your estimate.

2. Which items would you try hardest to sell? Explain why.

3. a) Which items, and how many of them, would you need to sell in order to earn $50?
b) Explain how you figured this out.
c) Is there another way to earn $50 by selling some of the items? Explain.

4. Reflect Describe one advantage and one disadvantage of being paid by commission.

Example 1: Calculate Commission Earnings

Devon has a summer job selling TV Listings subscriptions door-to-door. He is paid a commission of 40% of sales. Each new 1-year subscription sells for $25, including taxes. One week he sells 18 subscriptions. What is his commission for the week?

Solution

First, calculate the total sales.

Total sales = 18 × $25

   = $450

Then, calculate his commission.

Commission = 40% of $450

   = 0.40 × $450

   = $180

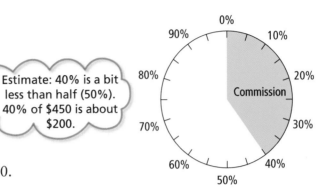

Estimate: 40% is a bit less than half (50%). 40% of $450 is about $200.

Devon's commission for the week is $180.

Example 2: Apply Rates to Commission

Refer to Example 1. Devon hopes to earn $1000 by the end of the summer. What total value must he sell?

Total Sales

Commission $1000

Solution

Method 1: Use Equivalent Ratios

40% commission means that he earns $40 for every $100 of sales.

$$\frac{\$40}{\$100} = \frac{\$1000}{\blacksquare}$$

Write the ratio $\frac{commission}{sales}$.

$$\overset{\times 25}{\frac{\$40}{\$100}} = \frac{\$1000}{\blacksquare}$$

I need to find how many times larger $1000 is than $40. 1000 ÷ 40 = 25

$$= \frac{\$1000}{\$2500}$$

Multiply the denominator by 25.

To earn $1000 in commission, Devon must sell a total of $2500.

Method 2: Use Systematic Trial

40% is less than half. To earn a $1000 commission, Devon's total sales must be a little more than double $1000. Start by trying sales of $2200.

Total Sales	Commission (40% of Total Sales)
$2200	$880
$2600	$1040
$2500	$1000

Too low. © 2200 × 0.4 = 880

Just a little high.

That's it.

Strategies

Use a table or a chart to organize the trials.

Devon must sell a total of $2500 to earn $1000.

- Many jobs in sales pay by commission.

- Commission is usually calculated as a percent of sales. For example, if commission is 20% of sales, for each $1.00 of sales, the salesperson earns $0.20.

Communicate the Ideas

1. Why do you think a company would choose to pay employees by commission?

2. a) What other ways are employees paid, other than by commission?
b) Describe advantages and disadvantages of each method of payment.

Check Your Understanding

Practise

For help with questions 3 to 5, refer to Example 1.

3. Jake earns 25% commission selling ice cream. How much does he earn for each day's sales?

a) Friday $100   **b)** Saturday $180

4. A school earns 35% commission on its book orders. Estimate, then calculate, the commission earned on each month's order.

a) October $309 **b)** November $1850

5. To raise funds, members of the drama club sell flower bulbs. They earn 30% commission. Estimate, then calculate how much each person earns for the club.

	Name	Total Bulb Sales
a)	Deanna	$125.00
b)	Pierre	$350.00

For help with questions 6 to 8, refer to Example 2.

6. Alana earns a 15% commission on bicycle sales. One week she earned $450. What were Alana's total bicycle sales for that week?

7. Yuri earns a 25% commission on sales of magazine subscriptions. One week he earned $220. What were Yuri's total sales for that week?

8. Monique earns a 30% commission on jewellery sales. She wants to earn $600 so she has spending money for her holidays. What amount of jewellery does she need to sell to reach her goal?

Apply

9. Jules earns a 20% commission on fruit sales. One week, his daily sales were as follows:

Monday $250
Tuesday $220
Wednesday $185
Thursday $208
Friday $310

a) What was Jules's commission for the week?

b) Find the answer to part a) using a different method. Does your answer check?

10. Manuel starts a job selling computer equipment. He earns 15% commission on all sales.

a) Find the total amount of Manuel's commission for the first three weeks.

Week	1	2	3
Sales	$1250	$2100	$2425

b) How much would Manuel need to sell in a week in order to earn $500?

Chapter Problem

9. There are four headliners and six supporting acts booked for your concert. Each of the headliners is paid a 5% commission on total ticket sales. The supporting acts are each paid 2%. Total ticket sales are $1 000 000.

a) How much does each headliner earn?

b) How much is paid to each supporting act?

c) Find the total amount paid to the bands.

d) Each headliner agrees to donate half of its commission to a local charity. How much will the charity receive?

12. Jackie sells beauty products on commission. She is paid a 25% commission on make-up items and 30% on bath products. Last month her make-up orders totalled $420.95 and the bath product orders totalled $325.00. How much did she earn?

13. Donna is paid a 25% commission on catalogue sales. She wants to earn $1200 to buy a computer. So far she has sales totalling $3670. How much more does she need to sell to reach her goal?

 14. Brian is offered a job that pays
Try This! $10/h or 8% commission on sales.

a) One Saturday he works 8 h and sells $500 worth of merchandise. Which payment option is better for him? Explain why.

b) Does your answer change if both rates are doubled? Explain.

c) Does your answer change if Brian sells twice as much in the same time period? Explain.

Extend

15. At last night's baseball game, Sandeep and Andre both sold hot dogs. Sandeep gets paid a commission of 20% of sales. Andre earns $30 per game plus a 15% commission. Show calculations to support your answers to the following:

a) Who earned more money if they both sold $500 in hot dogs?

b) Who earned more money if they both sold $700 in hot dogs?

c) For which amount of total sales would Sandeep and Andre earn the same amount of money?

Making Connections

You will apply graphing and algebra skills to solve problems of this type in high school.

Calculate Simple Interest

Suppose you receive a grade 8 graduation present of $200. You decide to deposit the money into a bank account until you finish high school, in 4 years. How much will be in the account when you graduate?

Materials

Optional:
• manipulatives (e.g., counters)
• grid paper

Discover the Math

How can you calculate simple interest?

simple interest
• amount earned for money borrowed or lent
• usually expressed as a percent per year

Suppose the bank pays 6% per year **simple interest**.

1. The interest is paid every year for 4 years. Without calculating, estimate how much the $200 deposit will amount to, with interest, at the end of 4 years.

> 6% interest means the bank pays $6 per year for each $100 deposited.

Strategies
Act it out

2. Find the amount of interest the $200 would earn after each time.

   a) 1 year   **b)** 2 years   **c)** 3 years   **d)** 4 years

3. **a)** How much does the $200 amount to when you graduate from high school?
   b) Compare this to your estimate in step 1.

4. **Reflect** What math operations are involved in step 2? Is there a faster way to find the total amount of interest? Explain your answer using words or symbols.

Example 1: Calculate Simple Interest

Amrik buys a $100 Canada Savings Bond that pays $7\frac{1}{2}$% per year simple interest. Amrik can cash the bond in 5 years, when it matures.
a) How much interest will the bond earn in 5 years?
b) What will the total value of the bond be in 5 years?

> $100   7.5% 5 Year Bond $100
> **CANADA SAVINGS BOND**
> *This is to certify that* **Amrik** *is entitled to a 7.5% 5 year bond payable by the Bank of Canada*
> **$100**
> $100 $100

Solution

a) Use the simple interest formula $I = P \times r \times t$, where

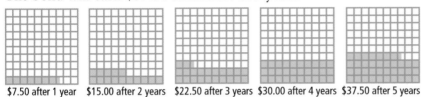

I is the interest, in dollars t is the time, in years

P is the **principal**, in dollars r is the interest rate per year, in decimal form

principal
• money invested or borrowed

$I = P \times r \times t$
$I = 100 \times 0.075 \times 5$ Write the interest rate as a decimal: 7.5% = 0.075.
$I = 37.50$ **Use two decimal places for money.**

The bond will earn $37.50 in interest in 5 years.

$7.50 after 1 year $15.00 after 2 years $22.50 after 3 years $30.00 after 4 years $37.50 after 5 years

b) Total amount = principal + interest
= $100 + $37.50
= $137.50

The total value of the bond in 5 years is $137.50.

Example 2: Calculate Simple Interest for Less Than One Year

Sue borrows $300 from her sister Darma. Sue agrees to pay 8% interest per year. If Sue repays the loan 6 months later, how much does she owe Darma?

Solution

Step 1: Find the interest.
$I = P \times r \times t$
$I = 300 \times 0.08 \times 0.5$
$I = 12$
Sue will owe $12 interest.

> The interest rate is 8%. Use $r = 0.08$.
> Time needs to be in years.
> 6 months is $\frac{6}{12}$ or $\frac{1}{2}$ year.
> Use $t = 0.5$.

Strategies
Choose a formula

Step 2: To find the amount owing, add the $300 borrowed.
Amount = $300 + $12
= $312
If Sue repays the loan 6 months later, she will owe $312 to Darma.

Key Ideas

- Simple interest is calculated when money is borrowed or lent.
- The formula for simple interest is $I = P \times r \times t$, where

  I is the interest, in dollars
  P is the principal, in dollars
  t is the time, in years
  r is the interest rate per year, in decimal form

- The total amount is found by adding the interest to the principal.

Communicate the Ideas

1. Describe three factors that affect the amount of interest your money earns in a simple interest account.

2. How can you use a fraction to express each time in years?

   a) 6 months   **b)** 4 months   **c)** 9 months

3. What's wrong? Kim deposits $100 into an account that pays 6% per year. Kim says, "Hey, if I leave this money in for 5 years, I'll earn over $3000 in interest! Look, I worked it out." Here is Kim's calculation:

   I = P x r x t
   I = $100 x 6 x 5
   I = $3000

   a) Find the error in Kim's solution and show a correct one.
   b) How can you tell Kim in a bad news/good news way about her mistake?

Check Your Understanding

Practise

For help with questions 4 to 6, refer to Example 1.

4. Suppose you deposit $250 into an account for 2 years. The account earns 5% interest per year.

   a) How much interest is earned in 2 years?
   b) What does the deposit amount to after 2 years?

5. Kelly buys a $500 bond that matures in 4 years. The bond pays 6% interest per year.

   a) Determine the total interest earned.
   b) What is the value of the bond after 4 years?

6. Tom leaves a deposit of $420 in a savings account for 3 years. The account earns 4.5% interest per year.

a) How much interest is earned in 3 years?

b) How much does the deposit amount to after 3 years?

For help with questions 7 to 9, refer to Example 2.

7. Pat deposits $325 into an account that earns 2.5% interest per year. Find

a) the interest after 6 months

b) the value of the deposit after 6 months

8. Cleo borrows $670 for 9 months. The loan company charges $12\frac{1}{2}$% interest per year.

a) How much interest does Cleo owe?

b) How much will she need to pay off the loan after 9 months?

9. Suppose you borrow $200 from a friend. Your friend charges $9\frac{1}{2}$% interest per year. You repay the loan after 3 months.

a) How much interest will you have to pay?

b) How much in total will you have to pay back?

Apply

10. You lend $1500 to a friend for 4 months, at an interest rate of $4\frac{3}{4}$% per year. What total amount will your friend have to pay back?

11. Eric deposits $175 for 6 months into an account that pays 7% interest per year. He deposits $200, for 6 months, into another account that pays 4% interest per year. Which account will earn more interest? Explain how you know.

12. Karen has $500 to invest for 4 years. Her bank offers two options.

Account A: earns 5.5% interest per year

Account B: earns $5\frac{3}{4}$% interest per year

Which account will pay me more interest?

a) Which account should Karen invest in?

b) How much more interest does it pay than the other account?

 Try This! **13.** Suppose you purchase a $500 Canada Savings Bond that earns 5.4% interest per year.

a) What will the value of the bond be when it matures in 4 years?

b) If you cash in the bond after 3 years, the bank reduces the interest rate by 1%. What is the value of the bond in this case?

Extend

14. When you check your options at the bank, you find an account that earns 5.5% compound interest. The teller explains that compound interest is calculated using the balance in your account after each year.

a) Use a table to find out the amount for a deposit of $500 after 4 years.

Year	Principal	Rate	Interest	Amount
1	$500.00	0.055	$27.50	$527.50
2	$527.50	0.055		
3				
4				

b) What is the total amount of interest earned? Explain how you found this.

c) How much more does compound interest provide than simple interest, at the same rate?

Key Words

For questions 1 to 6, match each definition to one of these words:

commission discount principal
proportion rate ratio
sales taxes simple interest speed
unit price unit rate

1. a comparison of quantities measured in different units

2. a statement that two ratios are equal

3. the price of one unit, used in shopping

4. an amount subtracted from a listed price to give a sale price

5. money collected by the government on purchases

6. a payment, expressed as a percent, earned on sales

5.1 Apply Ratio and Proportion, pages 150–155

7. Write a ratio, in simplest form, to compare the number of buttons of each colour.

   a) green to blue
   b) green to yellow

8. Find the missing number in each proportion.
   a) 12:8 = 6:■
   b) 3:■ = 12:20
   c) 7:2 = ■:10

9. A baseball team has a win-loss record of 30:25.

   a) Write this as a ratio in simplest form.
   b) Predict the team's final record at the end of a 165-game season. What assumption do you need to make?

5.2 Explore Rates, pages 156–161

10. Write each as a unit rate.

    a) Sonya walked 500 m in 5 min.
    b) It costs 99¢ for 3 lemons.
    c) Jordan typed 150 words in 6 min.

11. It costs $2.45 for 500 mL of soy sauce.

    a) Express this as a unit price per 100 mL.
    b) How much would 1.5 L of soy sauce cost?

12. Julie drove 150 km in 2 h, at a fairly constant speed.

    a) Express this as a unit rate.
    b) At this rate, how far will Julie travel in 5 h?
    c) Describe any assumptions you must make.

13. Which is the better buy? Justify your choice.

5.3 Apply Percent to Sales Taxes and Discounts, pages 162–165

14. Find the 7% GST and the 8% PST on each item.

	Item	Price
a)	Sweater	$28.95
b)	Bracelet	$10.99
c)	Camera	$239.00

15. Estimate, then calculate, each discount.

a) 30% off a picture frame, regular price $15.95

b) 25% off a filing cabinet, regular price $59.85

c) 20% off a magazine subscription, regular price $28.00

16. The regular price of a knapsack is $39.95. Now, it is marked down by 25%. It is subject to both 7% GST and 8% PST.

a) Estimate the final price.

b) Calculate the discount and the sale price.

c) Calculate the total sales tax and the final price.

d) Compare the final price to your estimate. How close were you?

17. The regular price of a snowboard is $349. Now, it is marked at 35% off.

a) What is the sale price?

b) Find the total price, including 7% GST and 8% PST.

5.4 Apply Percent to Commission, pages 166–169

18. Tomka earns 40% commission on the make-up that she sells. How much will she earn on each sale?

eye shadow $7.50   nail polish $4.59   lipstick $5.95   mascara $5.95

a) 1 eye shadow   **b)** 2 lipsticks

c) 1 mascara, 3 nail polishes, and 2 eye shadows

19. Aria earns a 3% commission on real estate sales.

a) What is her commission if she sells a house for $150 000?

b) Aria receives a commission cheque for a house sale. The cheque is for $6000. What was the selling price of the house?

5.5 Calculate Simple Interest, pages 170–173

20. Ian deposits $700 into an account that earns 6% interest per year.

a) How much interest is earned in 5 years?

b) What is the total amount after 5 years?

21. Suhanna borrows $350 for 18 months at a rate of $8\frac{1}{2}\%$ interest per year. What total amount must she pay when the loan is due?

22. $1000 is deposited into an account for 3 months. The account earns $5\frac{1}{4}\%$ interest per year. How much interest is earned?

CHAPTER

5

Practice Test

Strand	NSN	MEA	GSS	PA	DMP
Questions	1–11	2, 3, 6, 7, 11		1, 2	

Multiple Choice

For questions 1 to 5, choose the best answer.

1. The ratio 4:5 is equivalent to

   A 5:4   **B** 8:12

   C 12:15   **D** 15:12

2. The ratio of girls to boys in a class is 7:8. The class has 30 students. How many boys are there?

   A 14   **B** 15

   C 16   **D** 23

3. A plane travels 1200 km in 2.5 h at a constant speed. The unit rate is

   A 1200 km/2.5 h

   B 600 km/h

   C 2.5 km/h

   D 480 km/h

4. The regular price of a pair of jeans is $80. Now, the jeans are marked down by 25%. The sale price is

$80
25% off

   A $20

   B $50

   C $60

   D $65

5. Heather earns a 35% commission on shoe sales. One week she sold a total of $850. Her commission for that week is

   A $210.50

   B $297.50

   C $350.00

   D $552.50

Short Answer

6. a) Nathan is trying to decide which package of rolled oats to buy.
A: 500 g for $2.89
B: 300 g for $1.89
Which package would you recommend? Why?

   b) What assumption did you make in part a)?

7. a) Determine the unit price of each grocery item.

Item	Cost
Oranges	$3.50 for a dozen
Onions	$2.28 for 3 kg
Cereal (in bulk)	$4.40 for 350 g
Jam	$4.45 for 500 mL

   b) Determine the total cost for 5 oranges, 900 g of cereal, and 350 mL of jam.

8. Ron buys a $500 savings bond that earns 5% interest per year.

   a) How much interest is earned in the 3-year term?

   b) What is the total amount at the end of the 3 years?

9. Alvira earns a 4% commission on used car sales. One week Alvira's commission cheque was $780. What was the total amount of Alvira's car sales that week?

Extended Response

10. Identical hockey jerseys are on sale at two stores. At Slapshooters, the jersey is marked at 20% off its regular price of $95.00. At Ice Age, the jersey is marked at 15% off its regular price of $90.00. Both jerseys are subject to GST and PST.

a) Determine the discount and the sale price of a jersey at each store.

b) Calculate the total sales tax and the final price at each store.

c) Which store gives the better deal? How much would you save? Justify your answer.

11. Suppose you deposit $500 into a savings account for 4 months. The account earns $6\frac{1}{4}\%$ interest per year.

a) What amount of interest will you earn?

b) What will the total amount in the account be?

c) How much more interest would you earn if you left the money in the account for 20 months?

d) Would the amount, at the end of 20 months, be enough to buy a guitar that costs $514.99? Explain your answer.

Chapter Problem Wrap-Up

The concert starts at noon and lasts 10 h. Each headliner plays twice as long as each supporting act. Each band gets 25 min to set up. In question 14 on page 155 you found how many minutes acts get to play.

When planning the schedule, your marketing manager recommends that you follow these guidelines:
- Finish the concert with a headliner.
- Never schedule two headliners in a row.

Headliners	Supporting Acts
The Howlin' Cats	Moondancer
Virtual Thunder	C.U. L8er
The Crunch-Bunnies	Rap Pappy and Sonny Shine
3 Left Feet	New Girls Up the Street
	Breakdances With Woodchucks
	Flip Flop and the Clodhoppers

1. Design a schedule of bands. Include the times at which they are to start and stop performing, and a name for your concert event.

2. Keep a record showing your calculations and justifying how you have followed the guidelines.

3. Trade your schedule and record with a classmate. Check whether the schedule satisfies all the requirements.

4. If one of the headliners cancelled at the last minute, how could you adjust the schedule?

Patterning and Algebra

- Identify the relationships between numbers and variables.
- Identify, create, and discuss patterns using words and algebraic expressions.
- Apply and defend patterning strategies in problem solving situations.
- Write an algebraic expression for the nth term of a sequence.
- Present and explain solutions to patterning problems.

Data Management and Probability

- Interpret displays of data.
- Construct graphs and use the information to solve problems.

Number Sense and Numeration

- Explain the problem solving process in mathematical language.

Key Words

fractal

sequence

variable

nth term

CHAPTER 6

Patterning and Algebra

The art of paper folding is called origami. It has been popular in Japan for over 10 centuries. Origami creates interesting three-dimensional figures by folding very thin sheets of paper.

You probably fold many items in a pattern. You can fold napkins for a party, fold a sail to store it, or fold a gum wrapper, or a bus transfer in your pocket. You can create countless patterns by folding two-dimensional materials.

In this chapter, you will explore many patterns. You will create algebraic equations to describe patterns. You will solve problems using patterning skills and equations.

Chapter Problem

Create a pattern by folding a piece of paper in a similar way several times. Unfold the paper and describe all the patterns you can find. Use numbers and geometric shapes. How is the number of folds related to a feature of your pattern?

Patterns

Patterns can be described in words. They can be extended to find further terms. The **sequence** or number pattern 7, 9, 11, 13, ... begins with 7. You can find the next term by adding 2 to the previous term. The next three terms are 15, 17, and 19.

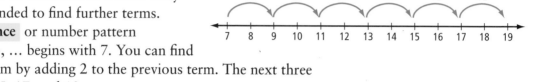

1. Write the next three terms in each sequence.
   a) 3, 9, 27, 81, ...
   b) $\frac{1}{2}, \frac{1}{4}, \frac{1}{6}, \frac{1}{8}, \ldots$
   c) 80, 70, 60, 50, ...
   d) 4, 7, 10, 13, ...

2. Describe each pattern in words. Then, show the next three terms.
   a) 10, 14, 18, 22, ...
   b)

   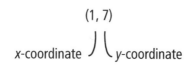

   c) 729, 243, 81, 27, ...
   d) $\frac{2}{3}, \frac{5}{3}, \frac{8}{3}, \frac{11}{3}, \ldots$

3. Describe each pattern. Then, show the missing terms.
   a) ■, ■, 15, 19, 23
   b)

   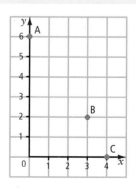

   c) ■, 16, 8, ■, 2
   d)

Days After Planting Grass Seed	Height of New Grass (mm)
1	5
2	10
3	
4	
5	25

Graphing Skills

In an **ordered pair**, the first number is the **x-coordinate**. The second number is the **y-coordinate**. To plot a point on a grid, find where the x-coordinate and y-coordinate meet. Then, mark a dot and label the ordered pair. The points A(0, 6), B(3, 2), and C(4, 0) are shown on the grid.

(1, 7)

x-coordinate ⎵ ⎵ y-coordinate

4. Write an ordered pair for each point on the grid.

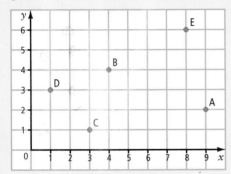

5. a) Plot the ordered pairs A(1, 2), B(1, 4), C(2, 3), D(2, 5), E(3, 4), and F(3, 6).
  b) Join A to B, B to C, and so on. Describe the pattern.
  c) Predict the next two ordered pairs in the pattern.

6. a) Plot the ordered pairs Q(2, 8), R(3, 7), S(5, 7), T(6, 6), U(8, 6), and V(9, 5).
  b) Join Q to R, R to S, and so on. Describe the pattern.
  c) Predict the next two ordered pairs in the pattern.

Pythagorean Relationship

The **Pythagorean relationship** connects the sides of any right triangle. The Pythagorean relationship can be used to find the length of one side of a right triangle if the other two sides are known.

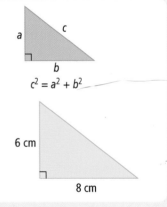

$c^2 = a^2 + b^2$ **Substitute the lengths of the legs for *a* and *b*.**
$c^2 = 6^2 + 8^2$
$c^2 = 36 + 64$
$c^2 = 100$ **Find the square root of 100.**
$c = 10$

The missing side length is 10 cm.

7. Find the missing side length in each right triangle.

a)

b)

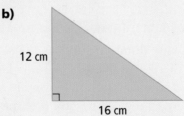

6.1 Identify Patterns

Focus on...

- patterns with numbers and shapes
- describing patterns
- extending patterns

French mathematician Blaise Pascal developed this number triangle in the 17th century. Look at the third diagonal. How can the sum 1 + 3 + 6 help you predict a number in the triangle? Describe at least three patterns in Pascal's triangle.

1
1   1
1   2   1
1   3   3   1
1   4   6   4   1
1   5   10 10 5   1

Discover the Math

Materials

- pattern blocks
- coloured tiles
- grid paper

How can you use patterns to make predictions?

1. Jeremy is making an ice cream sundae. He has two toppings: sprinkles and chocolate chunks.

   a) How many different sundaes can he make with no toppings? one topping? two toppings?

   b) Where can you find these numbers in Pascal's triangle?

2. Jodi has three toppings for her sundae: sprinkles, chocolate chunks, and blueberries.

   a) How many different sundaes can Jodi make with no toppings? one topping? two toppings? three toppings?

   b) Look at Pascal's triangle. Can you find these numbers?

   c) How many ways can Jodi serve her ice cream?

3. Liam found marshmallows too. He has four toppings available.

   a) Predict how many different sundaes Liam can make altogether.

   b) How many different sundaes can Liam make with no toppings? one topping? two toppings? three toppings? four toppings?

   c) Look at Pascal's triangle. Can you find these numbers?

4. **Reflect** What patterns do you see in the first six rows of Pascal's triangle? How can you use these patterns to make predictions?

Example 1: Extend a Fractal Tree

Fractal trees show a visual pattern. Examine this fractal tree.
a) Describe how new branches are created.
b) Copy the fractal tree onto grid paper. Extend the branches to one more stage.

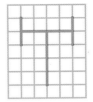

fractal
• a pattern of shapes, lines, or colours that gets smaller as it repeats

Solution

a)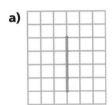

The trunk is four units.

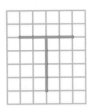

It splits into two at 90° angles. Each new branch is half as long as the trunk.

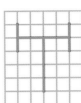

Each branch splits into two. Each new branch is half as long as the previous branch.

b)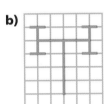

Example 2: Identify a Number Pattern

Describe and model each **sequence** . Then, write the next three terms.

a) $2\frac{1}{2}, 4\frac{1}{2}, 6\frac{1}{2}, 8\frac{1}{2}, \ldots$

b) 3, 6, 12, 24, …

c) 28, 24, 20, 16, …

sequence
• a pattern of numbers

Solution

a) Start with $2\frac{1}{2}$. Add 2 repeatedly.

The next three terms are $10\frac{1}{2}$, $12\frac{1}{2}$, and $14\frac{1}{2}$.

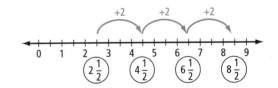

b) Start with 3. Repeatedly multiply by 2. The next three terms are 48, 96, and 192.

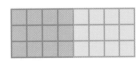

c) Start with 28. Subtract 4 repeatedly.
The next three terms are 12, 8, and 4.

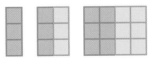

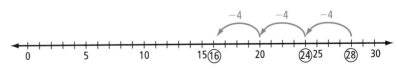

- Some patterns are based on geometric shapes or lines.

- Other patterns are based on number operations.

- To identify a pattern:
  - Find the first shape or number.
  - Describe how new shapes or numbers are generated.
  - Look for repeated sets of operations.

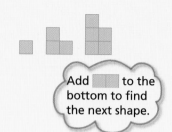

Add ▢ to the bottom to find the next shape.

Communicate the Ideas

1. Use words and numbers to describe one pattern in Pascal's triangle.

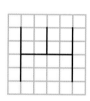

2. Is this a fractal tree? Explain.

3. a) Create a fractal tree. Show the first three stages. Explain how you know it is a fractal.

b) Challenge a classmate to identify a pattern in your fractal tree and to draw the next stage.

Check Your Understanding

Practise

4. Describe each number pattern.

a) 2, 6, 18, 54, ...

b) 110, 90, 70, 50, ...

5. Malina can bring up to four CDs on a car ride. How many different ways can she bring no CDs? one CD? two CDs? three CDs? four CDs?

6. During a graduation barbecue, students can choose up to five condiments for their burgers.

- ketchup
- mustard
- relish
- barbecue sauce
- steak sauce

How many different ways can students put condiments on their burgers?

For help with questions 7 and 8, refer to Example 1.

7. Copy the fractal tree onto triangle dot paper. Describe how new branches are created. Extend the branches to one more stage.

8. Look at the stages of the Sierpinski triangle fractal.

a) Explain how to extend the pattern.
b) Copy the fractal and draw the next stage.

For help with questions 9 to 11, refer to Example 2.

9. Describe each sequence.

a) 14, 17, 20, 23, …

b) $\dfrac{3}{2}, \dfrac{5}{2}, \dfrac{7}{2}, \dfrac{9}{2}, \ldots$

10. Write the next three numbers for each sequence in question 9.

11. What operation is used to extend each sequence? Write the next two numbers.

a) 1, 5, 25, 125, …
b) 243, 81, 27, 9, …
c) 2, 16, 30, 44, …

Apply

For questions 12 and 13, use Pascal's triangle.

12. Identify a pattern for finding the numbers in each row. Extend Pascal's triangle for three more rows.

13. a) Add the first three terms in the third diagonal (1 + 3 + 6). Where can you find this sum in Pascal's triangle?

b) Does this pattern happen on other diagonals? If so, how can you extend the pattern?

14. Look at the computer-generated fractal in this picture.

a) Describe a pattern of colours and shapes.

b) Design your own fractal. Challenge a classmate to identify your pattern.

Internet Connect Go to **www.mcgrawhill.ca/links/math8** and follow the links to explore some interesting fractal patterns.

Extend

15. a) Copy and complete the table.

Number	Sum Up To the Number	Result
1	1	
2	1 + 2	
3	1 + 2 + 3	
4		
5		
6		

b) Can you find each number and the sum up to that number in Pascal's triangle?

c) How can you use Pascal's triangle to find the sum of numbers up to any number?

Define Patterns Using Algebra

Focus on...
- geometric and number patterns
- modelling patterns
- translating patterns

A comet named Kohoutek was first seen in 1973. The comet orbits the Earth every six years. How can you use this information to explore the pattern of predicted future sightings of Kohoutek? How can you develop an equation to predict the year of a particular sighting?

Discover the Math

Materials
- toothpicks
- coloured marker

How can you use algebra to understand patterns?

1. Use a marker to colour one toothpick. Then, add toothpicks to make a row of squares.

2. Copy and complete the table for up to six toothpick squares.

Number of Squares	Number of Coloured Toothpicks	Number of Uncoloured Toothpicks	Total Number of Toothpicks

3. Describe the pattern of uncoloured toothpicks needed to extend a string of squares.

4. Write a formula to find the total number of toothpicks needed to form a given number of squares. Define your **variables** .

variable
- a letter that represents a number or numbers

5. If all four toothpicks in the first square are coloured, how will your results change?

6. Reflect How are your strings of toothpick squares similar? How are they different? How can formulas help you understand related toothpick patterns?

Example 1: Model a Pattern With a Formula

Examine the pattern of regular hexagons with side length 1 unit.

a) Describe the relationship between the number of hexagons and the perimeter of the shape.

b) Find the perimeter of a string of five hexagons.

c) Write a formula to model the perimeter of a string of *n* hexagons.

d) You have a string of 15 hexagons. Find the perimeter of the shape.

Solution

a) Let P represent the perimeter of a shape.

1 hexagon, $P = 6$
2 hexagons, $P = 10$
3 hexagons, $P = 14$
4 hexagons, $P = 18$

> Add 4 to find the perimeter of the next shape in the pattern.

As the number of hexagons increases by one, the perimeter of the shape increases by 4.

Strategies
What other patterns can you find?

b) The perimeter of a string of five hexagons is 18 + 4 or 22 units.

c) The formula is

perimeter of a shape ⟶

number of hexagons ⟵

$$P = 2 + 4n$$

end side lengths ⟶

top and bottom side lengths for each hexagon ⟵

Literacy Connections

Choosing a Variable
Any letter can be used as a variable. Choose a letter that helps you remember what the variable represents.

d) $P = 2 + 4n$
$P = 2 + 4(15)$ **Multiply.**
$P = 2 + 60$
$P = 62$

The perimeter of a string of 15 hexagons is 62 units.

> Fifteen hexagons means $n = 15$. I will substitute this value into the formula to find the perimeter.

Example 2: The *n*th Term of a Pattern

A theatre has 20 seats in the first row, 23 seats in the second row, 26 seats in the third row, and so on.

a) Describe the pattern in words.

b) Show the relationship between a row in the theatre and the number of seats in the row.

c) Develop an algebraic expression for the value of the **nth term** of the pattern.

d) How many seats are in row 12?

nth term
• an item in a sequence or pattern
• the variable, *n*, represents the position in the pattern

Solution

a) The first row has 20 seats. Each row has three more seats than the previous row.

b)

Theatre Row Number	Number of Seats	Pattern
1	20	20
2	23 = 20 + 3	20 + 3 × 1
3	26 = 20 + 3 + 3	20 + 3 × 2
4	29 = 20 + 3 + 3 + 3	20 + 3 × 3

This is the same as the theatre row number minus one.

Strategies
Make a table or chart

c) Let *n* represent the theatre row number.
The value of the *n*th term gives the number of seats in row *n* of the theatre.
The value of the *n*th term is $20 + 3 \times (n - 1)$.

If I know the row number, I can use this expression to find the number of seats in any row of the theatre.

d) The number of seats in row *n* is $20 + 3 \times (n - 1)$.

$$20 + 3 \times (12 - 1) \quad \textbf{Substitute } \textit{\textbf{n}} \textbf{ = 12.}$$
$$= 20 + 3 \times 11 \quad \textbf{Multiply.}$$
$$= 20 + 33$$
$$= 53$$

There are 53 seats in the 12th row of the theatre.

Row 12 means *n* = 12.

Key Ideas

◗ Patterns can be modelled using formulas.

◗ To develop a formula:
  – Create a table to identify the pattern.
  – Write a number sentence algebraically.

◗ You can use an expression for the value of the *n*th term to make predictions about a pattern.

Let *t* represent the number of toothpicks.
Let *s* represent the number of squares.
$$t = 1 + 3s$$
first toothpick   number of toothpicks added to form each square

5, 10, 15, 20, …
The value of the *n*th term is 5*n*.
n = 9 refers to the ninth term.
The value of the ninth term is 5(9) or 40.

Communicate the Ideas

1. a) Describe the sequence 1, 4, 7, 10, ….
   b) What is the value of the first term? third term?
   c) Explain how to find which term has a value of 19.

2. Brian and Leanne each got a different value for the nth of the pattern shown in the table. Who is correct? Why? What mistake did the other person make.

Term	Value	Pattern
1	6 = 3 + 3	3 × 2
2	9 = 3 + 3 + 3	3 × 3
3	12 = 3 + 3 + 3 + 3	3 × 4
4	15 = 3 + 3 + 3 + 3 + 3	3 × 5

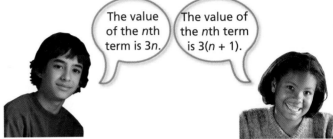

The value of the nth term is 3n.

The value of the nth term is 3(n + 1).

3. Tell your classmate how to find the 15th term in the sequence 2, 6, 18, 54, ….

4. Explain why the expressions 2 + 4n and 6 + 4(n − 1) can both be used to find the perimeter of a string of hexagons.

Check Your Understanding

Practise

For help with questions 5 and 6, refer to Example 1.

5. Examine the pattern of equilateral triangles.

   a) Describe the relationship between the number of triangles and the perimeter of the shape.
   b) Write a formula to model the perimeter of a row of triangles.
   c) Find the perimeter of a shape with 14 triangles.

6. Look at the pattern of cubes. Each cube has a smiley face sticker on every exposed face.

   a) Describe the relationship between the number of cubes and the number of smiley faces.
   b) Develop an equation to model the number of smiley faces.
   c) How many smiley faces are on 10 cubes?

For help with questions 7 and 8, refer to Example 2.

7. A theatre has 15 seats in the first row, 20 seats in the second row, 25 seats in the third row, and so on.

a) Describe the pattern.
b) Use a table to show the number of seats in each of the first five rows.
c) Develop a formula to model the number of seats in the nth row.
d) How many seats are in the 16th row?

8. A marching band has 3 musicians in the first row, 5 musicians in the second row, 7 musicians in the third row, and so on.

a) Explain the pattern in words.
b) Model the number of musicians in the nth row using a formula.
c) How many musicians are in the 10th row?

9. Copy and complete a table of values for each sequence. Show the first six terms.

Term	Value

a) $\frac{1}{3}, \frac{1}{4}, \frac{1}{5}, \frac{1}{6}, \ldots$
b) 486, 162, 54, 18, …
c) 5, 8, 11, 14, …
d) 99, 90, 81, 72, …

Apply

10. Look at the sequence
$1^2 + 1, 2^2 + 2, 3^2 + 3, 4^2 + 4, \ldots.$

a) Describe how the value of each term is related to the term number.
b) Which term in the sequence has a value of 12?
c) Write an expression for the value of the nth term.

11. Study the pattern of marbles.

Term 1   Term 2   Term 3

Copy and complete the table for the first six terms. Then, find an expression for the value of the nth term.

Term, n	Number of Marbles, m	Pattern
1	3	$1 + 2 \times 1$

Chapter Problem

12. Fold a square piece of paper along a diagonal. You made an isosceles triangle. Fold the base in half. Find the base of your new isosceles triangle. Fold it in half. Now, fold the base of this triangle in half.

a) Unfold the paper and describe all the different shapes you can find.
b) Show the relationship between the number of triangles on the paper and the number of times you folded the paper.
c) What other methods could you use to show this relationship?
d) Write a formula to model the number of triangles created after n folds.

13. Halley's Comet was seen in 1758.

a) If the comet appears every 76 years, write the years of the next three sightings.

b) Copy and complete the table.

Sighting After 1758	Year	Pattern
1	1834	1758 + 76
2		
3		
4		

c) Use an equation to model the year of the nth sighting of Halley's Comet after 1758.

d) Find the year of the 10th sighting after 1758.

Did You Know?

British astronomer Edmond Halley (1656–1742) showed that a comet he saw in 1682 was the same as a comet that had been seen in 1607 and 1531. Halley predicted that this comet would return in 1758. He was right!

Extend

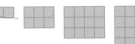

14. Examine the pattern of squares. The table shows how many squares are in each figure.

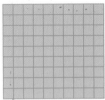

Figure	Number of Squares	Pattern
1	2	1 × 2
2	6	2 × 3
3	12	3 × 4
4	20	4 × 5

a) Find the number of squares in the seventh figure of the pattern.

b) Another figure in the pattern is shown. Which figure number is it? Justify your answer.

15. José is building a square pen for his pet rabbit. He wants to put five posts on each side. José draws this diagram.

a) How many posts will José need?

b) How many posts will Jose need to build any square pen? Explain your reasoning.

Making Connections

What does a tape measure have to do with finding your age?

Materials
• two-sided metric measuring tape

1. Fold the tape measure so that the zero end is matched up with 100 plus the last two digits of this year. If it is 2004, then line the end of the tape up with 100 + 04 = 104.

2. Ask a friend to point to the last two digits of his or her year of birth.

3. Look at the back of where your friend is pointing. That number is your friend's age.

For example, if your friend was born in 1990, the number across from 90 on the tape will be 14. Your friend is 14 years old. Try it for yourself or with a family member. Then, show why this works using the nth term.

Explore Relationships on a Grid

These students are exploring ways to measure a structure. How could you find the height of this structure?

Discover the Math

Materials
- foam cups
- ruler
- grid paper

How can you calculate the height of cups stacked inside each other?

1. Work with a partner and make stacks of one, two, three, four, and five cups. Measure the height of each stack of cups. Record your measurements in a table.

2. Plot the points on a coordinate grid.

3. Describe the pattern of points. If the number of cups increases by one, by how much does the height of the stack increase?

4. Write a formula relating the height of the stack to the number of cups.

5. Use your formula to predict the height of a stack of 10 cups.

6. Make a stack of 10 cups and measure it. How accurate is your formula?

7. **Reflect** How did you develop a formula from your measurements?

Strategies
What strategies are you using?

Example 1: Plot Points and Examine Relationships

The height of a stack of flowerpots can
be modelled with the formula $h = 9 + 3n$.

a) Define the variables.

b) Create a graph showing the heights of
one to four flowerpots.

c) Describe the pattern.

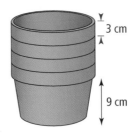

3 cm

9 cm

Solution

a) Let h represent the total height, in centimetres, of a stack of flowerpots.
Let n represent the number of flowerpots
in the stack.

b) To find the ordered pairs, substitute each number of flowerpots
into the formula. Then, calculate the height of the stack.

$h = 9 + 3n$	$h = 9 + 3n$	$h = 9 + 3n$	$h = 9 + 3n$
$h = 9 + 3(1)$	$h = 9 + 3(2)$	$h = 9 + 3(3)$	$h = 9 + 3(4)$
$h = 12$	$h = 15$	$h = 18$	$h = 21$

Strategies
Find needed
information

Number of Flowerpots, n	Height of Stack, h (cm)	(n, h)
1	12	(1, 12)
2	15	(2, 15)
3	18	(3, 18)
4	21	(4, 21)

> The first number in the
> ordered pair shows the
> number of flowerpots in a
> stack. The second number
> shows the height of the stack.

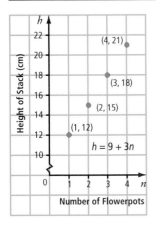

Strategies
What other ways can
you describe this
pattern? How will your
formula change?

c) The base of each flowerpot is 9 cm. The rim of each flowerpot is 3 cm.
Since they are stacked inside each other, the height of the stack is the
same as the height of the rims plus the height of one base.

Example 2: Use Ordered Pairs to Understand Relationships

The student council is organizing a school play. The total cost to buy up to five boxes of tickets is shown. The set-up fee to design the tickets is $30.

Number of Boxes, n	0	1	2	3	4	5
Total Cost, C ($)	30	45	60	75	90	105

a) Write the ordered pairs. Then, plot the points on a grid.

b) What does the ordered pair (0, 30) mean?

c) Describe the pattern of points. Then, write an equation to model the relationship.

d) How much will it cost for the student council to buy 35 boxes of tickets?

e) If the set-up fee is reduced to $27, how will your equation change?

Literacy Connections

Reading a Horizontal Table of Values

The variables are on the left.

• The top row shows the x-coordinates.

• The bottom row shows the y-coordinates.

(4, 90) is an ordered pair in this table of values.

Solution

a) (0, 30), (1, 45), (2, 60), (3, 75), (4, 90), (5, 105)

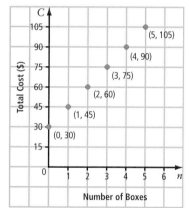

b) The set-up fee is $30.

We pay the set-up fee even if we don't buy any boxes.

c) The set-up fee is $30. As the number of boxes increases by one, the total cost increases by $15. The equation is $C = 30 + 15n$.

d) $C = 30 + 15n$ **Substitute n = 35. Then, evaluate.**
$C = 30 + 15(35)$
$C = 30 + 525$
$C = 555$
It will cost $555 to buy 35 boxes of tickets.

e) The set-up fee changes from $30 to $27.
The new equation is $C = 27 + 15n$.

Only the set-up fee changes.

- To explore a relationship:
  - Investigate the ordered pairs.
  - Plot the points on a grid.
  - Describe the pattern of points.

(1, 12), (2, 14), (3, 16), (4, 18), …

As the *x*-coordinate increases by one, the *y*-coordinate increases by two.

- You can use an equation to make predictions.

$h = 10 + 2n$. By substituting $n = 15$, you can predict that a stack of 15 flowerpots will be 40 cm high.

Communicate the Ideas

1. Cameron measures the heights of stacked linking cubes as shown.

Number of Cubes, n	Height, h (cm)
1	5
2	9
3	13
4	17

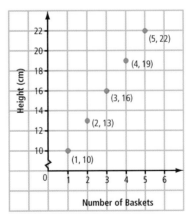

connector

a) Cameron lists the ordered pairs as (5, 1), (9, 2), (13, 3), (17, 4). Are the ordered pairs correct? Explain.

b) The pattern of heights is modelled with the formula $h = 4n + 1$. What does the number 1 mean? What does the number 4 mean?

2. The heights of up to five stacked baskets are plotted on a grid.

a) What information can you get from the graph?

b) Describe the pattern of points.

c) Develop a formula to calculate the height of any stack of these baskets.

d) Define the variables in your formula. Could you use any other letters? Explain.

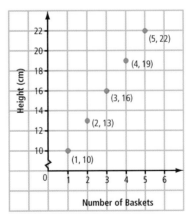

3. a) List the ordered pairs shown on the grid.

b) Describe the pattern of points. Then, create a question that leads to this pattern.

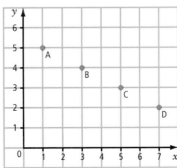

Practise

For help with questions 4 and 5, refer to Example 1.

4. The height of a stack of recycling bins can be modelled using the formula $h = 12 + 3n$.

a) Define each variable.
b) Complete a table of values for the heights of one to four bins.
c) Plot the ordered pairs on a grid.
d) Describe the pattern of points.

5. Zenaid looks at the pattern.

He writes the ordered pairs relating the number of circles to the number of lines (1, 4), (2, 8), (3, 12), (4, 16).

a) Complete a table of values using the ordered pairs.
b) Plot the points on a grid.
c) Describe the pattern.

For help with questions 6 and 7, refer to Example 2.

6. A camp counsellor buys T-shirts for his campers. The total cost of up to six T-shirts is shown. He pays a $25 fee to have the T-shirts designed.

Number of T-shirts	0	1	2	3	4	5
Total Cost ($)	25	31	37	43	49	55

a) Plot the ordered pairs on a grid.
b) Describe the relationship between the total cost and the number of T-shirts.
c) Write an equation modelling the total cost. Define your variables.

7. Hari measures the heights of stacked plastic cups.

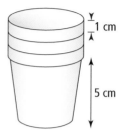

She records her results.

Number of Cups	1	2	3	4	5
Height (cm)	6	7	8	9	10

a) Plot the ordered pairs on a grid.
b) Describe the relationship between the number of cups and the height of a stack.
c) Develop an equation to model the height of a stack of cups.
d) What is the height of a stack of 40 cups?

Apply

8. Len buys baseball caps for the geography club. He pays the designer a $15 set-up fee. The cost for up to five bags of caps is shown.

Number of Bags	0	1	2	3	4	5
Cost ($)	15	30	45	60	75	90

a) Plot the ordered pairs on a grid. Justify your choice of scale on each axis.
b) Use a formula to find the cost of eight bags of baseball caps.
c) There are five baseball caps in each bag. Describe how to find the price per baseball cap for 5 to 12 caps.

9. Adriana works at a hot dog stand. She earns $50 per day, plus $0.20 per hot dog sold.

a) Copy and complete the table of values showing Adriana's earnings.

Number of Hot Dogs Sold per Day	Adriana's Earnings ($)
0	50
10	52
20	
30	
40	

b) Plot the ordered pairs on a grid.

c) Describe the relationship between Adriana's earnings and the number of hot dogs sold.

d) Express the relationship as an equation.

e) Adriana sells 100 hot dogs one day. How can you find her earnings that day?

Try This!

10. Most rulers start the zero line inside the edge of the ruler. One ruler starts the zero line 2 mm inside the edge.

a) Use pictures, words, and numbers to show the relationship between accurate measurement readings and measurements taken right from the edge of a ruler.

b) Develop an equation to model the relationship.

c) Create a table of values for your equation. Then, plot the points on a grid.

Extend

11. Describe the path of points shown. What could the variables, x and y represent?

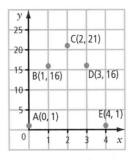

12. Advertising prices for the classified section of a newspaper are shown.

Number of Lines, n	Price, P ($)
1 to 6	$3 per line
7 to 12	$10 plus $1.00 per line
13 or more	$15 plus $1.25 per line

a) Develop an equation modelling the price for each length of advertisement.

b) Your advertisement has 15 lines, but it can be separated into smaller advertisements. How can you get the best price per line for your advertisement?

13. Ruth and Shawn are training for a cross-country running competition. They record the distance each person jogs.

Practice Number, n	Distance, d (km)	
	Ruth	Shawn
1	1.5	3.5
2	3	4.5
3	4.5	5.5
4	6	6.5

a) Describe the relationship between the distance that Ruth jogs and the practice number. Plot the ordered pairs on a grid.

b) Repeat part a) using Shawn's data. Plot the ordered pairs on the same grid.

c) What information can you find if you extend the patterns on the grid? When would you stop extending the pattern? Why?

6.4

Focus on...
• using patterns in problem solving
• selecting methods for solving problems

Apply Patterning Strategies

The cord attached to a bungee jumper stretches. The length of the stretch is related to the mass of the bungee jumper. This can be expressed as an equation. How can you find the maximum safe mass for a bungee jumper?

Discover the Math

Materials
• toothpicks
• grid paper

How can you apply formulas to solve problems?

A shelving unit can be made using boards that are the same length, including the vertical side pieces and the horizontal shelves. The shelves can be extended by placing sections side by side. This shelving unit is made in two sections and needs nine boards.

1. Use toothpicks to model one-, two-, and three-section shelving units. How many boards are needed for each? Organize the data for the shelving units.

2. Plot the data on a grid.

3. How many boards are added for each new section?

4. Write a formula relating the number of boards to the number of sections.

5. Explain how you developed your formula.

6. **Reflect** Why is it helpful to develop a formula for this type of problem?

Example 1: Find a Pattern to Plan a Picnic

Grade 8 students are setting up rows of tables for an outdoor picnic. The school has rectangular tables. The tables can seat three people on each side and one person at each end.

a) Develop a formula for the number of people that can sit at a row of n tables.

b) Use your formula to find how many people can sit at a row of 13 tables.

Solution

a) Let n represent the number of tables in a row.
Let s represent the number of seats.

Method 1: Draw a Diagram

Method 2: Complete a Table

Number of Tables, n	Number of Seats, s	Pattern
1	8	$s = 8$
2	$14 = 8 + 6$	$s = 8 + 6 \times 1$
3	$20 = 8 + 6 + 6$	$s = 8 + 6 \times 2$
4	$26 = 8 + 6 + 6 + 6$	$s = 8 + 6 \times 3$
5	$32 = 8 + 6 + 6 + 6 + 6$	$s = 8 + 6 \times 4$

The formula is $s = 8 + 6(n - 1)$.

> Three people can sit on each side of a table. That's $2 \times 3 = 6$ per table. I multiply 6 by the number of tables, n. Then, I add 2 for the ends.

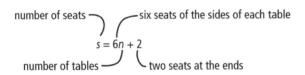

number of seats — six seats of the sides of each table

$$s = 6n + 2$$

number of tables — two seats at the ends

> Different methods of problem solving can give different formulas. Both are correct.

Strategies
What strategy are you using?

b) *Method 1*

$s = 6n + 2$
$s = 6(13) + 2$
$s = 78 + 2$
$s = 80$

> Substitute $n = 13$ into each formula. Then, evaluate.

Method 2

$s = 8 + 6(n - 1)$
$s = 8 + 6(13 - 1)$
$s = 8 + 6(12)$
$s = 8 + 72$
$s = 80$

Eighty students can sit at a row of 13 tables.

Example 2: Explore a Tournament Pattern

In a lacrosse tournament, a team that wins a match plays against another winning team in the next round. A team that loses a match is eliminated.

a) A lacrosse tournament takes six rounds to find the winning team. How many teams can enter the tournament?

b) How many teams can enter a tournament that takes n rounds to find the winner?

Solution

a) Organize the data in reverse order using a tree diagram.

Strategies
Work backward

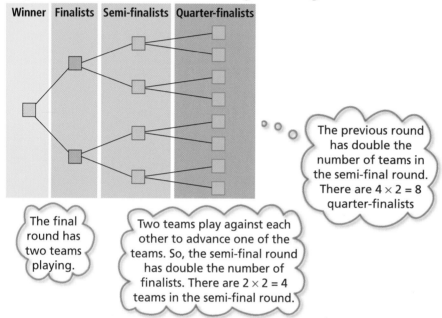

The previous round has double the number of teams in the semi-final round. There are $4 \times 2 = 8$ quarter-finalists

The final round has two teams playing.

Two teams play against each other to advance one of the teams. So, the semi-final round has double the number of finalists. There are $2 \times 2 = 4$ teams in the semi-final round.

Literacy Connections

Reading Tree Diagrams
Read tree diagrams from left to right. Each branch represents a team playing in that round.

Rounds Needed	Number of Teams	Pattern
1	2	2^1
2	$4 = 2 \times 2$	2^2
3	$8 = 2 \times 2 \times 2$	2^3
4	$16 = 2 \times 2 \times 2 \times 2$	2^4
5	$32 = 2 \times 2 \times 2 \times 2 \times 2$	2^5
6	$64 = 2 \times 2 \times 2 \times 2 \times 2 \times 2$	2^6

I can extend the pattern by multiplying each term by two.

Strategies
Make a table or chart

A tournament that has six rounds starts with 64 teams.

b) A tournament with n rounds starts with 2^n teams.

number of teams playing in each match —⌐⌐ number of rounds in a tournament

To solve a patterning problem,
  – Extend the pattern.
  – Organize the data in a table or a tree diagram.
  – Plot ordered pairs on a grid.
  – Explain the pattern in words.
  – Develop an equation to model the pattern.

Sometimes you need to use more than one method to solve a patterning problem.

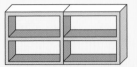

Shelving Units	Boards	Pattern
1	$5 = 1 + 4$	$1 + 4 \times 1$
2	$9 = 1 + 4 + 4$	$1 + 4 \times 2$
3	$13 = 1 + 4 + 4 + 4$	$1 + 4 \times 3$

Start with one board. Then, add four boards for each unit.

Let n represent the number of shelving units.
Let b represent the number of boards.
$b = 1 + 4n$

Communicate the Ideas

1. Jack planted a bean seed. He was told that, once the beanstalk was 2 m tall, it would double in height every day for 10 days. What is wrong with Jack's solution?

2. Describe a situation that can be modelled using the formula $C = 5n + 40$.

3. A checkers tournament takes seven rounds to find a winner. So, 2^7 players can enter the tournament. What is the meaning of the 7? What is the meaning of the 2?

Practise

For help with questions 4 and 5, refer to Example 1.

4. Square tables are arranged in rows for a parent-night presentation. Each side of a square table seats two people.

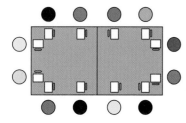

a) Draw a diagram to show how many people can sit at a row of four tables.

b) Describe a pattern for the number of people sitting at a row of *n* tables.

c) Use an equation to model your pattern.

5. James is helping grade 5 students arrange tables for reading groups. The school has trapezoid tables, which seat five people.

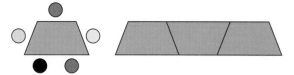

a) Describe a pattern relating the number of students that can sit at a row of *n* tables.

b) Use a table to organize your pattern.

c) Write a formula to model your pattern.

d) Use your formula to find how many students can sit at a row of seven tables.

e) Describe one way to check your answer. Check your answer. If it is not correct, revise your formula.

For help with questions 6 and 7, refer to Example 2.

6. You are planning a badminton tournament. A player who wins a match plays against another winner in the next round. A player who loses a match is eliminated.

a) How many badminton players can enter a tournament that takes four rounds to find the overall winner?

b) How many players can enter a tournament that takes *n* rounds?

7. Sari organizes a spelling competition. There are five rounds. At each round, half the students are eliminated. The final round has three competitors.

a) Organize the data using a tree diagram or a table.

b) How many students can enter the spelling competition?

Apply

8. Study the exposed smiley face cubes.

Diagram 1   Diagram 2   Diagram 3

a) Develop a formula to model the pattern.

b) What method did you use to find your formula? Justify your method.

9. A pattern is made of centimetre squares.

a) By how much does the perimeter of the shape increase with each new L-shape?

b) Describe the relationship between the perimeter of the shape and the number of L-shapes.

c) Find the perimeter of a shape that uses 12 L-shapes.

Chapter Problem

10. Start to fold a piece of paper into a fan. After each fold, open the paper and record the number of creases and sections.

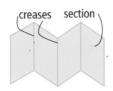

creases   section

a) How is the number of sections related to the number of creases?

b) Develop an equation to model the relationship.

c) What do your variables represent?

d) Justify the method you used for your investigation.

e) If your fan has 16 sections, how many creases will it have? Explain.

11. a) Find the length of the hypotenuse of each right triangle.

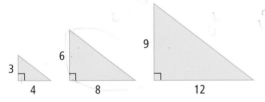

b) How are the triangles related? Identify the pattern and extend it to show one more triangle.

c) Create a similar pattern beginning with this triangle. Show the next two triangles.

12. Fernanda read about a cool Web site in her science book. She e-mails three friends to tell them about the site. Each of her friends e-mails three other friends and so on. How many levels of e-mails are needed to tell 1000 people?

Try This!

13. Look at the Olympic symbol.

a) Describe the relationship between the number of circles and the number of intersection points. How can the pattern be extended?

b) If the pattern is extended to a total of 100 circles, how many points of intersection will there be?

c) Create your own patterning problem. Ask a classmate to model your pattern using an equation.

Extend

14. Dr. Fournier wants to hire a student to walk dogs for her veterinary clinic. Two students apply for the job. Chandra charges $5 per dog. Sylvie charges $10 for the first dog and $3 for each additional dog.

a) How much does each student charge to walk one dog? two dogs?

b) Who should Dr. Fournier hire to walk the dogs? Why? Will Dr. Fournier change her mind depending on the number of dogs at the clinic? Explain.

Key Words

For questions 1 to 4, match each word to the correct definition.

1. a pattern of numbers

2. a pattern of shapes, lines, or colours that gets smaller as it repeats

3. an item in a pattern

4. a letter that represents a number or numbers

A fractal

B *n*th term

C origami

D sequence

E variable

6.1 Identify Patterns, pages 182–185

For questions 5 and 6, use Pascal's triangle.

5. Ben is making pancakes for his mother's birthday. He has two toppings: maple syrup and strawberry sauce. In how many different ways can Ben serve the pancakes?

6. Ben's sister Sara arrives home with bananas from the store. In how many different ways can Ben and Sara serve their pancakes now that they have maple syrup, strawberry sauce, and sliced bananas?

7. Create a fractal that starts with a quadrilateral. Show the first three stages of your fractal.

8. The first three rows of a number pattern are shown.

Column A	Column B	Column C	Column D	Column E
1	2	3	4	5
6	7	8	9	10
11	12	13	14	15

a) Copy the pattern and continue Column C for two more numbers.

b) Describe the diagonal pattern 2, 8, 14.

6.2 Define Patterns Using Algebra, pages 186–191

9. A garden has three rosebushes in the first row, five rosebushes in the second row, seven rosebushes in the third row, and so on.

a) Describe the pattern in words.

b) Use a table to show the number of rosebushes in each of the first five rows.

c) Write a formula to model the number of rosebushes in the *n*th row.

d) How many rosebushes are in the 10th row?

10. Copy and complete a table for each sequence. Extend your table to show two more terms for each sequence.

Term	Value

a) 3, 8, 13, 18, ...

b) $\dfrac{2}{3}, \dfrac{4}{3}, \dfrac{6}{3}, \dfrac{8}{3}, \ldots$

c) 70, 65, 60, 55, ...

d) $2^2, 3^2, 4^2, 5^2, \ldots$

6.3 Explore Relationships on a Grid, pages 192–197

11. Plot the ordered pairs on a grid. Describe the pattern. Then, write an equation that models the pattern.

x	0	1	2	3
y	5	9	13	17

12. At a skateboard park, there is a low rail to skate down. Makayla's height as she skates down the rail is recorded in the table.

Distance Travelled Along the Rail, *d* (m)	Makayla's Height Above the Ground, *h* (cm)
0	60
1	55
2	50
3	45

a) List the ordered pairs. Then, plot them on a grid.
b) Describe the pattern in words.
c) Write an equation to model the pattern.

13. a) Make a table of values for the ordered pairs plotted on the grid.

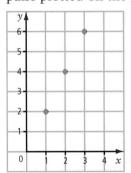

b) Extend your table to show three more values for *x* and *y*.
c) Describe the pattern of points.
d) Write an equation to model the pattern.

6.4 Apply Patterning Strategies, pages 198–203

14. Study the pattern of stacked 1-cm squares.

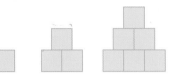

Diagram 1   Diagram 2   Diagram 3

a) Use a table to record the perimeter of each shape.
b) Describe the relationship between the perimeter of a shape and the diagram number.
c) Model the relationship with a formula.
d) Which diagram in the pattern would have a perimeter of 44 cm?

15. You are planning a checkers tournament. A player who wins a game advances to play against another winner in the next round. A player who loses a game is eliminated.

a) How many checkers players can enter a tournament that takes five rounds to find the overall winner?
b) How many players can enter a tournament that needs *n* rounds?

16. Is Maria correct in her thinking? Explain.

> Four people sit around each table. I have four tables—that's 16 people. No one sits at the insides because the tables are pushed together. So, I'll subtract 3. The number of people is 16 – 3 = 13.

Multiple Choice

For questions 1 to 6, select the best answer.

1. The next term in the sequence 5, 15, 45, 135, ... is

A 180   **B** 200

C 205   **D** 405

2. This is called a fractal because

A the pattern uses more than one colour

B the pattern involves only triangles

C the shapes get smaller as they repeat

D the outside triangle sides do not change

3. Which statement describes this pattern?

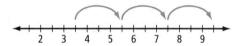

A Start with $3\frac{1}{2}$ and repeatedly add $2\frac{1}{2}$.

B Start with 3.5 and repeatedly multiply by 2.

C Start with $3\frac{1}{2}$ and repeatedly add 2.

D Start with $3\frac{1}{2}$ and repeatedly subtract 2.

4. For the sequence 2, 4, 6, 8, ..., the value of the sixth term is

A 4   **B** 6

C 12   **D** 36

5. The value of the nth term of a pattern is $3n + 2$. What is the value of the tenth term?

A 36   **B** 32

C 15   **D** 5

6. The value of the nth term in the sequence 2, 5, 8, 11, ... is

A $n + 1$ **B** $2n$

C $n + 2$ **D** $3n - 1$

Short Answer

7. A school band plays in an outdoor music festival. The first row has four band members. Each row has three more members than the previous row.

List two ways to model this pattern. Show examples.

8. Write the sixth and eighth terms of the sequence $\frac{3}{5}, \frac{6}{5}, \frac{9}{5}, \frac{12}{5}, \ldots$

9. Examine the pattern of regular hexagons with side length 1 unit.

a) Describe the relationship between the number of hexagons and the perimeter of the shape. Record your data in a table.

b) Write a formula to model the perimeter of a string of n hexagons.

c) You have a string of 17 hexagons. Find the perimeter of the shape.

10. a) Plot the points on a grid.
b) Describe the pattern.
c) Write an equation relating x and y.

x	y
2	7
3	9
4	11
5	13
6	15

Extended Response

11. A family tree shows Gavin's ancestors.

Gavin	Parents	Grandparents	Great-grandparents
		F	F
	F	M	M
			F
		F	M
	M		F
		M	M
			F

If he extends the tree to seven generations, how many ancestors will there be? Justify the method you used. What other methods could you use?

12. During volleyball team practices, the coach demonstrates serving the ball in the court. The team records how many serves out of 20 land in the court.

Practice Number, n	1	2	3	4	5
Serves in Court, S	4	6	8	10	12

a) Plot the ordered pairs on a grid.
b) Describe the pattern in words. Then, model the pattern with an equation.
c) Predict in which practice the coach expects to get all of her serves in the court.

13. Yasmin wants to lease a computer for six months. The plan she likes costs $100 initially, plus $75 per month.

a) Write a formula for the cost of leasing the computer.
b) If the computer costs $1500 to buy, after how many months will Yasmin be losing money by leasing it?

Chapter Problem Wrap-Up

Create and analyse your own folding pattern.

1. Develop a plan for repeatedly folding a piece of paper in a pattern. Describe your plan.

2. After each fold, examine your piece of paper and describe new sections, new creases, and new shapes. Record your data.

3. Investigate and describe any relationships you find.

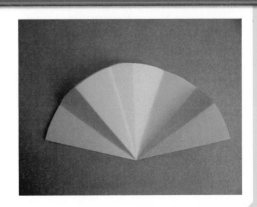

What does math have to do with riding a bicycle?

Have you ever ridden a bicycle that has more than one gear? Selecting the proper gear can either make you go faster or make it easier to climb hills. How do the gears work?

As you pedal, the chain passes a force from the pedals to the rear wheel. Then, the rear wheel turns, moving the bicycle forward. As you change gears, the chain moves to a different gear on the pedal sprocket or the rear wheel sprocket.

The level of difficulty of pedalling is related to the ratio of the number of teeth on the pedal sprocket to the number of teeth on the rear wheel sprocket.

When the ratio $\dfrac{\text{pedal teeth}}{\text{rear wheel teeth}}$ is high,

the pedals are harder to turn, but you are able to go faster.

When the ratio $\dfrac{\text{pedal teeth}}{\text{rear wheel teeth}}$ is low, the pedals are

easier to turn. This makes it easier to ride up a hill.

The gear is a type of simple machine. Other examples of simple machines are the wheel, ramp, and lever. Simple machines have been used for hundreds of years. Understanding ratios is important for exploring simple machines.

 To learn more about simple machines, go to **www.mcgrawhill.ca/links/math8** and follow the links.

What's the Best Buy?

1. Look at the floorplan of a mall. Find as many patterns as you can.
   Explain your patterns in more than one way.

Floorplan of Three Stores

Store 1   Store 2   Store 3

2. Describe how stores are added. You want to add stores that are the
   same size. How many squares do you need to design the floorplan for
   four stores? five stores? *n* stores?

3. You have 45 squares to design the floorplan. How many stores can be
   in the mall?

4. Design a structure for your own mall. How many squares do you need
   for the floorplan of two stores? three stores? *n* stores? What is the
   maximum number of stores you can have with up to 45 squares?

5. The signs in the window suggest a price war. Which bike is the best
   deal? Justify your choice.

6. You own Dynamic Duos. What sale will you offer on bikes? Justify
   your price.

Number Sense and Numeration

• Express repeated multiplication as powers.

• Understand and apply the order of operations with brackets and exponents in evaluating expressions that involve fractions.

• Represent whole numbers in expanded form using powers and scientific notation.

• Use a calculator for operations beyond the proficiency expectations for using pencil and paper and for multi-step calculations involving whole numbers and decimals.

• Justify the choice of method for calculations, and use estimation to assess reasonableness.

• Use mathematical language to explain the process and the conclusions in problem solving and investigations.

• Reflect on learning experiences and interpret and evaluate mathematical issues using appropriate mathematical language.

Patterning and Algebra

• Describe and justify a rule in a pattern.

• Present solutions to patterning problems and explain the thinking behind the solution process.

Key Words

power

base

exponent

order of operations

scientific notation

CHAPTER 7

Exponents

Many people around the world play board games. Some of the games are very old. For example, one version of chess originated in India around the 6th century. Over 200 million people play chess in China alone.

The modern version of chess uses a board with 64 small squares on it. The same board is used in the game of checkers. In this chapter, you will use this board to solve problems that deal with patterns and large numbers. You will also learn a new way to write large numbers such as 200 million.

Chapter Problem

Imagine placing toonies on the 64 small squares of a chessboard. You put one toonie on the first square. You put two toonies on the second square. You put four toonies on the third square. You put eight toonies on the fourth square, and so on.

How much would the toonies on the 64th square be worth? Would this stack of toonies reach the Moon?

By the end of this chapter, you will be able to answer these questions.

Areas of Circles

The area, A, of a circle with radius r is given by the equation $A = \pi \times r^2$.
The value of π is about 3.14.

Find the area of a circle with a radius of 10 cm.
Show your answer to the nearest square centimetre.
$A = \pi \times r^2$
$A = \pi \times 10^2$ $\boxed{c}\,\boxed{\pi}\,\boxed{\times}\,\mathbf{10}\,\boxed{x^2}\,\boxed{=}$ 314.1592654
$A \doteq 314$
The area of the circle is about 314 cm².

10 cm

Estimate: $3 \times 100 = 300$

1. Calculate the area of a circle with each radius, to the nearest square unit.

   a) 5 m   **b)** 12 cm

2. Calculate the area of a circle with each radius, to the nearest tenth of a square unit.

   a) 6 m   **b)** 30 cm

Expanded Form

The number 342 067 is written in **standard form**. **Expanded form** shows the total value of each digit. Use the table to write the number 342 067 in expanded form.

Hundred Thousands	Ten Thousands	Thousands	Hundreds	Tens	Ones
3	4	2	0	6	7

342 067 = 300 000 + 40 000 + 2000 + 60 + 7

3. Write each number in expanded form.

   a) 583   **b)** 50 601
   c) 567 233   **d)** 4 035 120

4. Write each number in standard form.

   a) 100 000 + 20 000 + 4000 + 700 + 30 + 9
   b) 2 000 000 + 70 000 + 300 + 1

Order of Operations

To evaluate an expression involving more than one operation, use **BEDMAS**.

$5 + (3 - 2) \times 4 \div 2$ **Brackets.**
$= 5 + 1 \times 4 \div 2$ **Multiply.**
$= 5 + 4 \div 2$ **Divide.**
$= 5 + 2$ **Add.**
$= 7$

B   Brackets
E   Exponents
D ⎫ Division and Multiplication, in
M ⎭ order from left to right
A ⎫ Addition and Subtraction, in
S ⎭ order from left to right

5. Evaluate.

a) $10 + 2 \times 3 - 5$ **b)** $4 \times 3 + 6 \div 2$
c) $40 \div 4 - 2 \times 3 + 7$ **d)** $3 + 4 \times 2 - 16 \div 8$

6. Evaluate.

a) $(4 - 1) \times 3 + 2$ **b)** $8 \div (2 \times 2) - 1$
c) $16 \div (2 \div 2) \div 2$ **d)** $20 - 4 \times (3 + 2)$

Prime Factors

You can use a **factor tree** to write a **composite number** as the product of its **prime factors**.

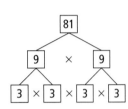 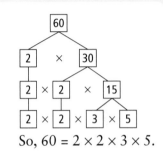

So, $81 = 3 \times 3 \times 3 \times 3$.   So, $60 = 2 \times 2 \times 3 \times 5$.

7. Write each number as the product of its prime factors.

a) 54   **b)** 128   **c)** 500

8. Which of the following numbers have 2 as a prime factor? How can you tell?

100   301   456   294   279   193

Volume of a Rectangular Prism

You can find the volume of a rectangular prism using one of these relationships:

Volume = area of base × height $V = l \times w \times h$

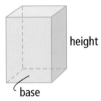 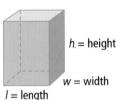

9. Find the volume of this rectangular prism.

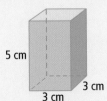

5 cm   3 cm   3 cm

10. Find the volume of this rectangular prism.

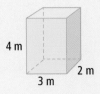

4 m   2 m   3 m

Pattern With Powers and Exponents

The security of people and property is important. Think of ways you protect your security. Which of them require you to use numbers?

Many electronic security devices are remote controlled. Examples include electronic car-door locks, car alarms, and home security systems. There would be no security if the same remote operated more than one security device. Therefore, security devices use different codes.

Discover the Math

Materials
- scientific calculator

Optional:
- BLM 7.1A Codes Worksheet

How can you write and evaluate numbers with exponents?

In many security devices, a bank of electronic switches determines the number of codes. The simplest switches have only two possible settings, OFF and ON. The table shows the number of possible codes for 2 and 3 switches. Each number of possible codes is written in three ways.

Number of Switches	Possible Settings	Number of Possible Codes		
		Standard Form	Repeated Multiplication	Exponential Form
2	OFF-OFF OFF-ON ON-OFF ON-ON	4	2×2	2^2
3	OFF-OFF-OFF OFF-OFF-ON OFF-ON-OFF OFF-ON-ON ON-OFF-OFF ON-OFF-ON ON-ON-OFF ON-ON-ON	8	$2 \times 2 \times 2$	2^3

Strategies
Act it out

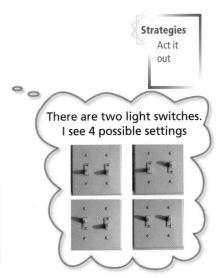

There are two light switches. I see 4 possible settings

1. Copy the table and continue it for 4 switches.

2. a) Describe the patterns in the table in words.
   b) Without listing the possible settings, continue the table for 5 switches and 6 switches.

Strategies
Look for a pattern

3. Describe the meaning of the 4 in 2^4.

4. Explore how to use the power key on your calculator to evaluate 2^5 correctly. List the steps in the method you used.

5. One type of home security system has 16 electronic switches, each with 2 settings. How many possible codes are there? Give your answer in exponential form and in standard form.

6. **Reflect** Is there an advantage to writing numbers in exponential form, instead of as repeated multiplications? Explain.

Technology Tip

• On some calculators, the power key will appear as $\boxed{y^x}$. On others, the power key may appear as $\boxed{a^x}$ or $\boxed{x^y}$.

Example 1: Write Powers

Write each expression as a **power**.
a) $8 \times 8 \times 8 \times 8 \times 8 \times 8 \times 8$
b) $6 \times 6 \times 6 \times 6 \times 6 \times 6 \times 6 \times 6$

Solution

a) $8 \times 8 \times 8 \times 8 \times 8 \times 8 \times 8 = 8^7$ 8 is the base. 7 is the exponent.

b) $6 \times 6 \times 6 \times 6 \times 6 \times 6 \times 6 \times 6 = 6^8$ 6 is the base. 8 is the exponent.

power

• a number in exponential form
• includes a **base** and an **exponent**

exponent

power → 4^3

base

base

• the factor you multiply

exponent

• the number of factors you multiply

Powers with the same base can be described as a family. For example, 4^2, 4^3, and 4^4 are powers of four. They represent the repeated multiplication of 4 by itself.

Literacy Connections

Reading Powers
You can name powers in words by describing the base and the exponent. The power 4^5 can be named
- four to the fifth
- four to the exponent five
- the fifth power of four

Example 2: Write Powers

a) Write 729 as a power of 3.

b) Write 10 000 000 as a power of 10.

Solution

a) $729 = 3 \times 3 \times 3 \times 3 \times 3 \times 3$

  $= 3^6$

> Multiply 3s until you reach 729.

b) $10\ 000\ 000 = 10 \times 10 \times 10 \times 10 \times 10 \times 10 \times 10$

  $= 10^7$

> Multiply 10s until you reach 10 000 000.

Example 3: Evaluate Powers

Evaluate.

a) 2^6

b) 1.5^3

Solution

a) $2^6 = 2 \times 2 \times 2 \times 2 \times 2 \times 2$

  $= 4 \times 2 \times 2 \times 2 \times 2$

  $= 8 \times 2 \times 2 \times 2$

  $= 16 \times 2 \times 2$

  $= 32 \times 2$

  $= 64$

> I see two sets of $2 \times 2 \times 2$.
> $2^6 = (2 \times 2 \times 2) \times (2 \times 2 \times 2)$
> $= 8 \times 8$
> $= 64$

b) Use a calculator.

  ⓒ 1.5 y^x 3 = 3.375

Key Ideas

- Powers express repeated multiplication.

- A power is written in exponential form.

- In a power,
  - the factor being multiplied is the base
  - the number of factors being multiplied is the exponent

power → 4^3 (exponent above the 3, base below the 4)

1. When Asabi saw the expression $4 \times 4 \times 4 \times 4 \times 4$, she knew she could write it as 4^5. How did she know?

2. Suppose Vishal asked you this question about powers. What answer would you give? Justify your answer.

Does the exponent show how many times the base is multiplied by itself?

3. Use words and numbers to describe a method you could use to write 1296 as a power of 6.

4. Describe how you would evaluate 3^5 using

   a) paper and pencil   **b)** a calculator

Check Your Understanding

Practise

For help with questions 5 and 6, refer to Example 1.

5. Express as a power.

   a) $2 \times 2 \times 2$
   b) $8 \times 8 \times 8 \times 8 \times 8$
   c) $7 \times 7 \times 7 \times 7 \times 7 \times 7$

6. Write as a power. Do not evaluate.

   a) $3.1 \times 3.1 \times 3.1 \times 3.1$
   b) $7.6 \times 7.6 \times 7.6 \times 7.6 \times 7.6 \times 7.6$

For help with questions 7 and 8, refer to Example 2.

7. Write each power.

   a) 32 as a power of 2
   b) 256 as a power of 4
   c) 1331 as a power of 11
   d) 100 000 as a power of 10

8. Write each power.

   a) 625 as a power of 25
   b) 729 as a power of 9
   c) 3125 as a power of 5
   d) 100 000 000 as a power of 10

For help with questions 9 to 12, refer to Example 3.

9. Evaluate.

   a) 2^7
   b) 3^4
   c) 6^3

10. Evaluate.

   a) 4^5
   b) 1^{20}
   c) 10^6

11. Evaluate.

   a) 1.6^2
   b) 0.1^4
   c) 0.5^3

12. Evaluate.

   a) 3.2^2
   b) 2.3^3
   c) 0.5^4

Apply

13. Find the area of a square with each side length.

    a) 4 m

    b) 3.6 cm

14. Find the volume of a cube with each edge length.

    a) 5 cm

    b) 2.5 mm

15. Pierre used pictures and words to explain each of the following statements to Marc. Show how Pierre might have explained each statement.

    a) Powers with the exponent 2 are commonly known as squares.

    b) Powers with the exponent 3 are commonly known as cubes.

16. a) Without using a calculator, express 2401 as a power of 7. Explain your method.

    b) Describe another method that does not require a calculator.

17. Find the unknown number in each equation.

    a) $5^3 = \blacksquare$

    b) $2^{\blacksquare} = 128$

    c) $\blacksquare^4 = 256$

18. How many prime factors does 3^4 have? Explain.

> ### Making Connections
> You worked with prime factors in Chapter 3.

19. Consider powers of 3 with natural number exponents.

    a) Is every power of 3 a multiple of 3? Explain why or why not.

    b) Is every multiple of 3 a power of 3? Explain why or why not.

20. The first four numbers in a pattern are as follows.

    1   4   27   256

    a) Describe the pattern in words.

    b) Write the next three numbers in the pattern as powers and in standard form.

    c) Write an expression for the nth term in the pattern.

21. The number 81 can be written as 9^2 or as 3^4. Write each of the following numbers as a power with an exponent greater than 1 in three ways.

    a) 256

    b) 729

    c) 1 000 000

22. Express the number of wheels on 16 cars as

    a) a power of 8

    b) a power of 4

    c) a power of 2

23. a) Copy and complete the first five lines of this pattern.

$$1^2 - 0^2 = \blacksquare$$
$$2^2 - 1^2 = \blacksquare$$
$$3^2 - 2^2 = \blacksquare$$
$$4^2 - 3^2 = \blacksquare$$
$$5^2 - 4^2 = \blacksquare$$

    b) How could you find each difference without squaring or subtracting?

    c) Evaluate $1\,000\,000^2 - 999\,999^2$ without using a calculator.

24. There are squares of different sizes on a chessboard. The diagram shows a square of side length 1 unit and a square of side length 2 units.

a) What is the side length of the largest square on the board?

b) There are 64 squares of side length 1 unit. Express this number of squares as a power with exponent 2.

c) How many squares are there with a side length of 2 units? Express this number of squares as a power with exponent 2.

Try This!

25. a) Copy and complete the first four lines in this pattern.

$101^2 = \blacksquare$
$202^2 = \blacksquare$
$303^2 = \blacksquare$
$404^2 = \blacksquare$

b) Predict the value of 707^2. Check the value on a calculator.

c) Now, predict the value of 808^2. Is the value as you predicted? Explain the observed value.

Extend

26. Predict the last digit when 3^{19} is written in standard form.

27. a) Copy and complete the table.

b) Complete a similar table for 3^4, 3^3, 3^2, and 3^1.

Power	Standard Form
10^4	
10^3	
10^2	
10^1	

c) Use the patterns to predict the values of 10^0 and 3^0.

d) Predict the value of any power with a natural number base and exponent 0.

e) Use a scientific calculator to check your prediction.

f) Check the values of powers with decimal bases and exponent 0.

g) Make a general statement about the value of powers with exponent 0.

Making Connections

Modelling Powers

Tear a strip from the longer side of a sheet of paper. Mark one surface of the strip with the word "top." With the top facing you, fold the left end of the strip onto the right end. Partially open the strip with the top facing you, as shown in the diagram. You will see a V-shape that points downward. Call it a "down V."

Return the strip to its folded shape. Then, fold the left end onto the right end again. Unfold the paper and look at the top. You will see two down Vs and one "up V," as shown in the diagram.

1. Continue folding the paper left over right. After each extra fold, look at the top of the strip. Count the numbers of down Vs and up Vs. Extend the table.

2. Describe patterns in the table.

Number of Times You Folded	Number of Down Vs	Number of Up Vs	Total Number of Vs
1	1	0	1
2	2	1	3

Order of Operations With Exponents

You perform many tasks in a certain order. For example, in the morning, you put on your socks before your shoes.

Think of the steps you would follow to create the flower garden shown in the photo. List the steps in order.

In math, we evaluate expressions by applying operations in an agreed-upon order.

Discover the Math

Materials
• calculator

How can you choose the order in which you should perform operations?

Karen, Matt, and Maria are trying to find the area of the grass in this backyard.

They agree on the following expression for the area of the grass.
$A = 12^2 - 4 \times 3^2$

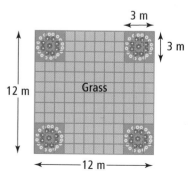

They are unsure if the expression can be evaluated in different ways.
The students decide to check.

I will square twelve, then subtract four, and then multiply by three squared.

I will multiply four by three, and then square the product. Then, I will subtract the result from twelve squared.

I will square twelve. Then, I will square three and multiply the answer by 4. Then, I will subtract the second result from the first result.

1. Complete the calculation by each student's method.

2. Which answer is correct? Explain how you know.

3. Reflect

   a) Explain why you need to specify the order in which the operations are performed.

   b) On your calculator, input the operations in the order they appear in $12^2 - 4 \times 3^2$. Does your calculator automatically perform the operations in the right order? How do you know?

Example 1: Evaluate Expressions With Exponents

Use the **order of operations** to evaluate $3^4 + 7(2 + 4) - 1$.

Solution

$3^4 + 7(2 + 4) - 1$ **Brackets.**

$= 3^4 + 7(6) - 1$ **Exponent.**

$= 81 + 7(6) - 1$ **Multiply.**

$= 81 + 42 - 1$ **Add and subtract in order from left to right.**

$= 123 - 1$

$= 122$

Remember that 7(6) means 7×6.

Estimate: $80 + 40 = 120$

order of operations

- correct sequence of calculations for evaluating an expression

B   Brackets, then
E   Exponents
D ⎫ Division and
M ⎭ Multiplication, in order from *left to right*
A ⎫ Addition and
S ⎭ Subtraction, in order from *left to right*

Example 2: Evaluate Expressions With Fraction Bars

Evaluate $\dfrac{7-1}{2} + 5^2$.

Solution

Method 1: Keep the Fraction Bar

A fraction bar acts as a grouping symbol, like brackets. I can write $\dfrac{7-1}{2} + 5^2$ as $\dfrac{(7-1)}{2} + 5^2$.

$$\dfrac{7-1}{2} + 5^2$$

$= \dfrac{(7-1)}{2} + 5^2$ **Brackets.**

$= \dfrac{6}{2} + 5^2$ **Exponent.**

$= \dfrac{6}{2} + 25$ **Divide.**

$= 3 + 25$ **Add.**

$= 28$

Method 2: Eliminate the Fraction Bar

A fraction bar is a division symbol. I can write $\dfrac{7-1}{2} + 5^2$ as $(7-1) \div 2 + 5^2$.

$$\dfrac{7-1}{2} + 5^2$$

$= (7-1) \div 2 + 5^2$ **Brackets.**

$= 6 \div 2 + 5^2$ **Exponent.**

$= 6 \div 2 + 25$ **Divide.**

$= 3 + 25$ **Add.**

$= 28$

Key Ideas

- To evaluate expressions, follow the order of operations. BEDMAS can be used to help remember the order.

B	Brackets
E	Exponents
D **M**	Division and Multiplication, from left to right
A **S**	Addition and Subtraction, from left to right

- A fraction bar acts as a grouping symbol, like brackets.
  $\dfrac{5+7}{3}$ can be written as $\dfrac{(5+7)}{3}$.

- A fraction bar is also a division symbol.
  $\dfrac{5+7}{3}$ can be written as $(5+7) \div 3$.

Communicate the Ideas

1. Is the area of the blue shaded region represented by $(4 - 2)^2$ or $4^2 - 2^2$? Explain your reasoning.

2. Explain why you need to know the order of operations.

3. Describe the method you would use to evaluate $4^2 - \dfrac{7 + 3}{5}$.

Check Your Understanding

Practise

For help with questions 4 and 5, refer to Example 1.

4. Evaluate.
   a) $4 \times 3 + 5^2$
   b) $7^2 \div (9 - 2)$
   c) $3^2 + 4^2 - 5^2$
   d) $(8 - 6)^4 - 8 \div 4$

5. Evaluate.
   a) $2^3 + 5(8 - 2) - 6$
   b) $(7 - 5)^2 + 3^2$
   c) $4(3 - 1)^3$
   d) $2^3 \div (1 + 2^2)$

For help with questions 6 and 7, refer to Example 2.

6. Evaluate.
   a) $\dfrac{10 - 4}{2}$
   b) $7 - \dfrac{6 + 2}{4}$

7. Evaluate.
   a) $2^2 + \dfrac{10 - 2}{4 \times 2}$
   b) $\dfrac{3^2 - 5}{2^3 \times 3}$

8. Evaluate. Justify each step.
   a) $(7 - 5)^4 \div 8$
   b) $(3 \times 2 - 5)^{10}$
   c) $39 - (4 + 6 \div 3)^2$

9. Evaluate.
   a) $2\left(\dfrac{10 - 1}{3}\right)$
   b) $\left(\dfrac{2 + 6}{2^2}\right) - \dfrac{1}{2}$
   c) $6.5 - \left(\dfrac{3^2 - 1}{4^2}\right)$
   d) $4 + \left(\dfrac{6}{2 + 1}\right) \times 2^3$

Apply

10. Does $(2 + 3 + 4)^2 = 2^2 + 3^2 + 4^2$? Justify your answer.

11. a) Write an expression to represent the area of this shape.

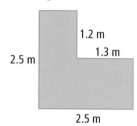

b) Calculate the area.

12. a) Write an expression to represent the surface area of this rectangular prism.

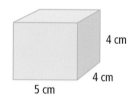

b) Evaluate the surface area.

Making Connections

You found the surface area of rectangular prisms in Grade 7.

13. Each statement is *false*. Copy each statement and add one set of brackets to make it true.

a) $2 + 4^2 - 3 \times 5 = 21$
b) $2 + 4^2 - 3 \times 5 = 67$
c) $2 + 4^2 - 3 \times 5 = 75$

14. Copy each statement. Replace each ■ with an operation $(+, -, \times, \text{ or } \div)$ to make the statement true.

a) $3^3 \; ■ \; 4 \; ■ \; 5 = 7$
b) $(5 \; ■ \; 3)^2 - 40 \; ■ \; 2 = 44$
c) $4\left(\dfrac{6 \; ■ \; 3}{3}\right) ■ \; 9 = 3$

15. Write one problem like those in question 13 and one problem like those in question 14. Have a classmate solve your problems.

16. Olga's patio is a 5 m by 6 m rectangle. She wants to cover most of it with interlocking bricks. The exception is a circular tree planter of radius 1 m near one corner of the patio. What area is she covering with bricks, to the nearest square metre?

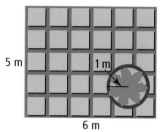

Making Connections

You found the area of circles in Chapter 1.

17. Michel's garden has the shape shown in the diagram. What is the area of his garden?

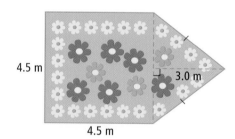

Making Connections

You found the area of composite shapes in grade 7.

18. In a magic square, the sum of the numbers in each column, row, and diagonal is the same. Copy and complete this magic square.

2^4	3^2	■
11	■	■
12	■	■

19. a) Copy and complete the first four lines of this pattern.

$2^3 - (1 \times 2 \times 3 + 2) = $ ■
$3^3 - (2 \times 3 \times 4 + 3) = $ ■
$4^3 - (3 \times 4 \times 5 + 4) = $ ■
$5^3 - (4 \times 5 \times 6 + 5) = $ ■

b) Predict the next two lines of the pattern.

Try This!

20. Here are two ways of using five 2s and the order of operations to make the number 0.

$$2 - \frac{2}{2} - \frac{2}{2} = 0$$

$$2 \times (2^2 - 2^2) = 0$$

a) Use five 2s and the order of operations to make each number from 1 to 9.
b) Make each number from 0 to 9 using four 4s.
c) Make each number from 0 to 9 using four 3s.
d) Choose a digit from 0 to 9 and use it several times to make other numbers.

Extend

21. a) Copy and complete the first four lines of this pattern.

$1^2 + 3^2 - 6 = $ ■
$2^2 + 4^2 - 11 = $ ■
$3^2 + 5^2 - 18 = $ ■
$4^2 + 6^2 - 27 = $ ■

b) Predict the next two lines of the pattern. Check them with a calculator.
c) Predict the 20th line of the pattern.

22. The French mathematician Pierre de Fermat (1601–1665) believed that every whole number could be expressed as the sum of four or fewer perfect squares. For example,

$17 = 1^2 + 4^2$

or

$17 = 2^2 + 2^2 + 3^2$

$20 = 2^2 + 4^2$

or

$20 = 1^2 + 1^2 + 3^2 + 3^2$

Express each number as the sum of four or fewer perfect squares. Find as many answers as possible for each number.

a) 27
b) 30
c) 50
d) 99
e) 130

Discover Scientific Notation

We like lots of sounds, such as our favourite music or the voice of a friend. We think of sounds we do not like as noise. For many people, an example of noise is the sound of an aircraft taking off. Give examples of sounds you like and sounds you think of as noise.

Discover the Math

Materials
- scientific calculator

Optional:
- BLM 7.3A
  Sound Level Worksheet

How can you use powers of 10 to write large numbers?

The table lists a variety of sounds. The level of each sound is expressed in a unit called a decibel (symbol dB). Loud sounds have higher sound levels than quiet sounds.

The quietest sound that people can hear is called the threshold of hearing (TOH). The table shows how sound levels compare to the TOH. For example, the sound level of rustling leaves is 10 times the TOH. The sound level of a whisper is 100 times the TOH.

1. Copy the table.
   a) Describe the patterns in the three columns under the "Number of Times the TOH" heading.
   b) Explain why the number 10^1 is not shown as a repeated multiplication in the table.
   c) Use the patterns to complete the table.

Example	Sound Level (dB)	Number of Times the TOH		
		Standard Form	**Repeated Multiplication**	**Exponential Form**
Rustling leaves	10	10		10^1
Whisper	20	100	10×10	10^2
	30	1 000	$10 \times 10 \times 10$	10^3
Quiet conversation	40	10 000	$10 \times 10 \times 10 \times 10$	10^4
	50	100 000	$10 \times 10 \times 10 \times 10 \times 10$	10^5
Normal conversation	60			
Busy traffic	70			
Vacuum cleaner	80			
Thunder	90			
Personal stereo (on full volume)	100			
Rock concert (front rows)	110			
	120			
(Pain threshold)	130			
Military jet takeoff	140			

2. Look at the sound levels in decibels. Describe the relationship between these values and the other numbers in the table.

3. Use a scientific calculator to perform the repeated multiplication of 10.
   a) What is the greatest number of 10s you can multiply to get an answer displayed in standard form?
   b) Multiply more 10s than the number you found in part a). How does the calculator display the value of the product?

4. **Reflect** Compare the advantages and disadvantages of expressing powers of 10 in standard form, as repeated multiplications, and in exponential form.

Example 1: Write Numbers in Expanded Form Using Powers of 10

Use powers of 10 to write the number in each statement in expanded form.
a) The radius of Earth is 6378 km.
b) The distance from Earth to the Moon is 384 000 km.

Solution

a) $6378 = 6000 + 300 + 70 + 8$
$= 6 \times 1000 + 3 \times 100 + 7 \times 10 + 8$
$= 6 \times 10^3 + 3 \times 10^2 + 7 \times 10^1 + 8$

b) $384\ 000 = 300\ 000 + 80\ 000 + 4000$
$= 3 \times 100\ 000 + 8 \times 10\ 000 + 4 \times 1000$
$= 3 \times 10^5 + 8 \times 10^4 + 4 \times 10^3$

> There are no 100s, 10s, or 1s in the number

Example 2: Write Numbers in Scientific Notation

The diameter of the planet Jupiter is 143 000 km. Write 143 000 in **scientific notation** .

Solution

Method 1: Write a Product

I can rewrite 143 000 as the product of two numbers.

I need the first number to be greater than or equal to 1 but less than 10. I will put the decimal point between 1 and 4.

$$143\ 000 = 143 \times 1000$$
$$= 1.43 \times 100 \times 1000$$
$$= 1.43 \times 100\ 000$$
$$= 1.43 \times 10^5$$

Now I need to show 100 000 as a power of 10. There are five zeros. So, 100 000 is 10^5.

Method 2: Move the Decimal Point

I will move the decimal point to the left to make a number that is greater than or equal to 1 but less than 10. I can count the number of places that the decimal point moves.

143 000.

The decimal point starts here.

1.43 000

The decimal point ends here. The decimal point moves 5 places to the left.

So, $143\ 000 = 1.43 \times 100\ 000$
$$= 1.43 \times 10^5$$

The exponent is the same as the number of places the decimal point moved to the left.

Example 3: Convert to Standard Form

The planet Mercury is 5.79×10^7 km from the Sun. Express 5.79×10^7 in standard form.

Solution

$$5.79 \times 10^7 = 5.79 \times 10\ 000\ 000$$
$$= 57\ 900\ 000$$

10^7 has 7 zeros. Move the decimal point 7 places to the right.

5.79

scientific notation

• the product of two numbers:
  – the first number is greater than or equal to 1 but less than 10
  – the second number is a power of 10
• example is 2.4×10^4

Literacy Connections

Reading Scientific Notation

You can read 1.43×10^5 as

• one decimal four three times ten to the fifth
• one decimal four three times ten to the exponent five
• one decimal four three times the fifth power of ten

Technology Tip

• Some scientific calculators convert numbers from standard form to scientific notation, and vice versa. Explore how to do the conversions. Compare the ways that different calculators display numbers in scientific notation.

- The expanded form of a number shows the value of each digit in the number.
  $5489 = 5000 + 400 + 80 + 9$

- Powers of 10 can be used to write numbers in expanded form.
  $5489 = 5 \times 10^3 + 4 \times 10^2 + 8 \times 10^1 + 9$

- A number in scientific notation is the product of two numbers. The first is greater than or equal to 1 but less than 10. The second is a power of 10.
  $5489 = 5.489 \times 10^3$

Communicate the Ideas

1. Explain why it is helpful to write a large number, such as 125 000 000 000, in scientific notation.

2. Svetlana and Darcy each wrote 4.1×10^5 in standard form. Who is correct? Explain. What mistake did the other person make?

   Svetlana's answer: Darcy's answer:
   $4.1 \times 10^5 = 410\ 000$ $4.1 \times 10^5 = 4\ 100\ 000$

3. Write 8500 in expanded form using powers of 10 and in scientific notation. How are your answers similar? How are they different?

Check Your Understanding

Practise

For help with questions 4 and 5, refer to Example 1.

4. Write each number in expanded form.

   a) 721
   b) 2005
   c) 21 002
   d) 7 802 500

5. Use powers of 10 to write each number in expanded form.

   a) 345
   b) 5401
   c) 65 020
   d) 1 005 200

For help with questions 6 and 7, refer to Example 2.

6. What power of 10 would you use to write each number in scientific notation?

   a) 3200
   b) 635 000
   c) 1 252 000
   d) 40 001

7. Write each number in scientific notation.

   a) 500
   b) 28 000
   c) 95 400
   d) 8 432 000
   e) 456 721
   f) 65 010

For help with questions 8 and 9, refer to Example 3.

8. Express each number in standard form.

   a) 8×10^3 b) 5.3×10^4
   c) 9×10^5 d) 1.25×10^8

9. Express each number in standard form.

   a) 4×10^4 b) 6.2×10^3
   c) 3×10^5 d) 2.05×10^7

Apply

10. Without using a calculator, decide which of these two numbers is larger, 1×10^7 or 9×10^6. How do you know?

11. Without using a calculator, explain how you would decide which number is greater, 4.55×10^5 or 456 000.

12. Express each number in standard form.

    a) $6 \times 10^4 + 7 \times 10^3 + 5 \times 10^2 + 3 \times 10^1 + 9$
    b) $8 \times 10^5 + 6 \times 10^3 + 2$

13. Without using a calculator, arrange the numbers in order from least to greatest.

    a) 1.23×10^4
       $1 \times 10^4 + 2 \times 10^2 + 3 \times 10^1$
       12 310
    b) 350 000
       3.51×10^5
       $3 \times 10^5 + 5 \times 10^4 + 5 \times 10^2$

14. a) Write the numbers 1, 2, and 3 once each in this expression in as many different ways as possible.
       $\blacksquare . \blacksquare \times 10^{\blacksquare}$
    b) List the numbers from part a) in order from least to greatest.

15. Is each number written correctly in scientific notation? If not, correct it. Explain your reasoning.

    a) 25×10^2 b) 1.003×10^6
    c) 0.55×10^4 d) 1×10^{12}

16. Chemists measure enormous numbers of tiny particles, such as atoms and molecules. The unit that chemists use is the mole. The number of particles in one mole is about 6.02×10^{23}. Express this number in standard form.

Making Connections

High school chemistry often uses the mole as a unit. To understand this measurement unit, you must know scientific notation.

17. Rewrite each value using scientific notation.

    a) The diameter of the planet Venus is 12 100 km.
    b) A tiny insect called the common midge can beat its wings up to 132 000 times per minute.
    c) Earth is about 150 000 000 km from the Sun.
    d) Lake Ontario holds about 1 640 000 000 000 m³ of water.

18. Over 200 million people play chess in China. Express 200 million in scientific notation.

19. Astronomers have estimated the number of stars within range of our telescopes to be 70 sextillion. This number is 70 000 000 000 000 000 000 000. Write this number in scientific notation.

Did You Know?

Astronomers often need to express very large numbers, distances, and times. Helen Sawyer Hogg (1905–1993) of the University of Toronto was a famous Canadian astronomer. She studied some of the oldest stars in our galaxy. They are about fourteen billion years old. Fourteen billion is 14 000 000 000 or 1.4×10^{10}.

20. Imagine placing toonies on the 64 small squares of a chessboard. You put one toonie on the first square. You put two toonies on the second square. You put four toonies on the third square. You put eight toonies on the fourth square, and so on.

a) Describe the pattern in the numbers of toonies on the squares in the first row.

b) How many toonies are on the last square in the first row? Express this answer as a whole number.

c) How many toonies are on the 12th square? Express this answer as a power of 2.

d) What is the value, in dollars, of the toonies on the 12th square? Express this answer in scientific notation.

21. Geologists have divided the history of Earth into periods. The Rocky Mountains appeared during the Jurassic Period.

a) The Jurassic Period began about 180 million years ago. It ended about 135 million years ago. So, it lasted about 45 million years. Express each of these numbers in scientific notation.

b) To find out more about geological periods, go to **www.mcgrawhill.ca/links/math8** and follow the links. Choose a period other than the Jurassic Period. Find out when it began, when it ended, and how long it lasted. Express each of these numbers in scientific notation.

22. Calculate each product or quotient. Express your answers in scientific notation.

a) $1\ 000\ 000 \times 10\ 000\ 000$
b) $25\ 000 \times 3\ 000\ 000$
c) $50\ 000\ 000 \div 2000$
d) $25\ 000\ 000 \div 40\ 000$

Try This! **23.** Huge numbers of tiny particles, called neutrinos, reach Earth from stars every day. Neutrinos pass right through Earth and right through you.

a) About 60 billion neutrinos strike each square centimetre of your skin every second. Express this number in scientific notation.

b) Estimate the number of neutrinos that pass though one of your hands every second. Express the number in scientific notation. Justify your reasoning.

Extend

24. The frequency of a radio signal shows the number of radio waves that reach your radio every second. The frequencies of AM stations are usually measured in kilohertz (kHz). The frequencies of FM stations are usually measured in megahertz (MHz). Convert each frequency to hertz (Hz). Express each frequency in scientific notation.

a) an AM station broadcasting at 860 kHz
b) an FM station broadcasting at 91.1 MHz
c) the frequency of your favourite radio station

Literacy Connections

The prefix *kilo-* means one thousand.
The prefix *mega-* means one million.

25. The speed of light in space is about 300 000 km/s. A light-year is the distance that light travels through space in a year. How far is a light-year, in kilometres? Express your answer in scientific notation.

Solve Fermi Problems

How many trees are there in Ontario?

How many years would it take you to count by ones to one billion?

Estimation problems like these are called Fermi problems. Enrico Fermi (1901–1954) was a famous scientist. He liked to ask his students to solve these problems.

To solve Fermi problems, you need to find missing information, make assumptions, and use estimation. Other problem solving strategies may also be useful.

Remember that your answer to a Fermi problem will be approximate. Your answer may be different from the answers of your classmates. Use different answers to compare the assumptions and approximations you made.

Discover the Math

How can you solve an estimation problem that seems impossible?

Example: Water in an Olympic Pool

How many glasses of water would fill an Olympic swimming pool?

Solution

Method 1: Use the Volumes

Understand

Find out how many small volumes are in a large volume.

I can solve the problem in three steps.

Plan

1. Estimate the volume of a glass of water.

2. Find the volume of an Olympic swimming pool.

3. Divide the volume of the glass of water into the volume of the swimming pool.

Do It!

Strategies
Make an assumption

1. Different glasses have different sizes. A drinking glass might be 6 cm wide and 11 cm high. Estimate the volume of the glass by finding the volume of a rectangular prism with a square base of side length 6 cm, and a height of 11 cm.

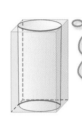

The glass roughly fills the space inside a rectangular prism.

Approximate volume of glass = 6 cm × 6 cm × 11 cm
$$= 396 \text{ cm}^3$$
The volume of the glass is about 400 cm^3.

Strategies
Find needed information

2. Find the volume of an Olympic swimming pool.
An Olympic swimming pool is 50 m long. The width and depth can vary from one pool to another. A width of 25 m and a depth of 2 m are fairly typical. Convert the length, width, and depth to centimetres.

50 m = 50 × 100 cm	25 m = 25 × 100 cm	2 m = 2 × 100 cm
= 5000 cm	= 2500 cm	= 200 cm

Volume = length × width × depth
$$= 5000 \times 2500 \times 200$$
$$= 2\ 500\ 000\ 000$$
The volume is 2 500 000 000 cm^3.

The glass is measured in centimetres. The pool is measured in metres. To divide the volumes, the units must be the same.

The number 6 250 000 can be written in scientific notation as 6.25×10^6.

3. Divide the volume of the glass of water into the volume of the swimming pool.

Number of glasses of water = $\dfrac{2\ 500\ 000\ 000}{400}$

Estimate: 2 400 000 000 ÷ 400
= 6 000 000

$$= 6\ 250\ 000$$
About 6 250 000 glasses of water would fill an Olympic swimming pool.

Look Back

Can you think of another way to solve the problem?
After you think about this, look at Method 2 on the next page.

Method 2: Solve a Simpler Problem

Strategies
Solve a
simpler
problem

1 m

1 m

1 m

I am going to estimate the number of glasses of water that would fill a 1 m by 1 m by 1 m cube.

The edge length of the cube is 1 m.
Different glasses have different sizes. A drinking glass might be 6 cm wide and 11 cm high.

Change the edge length of the cube to centimetres.
1 m = 100 cm

My measurements need to have the same units.

Find the number of glasses that will fit along each edge of the cube.
Length: 100 ÷ 6 ≐ 17
Width: 100 ÷ 6 ≐ 17
Height: 100 ÷ 11 ≐ 9

I can find each number by dividing.

I need to multiply the numbers of glasses along three edges.

Find the total number of glasses inside the cube.
$17 \times 17 \times 9 = 2601$
The number of glasses that would fill 1 m³ is about 2600.

The volume of the swimming pool is
$50 \text{ m} \times 25 \text{ m} \times 2 \text{ m} = 2500 \text{ m}^3$
This volume is 2500 times the volume of the 1 m by 1 m by 1 m cube.

Find the number of glasses of water needed to fill the swimming pool.
$2500 \times 2600 = 6\ 500\ 000$

About 2600 glasses of water fill 1 m³. I can multiply to find out how many glasses of water would fill 2500 m³.

About 6 500 000 glasses of water would fill an Olympic swimming pool.

The answers to Method 1 and Method 2 are both very large. Both numbers are between 6 000 000 and 7 000 000, so both answers seem reasonable.

Key Ideas

- To solve a Fermi problem, research missing information and make assumptions.

- The answer to a Fermi problem is an estimate.

- The same Fermi problem may have many different solutions.

1. Why might the answers to some Fermi problems be expressed in scientific notation?

2. Suppose two students get two different answers to a Fermi problem. Do you think that at least one of the answers must be wrong? Explain.

Check Your Understanding

Apply

In each question, explain and justify the process that you used to get the result.

For help with question 3, refer to the Example.

3. How many volleyballs would fill a school gymnasium?

4. Yonge Street extends from Toronto to Rainy River. It is the longest street in the world. How many strides would it take you to walk the length of Yonge Street?

5. a) How long does it take to write the number 8 enough times to fill a page?
   b) How many 8s are on the page?
   c) Estimate the number of hours you would need to write 10 000 000 number 8s.
   d) How many pages would you need for 10 000 000 number 8s?

6. How much would it cost to paper the walls of your classroom with $10 bills?

7. Estimate the number of blades of grass on a soccer field.

8. Estimate the mass of garbage your school produces in a year.

9. Estimate the number of times a dog wags its tail in its lifetime.

10. How many trees are there in Ontario?

11. About how many years would it take you to count by ones to one billion?

12. Estimate the number of batteries that Canadians discard in a year.

13. Estimate the total cost of all the T-shirts that Canadians own.

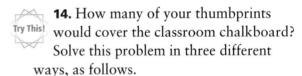
14. How many of your thumbprints would cover the classroom chalkboard? Solve this problem in three different ways, as follows.

   a) Assume that your thumbprint approximates a rectangle. Estimate the area it covers. Complete the solution.
   b) Use a different method to estimate the area covered by your thumbprint. Solve the problem again. Compare your solution with the one from part a). Is one solution better than the other? Explain.
   c) Use a method that does not involve estimating the area of your thumbprint.

Extend

15. If a golf ball were as big as Earth, about how deep would each dimple be?

Key Words

For questions 1 to 4, copy the statement and fill in the blanks. Use some of these words:

base   expanded form
exponent   exponential form
power   scientific notation

1. The number 4^5 is written as a ▪▪▪▪◯.

2. In 9^3, 9 is the ▪▪▪◯ and 3 is the exponent.

3. The number $5 \times 100 + 3 \times 10 + 9 \times 1$ is written in ▪▪▪▪▪▪▪▪▪ ▪▪▪◯.

4. The number 2.45×10^4 is written in ▪▪▪▪▪▪◯▪▪ ▪▪▪▪▪◯▪▪.

5. Rearrange the circled letters in questions 1 to 4 to describe a type of problem you solved in this chapter.

7.1 Pattern With Powers and Exponents, pages 214–219

6. Express as a power.

a) $3 \times 3 \times 3 \times 3 \times 3$
b) $1 \times 1 \times 1 \times 1 \times 1 \times 1 \times 1$
c) $7.9 \times 7.9 \times 7.9 \times 7.9$

7. Evaluate.

a) 2^8
b) 9^5
c) 3.3^3

8. The numbers 3 and 12 are not perfect squares. Explain why the product of 3 and 12 is a perfect square.

9. A bit is the smallest amount of information that a computer can process. A byte is 8 bits. Express the number of bits in 32 bytes as

a) a power of 4
b) a power of 2

10. a) Copy and complete the first four lines of this pattern.
$1^2 = $ ▪
$11^2 = $ ▪
$111^2 = $ ▪
$1111^2 = $ ▪

b) Predict the value of $1\ 111\ 111^2$.

c) Identify the first square for which this pattern breaks down. Explain why.

7.2 Order of Operations With Exponents, pages 220–225

11. Evaluate.

a) $4^3 \div (18 - 4^2)$
b) $2 \times 4 + (6 - 4)^4$
c) $13 - \left(\dfrac{4^2 + 8}{3} \right)$

12. The diagram shows a circular flowerbed around a circular fountain. What is the area of the flowerbed, to the nearest tenth of a square metre?

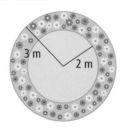

13. Compare the meanings of $3 + 5^2$ and $(3 + 5)^2$.

14. Two cubes have edge lengths of 3 cm and 4 cm.

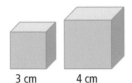

3 cm   4 cm

a) Write an expression that represents the difference in their volumes.
b) Calculate the difference in their volumes.
c) Write an expression that represents the difference in their surface areas.
d) Calculate the difference in their surface areas.

7.3 Discover Scientific Notation, pages 226–231

15. Express each number in expanded form using powers of 10.

a) 3562   b) 204 310

16. Express each number in scientific notation.

a) 1 000 000   b) 930 000
c) 14 500 000 000   d) 420 050

17. Without using a calculator, arrange these numbers in order from least to greatest.

542 000
5.421×10^5
$5 \times 10^5 + 4 \times 10^4 + 2 \times 10^2$

18. a) Evaluate 3^2, 33^2, 333^2, and 3333^2.
b) Predict the value of $3\ 333\ 333^2$.
c) Can you use a calculator to check your prediction? Explain.

19. A parsec is a very large unit of distance. Astronomers use this unit to describe distances between stars in space. One parsec is about 31 trillion kilometres. Express this number in scientific notation.

20. When a car is driven at normal speeds, the spark plugs in the engine fire about 20 times per second. How many times would they fire in an 8-h drive? Express your answer in scientific notation.

7.4 Solve Fermi Problems, pages 232–235

In each solution, explain and justify the process that you used to get the result.

21. Estimate the number of times an elephant's heart beats in its lifetime.

22. How many footsteps do you take in a year?

23. How many pencils would stretch from Earth to the Moon?

24. Estimate the number of hockey pucks needed to cover an ice rink.

Multiple Choice

For questions 1 to 4, choose the best answer.

1. The number 3^4 means

   A $4 \times 4 \times 4$ **B** 3×4

   C $3 \times 3 \times 3 \times 3 \times 3$ **D** $3 \times 3 \times 3 \times 3$

2. The value of the expression $1 + (9 - 2^3) \div 5$ is

   A 0.4   **B** 0.8

   C 1.2   **D** 8.4

3. The number 3×10^4 equals

   A $3 \times 10\ 000$ **B** 30^4

   C 300 000   **D** $3^4 \times 10\ 000$

4. The number 200 045 written in expanded form is

   A $2 \times 10^3 + 4 \times 10^1 + 5$

   B $2 \times 10^5 + 4 \times 10^1 + 5$

   C 2.00045×10^5

   D $200\ 000 + 45$

Short Answer

5. Evaluate.

   a) 2^5 **b)** 4^3 **c)** 1.1^2

6. a) Copy and complete the first four lines of this pattern.

   $4^2 = \blacksquare$

   $34^2 = \blacksquare$

   $334^2 = \blacksquare$

   $3334^2 = \blacksquare$

   b) Predict the value of $33\ 333\ 334^2$.

7. Evaluate.

   a) $3^3 - 5 \times 3$

   b) $6 \times 2 - (3^3 - 2^4)$

   c) $\left(\dfrac{2^3 + 1}{4 - 1} \right) + 5$

8. Jake gave Syreeta a card on her birthday. As a joke, Jake wrote in the card, "Happy $3^2 + (14 - 4) \div 2$ birthday." How old was Syreeta?

9. Express the number of eggs in 18 dozen eggs as a power of 6.

10. Express each number in expanded form using powers of 10 and in scientific notation.

   a) The mass of a blue whale is about 75 000 kg.

   b) The total area of the Great Lakes is about 244 000 km².

   c) The planet Venus is about 108 000 000 km from the Sun.

11. Raj decided to plant two flowerbeds in his backyard. One flowerbed is a 3 m by 4 m rectangle. The other flowerbed is a circle with a radius of 2 m.

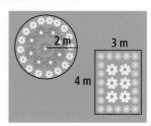

   a) Write an expression that represents the total area of the flowerbeds.

   b) Calculate the total area, to the nearest square metre.

12. a) Write an expression that represents the area of this shape

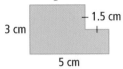

3 cm — 1.5 cm

5 cm

b) Calculate the area.

13. a) Copy and complete the first four lines of this pattern.
$3 \times 1 + 1 = \blacksquare$
$4 \times 2 + 1 = \blacksquare$
$5 \times 3 + 1 = \blacksquare$
$6 \times 4 + 1 = \blacksquare$

b) Write the next line of the pattern.

c) Use the pattern to evaluate 101^2 without using a calculator. Explain your reasoning.

Extended Response

14. Describe how you would solve one of the following problems. In your description, list the missing information you would need and the assumptions you would make.

a) Estimate the number of pages in all the books in your school.

b) How many car trips have all the students in your class taken since they were born?

c) How many tennis balls would fill a school bus?

Chapter Problem Wrap-Up

In question 24 on page 219, you found the numbers of squares of two different sizes on a chessboard. In question 20 on page 231, you found the value of a stack of toonies on a given square of a chessboard.

Suppose you were given a choice between the amounts of money described in options A and B.

Option A: The value of the toonies on the 64th small square of a chessboard if the toonies are placed as follows: One toonie is on the first small square. Two toonies are on the second small square. Four toonies are on the third small square. Eight toonies are on the fourth small square, and so on.

Option B: $1 000 000 000 for each square of any size on a chessboard.

1. Which option would you prefer? Explain your reasoning.

2. a) Estimate the number of toonies in a stack that reaches from Earth to the Moon.

b) Would the stack of toonies in Option A be tall enough to reach from Earth to the Moon? Explain.

Geometry and Spatial Sense
- Recognize, sketch, and build representations of three-dimensional figures from front, top, and side views.

Measurement
- Identify relationships between and among measurement concepts.
- Develop and apply the formulas for finding the surface area and the volume of a triangular prism.

Number Sense and Numeration
- Justify the choice of method for calculations: estimation, mental computation, concrete materials, pencil and paper, algorithms, or calculators.
- Explain the process used and any conclusions reached in problem solving and investigations.

Patterning and Algebra
- Evaluate algebraic expressions.

Key Words
polyhedron

net

skeleton

Three-Dimensional Geometry and Measurement

Many towns and cities have built skateboard parks so riders have a safer location in which to enjoy their sport.

Concepts of three-dimensional geometry and measurement are needed to design and build a skateboard park.

Think about a skateboard park. What geometric shapes do you expect to see?

In this chapter, you will extend your skills with three-dimensional geometry and measurement to include work with triangular prisms.

Chapter Problem

Consider the design of a simple skateboard ramp. If you plan to build it using plywood, what shapes will you need to cut? What area of plywood will you need?

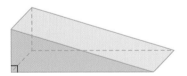

Area of a Triangle

Find the area of the triangle.

$$\text{Area} = \frac{1}{2} \times \text{base} \times \text{height}$$

$$A = \frac{1}{2} \times 10 \times 7$$

$$A = 35$$

The area of the triangle is 35 cm².

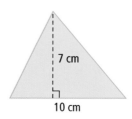

7 cm

10 cm

1. Find the area of each triangle.

a)
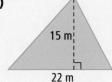

15 m

22 m

b)
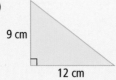

9 cm

12 cm

2. What is the height of the right triangle if its area is 12 cm²?

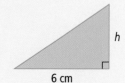

h

6 cm

Vocabulary of Three-Dimensional Figures

Mathematicians describe three-dimensional figures in terms of their **faces**, **edges**, and **vertices**.

Prisms have a base and a top face that are congruent and parallel. Their other faces are all rectangles. **Pyramids** have one polygon base, and their other faces are all triangles. Prisms and pyramids are named according to their base shape. The figure shown is a rectangular prism.

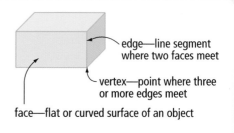

edge—line segment where two faces meet

vertex—point where three or more edges meet

face—flat or curved surface of an object

3. Match each prism with its name: triangular prism, cube, rectangular prism, or pentagonal prism.

a)

b)

c)

d)
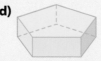

4. Match each pyramid with its name: triangular pyramid, square-based pyramid, rectangular pyramid, or pentagonal pyramid.

a)

b)

c)

d)

Surface Area and Volume of a Rectangular Prism

Find the surface area and the volume of the rectangular prism with length 8 cm, width 3 cm, and height 5 cm.

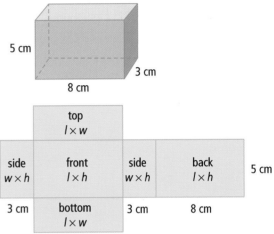

A **net**, which is a flat pattern that can be folded to form the figure, can help you find the areas of the six faces that make up the surface area.

Surface Area = (front + back faces) + 2 side faces + (top + bottom faces)

S.A. = $2 \times (8 \times 5) + 2 \times (5 \times 3) + 2 \times (8 \times 3)$

S.A. = $80 + 30 + 48$

S.A. = 158

The surface area is 158 cm².

Volume = area of base × height or $V = l \times w \times h$

$V = 8 \times 3 \times 5$

$V = 120$

The volume is 120 cm³.

---

5. Find the surface area of each rectangular prism.

a)
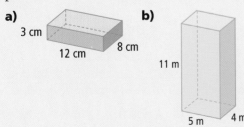
3 cm
12 cm
8 cm

b)
11 m
5 m
4 m

6. Find the volume of each rectangular prism in question 5.

7. A cube has a volume of 1000 cm³.

a) What are the dimensions of the cube?

b) Find the surface area of the cube.

8.1

Recognize and Sketch Three-Dimensional Figures

Focus on...

- recognizing three-dimensional figures from views

Brian is babysitting his cousins Allison and Eric. The children are building a fort with large plastic blocks. They decide to make each wall 4 blocks long, 4 blocks high, and 1 block thick. How many blocks do they need to build the fort? Children learn much about our three-dimensional world by playing like this.

Discover the Math

Materials

Optional:

- linking cubes

How can you distinguish three-dimensional figures from views?

1. After the children finish their fort, Brian draws a front view, top view, and side view.

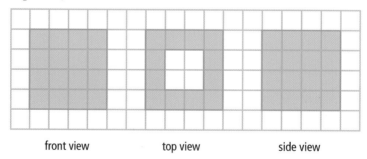

front view   top view   side view

Which view(s) tell you the height of the fort walls? Which view(s) tell you the width and the length of the fort?

2. Reflect Provide examples to illustrate your answers to the following.

a) Can a three-dimensional figure have the same front view, top view, and side view?

b) Can two different three-dimensional figures have the same front view? Can they also have the same top view? side view?

Example 1: Draw Front, Top, and Side Views

Draw the front view, top view, and side view of this three-dimensional figure.

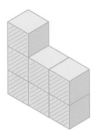

Solution

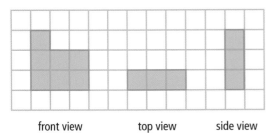

front view   top view   side view

Example 2: Identify Geometric Figures From Views

Identify and sketch the **polyhedron** with these three views.

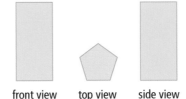

front view   top view   side view

polyhedron

- a three-dimensional figure with faces that are polygons
- plural is polyhedra

Solution

From the front view and the side view, this might be any prism, or even a cylinder.
The top view reveals that it is a prism with pentagonal bases.
The three views together indicate a pentagonal prism.

Key Ideas

- A three-dimensional object can be represented by its front view, top view, and side view.

- Given the front view, top view, and side view, you can identify simple three-dimensional figures.

1. Refer to the model of the fort at the beginning of this section. If the children decide to add an extra block onto each corner to create watchtowers, how would the front view, top view, and side view of the fort change? Draw them.

2. Does an object always have the same front face? Explain.

3. Compare the top views of a cube and a square-based pyramid. How are their top views different from each other?

cube   square-based pyramid

top view   top view

Check Your Understanding

Practise

For help with questions 4 to 6, refer to Example 1.

4. Draw the front, top, and side views of this figure.

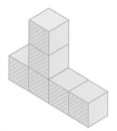

5. Sketch the front, top, and side views of each three-dimensional figure.

 a) pentagonal prism **b)** pentagonal pyramid

6. Sketch the front, top, and side views of each three-dimensional figure.

 a) hexagonal prism
 b) octagonal prism
 c) decagonal prism

For help with questions 7 to 9, refer to Example 2.

7. The top views of some objects are shown. Name two possible three-dimensional figures each might be.

 a)   **b)**

8. Identify each geometric figure from the front, top, and side views.

 a)

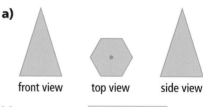

 front view   top view   side view

 b)

 front view   top view   side view

9. The diagrams show the front, top, and side views of an object. Make a sketch to show the overall shape of the three-dimensional object.

front view   side view   top view

Apply

10. Sketch the front, top, and side views of each three-dimensional object.

  a) carton of milk
  b) CD box
  c) can of pop

11. Choose three objects in your classroom with different shapes and sketch the front, top, and side views of each.

Chapter Problem

12. a) Draw three views of a skateboard ramp.

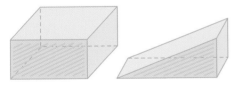

  b) If the ramp is curved, which view will change? Draw what it might look like.

13. Suppose you have a rectangular prism and a triangular prism.

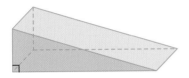

  a) Is it possible for these two polyhedra to have the same top view? Explain.
  b) Is it possible for these two polyhedra to have the same side view? Explain.
  c) Is it possible for these two polyhedra to have the same front view? Explain.

 14. Draw the front, top, and side views for each combination of simple objects.

  a) two cubes placed horizontally side by side

  b) one square-based pyramid placed on top of a cube

  c) one cylinder placed on top of a cube

Extend

15. Find all the ways that four cubes can be placed on the table so that at least one face of each cube is matched with one face of another cube. Draw the front, top, and side views for each figure.

16. You are hired by a company to draw designs for a house built using six hollow cubes. Each cube has a side length of 4 m.

  a) Draw three different house designs using the six cubes.
  b) Compare the number of walls, area of roof, and amount of floor space among the three designs. If each square metre of wall costs $120 to construct, each square metre of roof costs $200, and each square metre of floor costs $100, which house design is least expensive?

Build Models of Three-Dimensional Figures

Focus on...
• building representations of three-dimensional figures

Each year, Skills Canada-Ontario organizes a cardboard boat race competition, which gives students the opportunity to incorporate and apply their math, science, and technology skills in a problem solving situation. Students are asked to design and construct a boat out of two sheets of cardboard. Among other things, they are judged on the drawings of the boat, including the **net** and different views.

net

• a single pattern piece that can be folded to form a three-dimensional figure

To find out more about Skills Canada-Ontario and this contest, go to **www.mcgrawhill.ca/links/math8** and follow the links.

Internet Connect

Discover the Math

Materials
• linking polygons

Alternative:
• BLM 8.2A Nets

How can you model three-dimensional figures?

1. a) Use linking polygons to construct the nets of these prisms. Which faces are congruent? How many bases and how many faces does each prism have?

| triangular prism | square-based prism | pentagonal prism |

b) What patterns do you see in the nets? Draw the next two nets in the pattern.

2. a) Study these nets of different figures. How do these diagrams differ from the ones in step 1? How are they the same? Predict the shape when these nets are folded.

b) What patterns do you observe in their bases and number of faces? Draw the next two nets in the pattern.

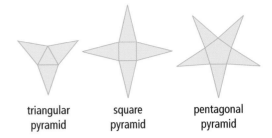

triangular pyramid   square pyramid   pentagonal pyramid

3. Reflect Describe how to draw a net for any prism. Describe how to draw a net for any pyramid.

Example 1: Build a Model Using a Net

Make a model of a cube using a net.

Solution

Method 1: Draw a Diagram

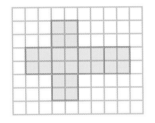

> A cube has six square faces. I can draw its net on grid paper or I can use TABS+ software to create and print the net. I'll add some tabs so I can glue the edges together.

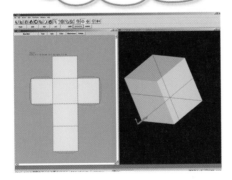

Method 2: Use a Manipulative

> I can use six squares to make the net.

Example 2: Build a Model Using a Skeleton

a) Make a model of a cube using a **skeleton** .
b) How many vertices and how many edges does the cube have?

> **skeleton**
> • a framework for a three-dimensional figure, made of its edges

Solution

a) *Step 1:* Join four straws with modelling clay at the vertices to form the square base. Make another square, just the same, for the top face.
Step 2: Place four straws vertically to form the edges of the side faces.
Check: The resulting figure has six congruent square faces. It is a cube.

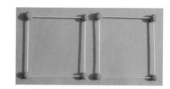

b) There are 4 vertices around the base and 4 around the top face. A cube has 8 vertices.
There are 4 edges around the base, 4 edges around the top face, and 4 vertical edges forming the side faces. A cube has 12 edges.

Key Ideas

- A net shows all the faces that make up the surface of a three-dimensional figure.

- A net can be used to construct a model of a three-dimensional figure.

- A skeleton is a frame formed by joining the edges of a three-dimensional figure.

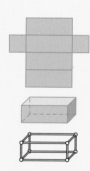

Communicate the Ideas

1. Compare nets and skeletons. How are they alike? How do they differ?

2. Which of these cubes can you make with this net? Justify your answer.

A   B   C

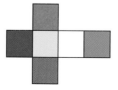

Practise

For help with questions 3 to 5, refer to Example 1.

3. Use a net to construct a model of the rectangular prism.

4. Use a net to construct a model of the square-based prism.

5. Make a copy of the net on grid paper. Add flaps and then use the net to construct a three-dimensional figure. What type of figure is it?

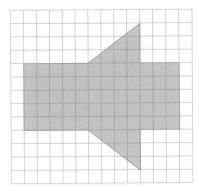

For help with questions 6 to 9, refer to Example 2. Use toothpicks or straws and modelling clay to make the models.

6. Sketch the skeleton of each three-dimensional figure. How many pieces of straws do you need to build each polyhedron?

a) cube
b) triangular prism
c) pentagonal prism

7. Sketch the skeleton of each three-dimensional shape. How many straws do you need to build each polyhedron?

a) hexagonal prism
b) octagonal prism
c) decagonal prism

8. Construct a skeleton of each prism. Record the number of edges and the number of vertices for each.

a) triangular prism
b) rectangular prism
c) pentagonal prism

9. Construct a skeleton of each pyramid. Record the number of edges and the number of vertices for each.

a) triangular pyramid
b) square pyramid
c) pentagonal pyramid

Apply

10. The frames for two different children's tents are shown. Find the number of faces, vertices, and edges of each.

a) 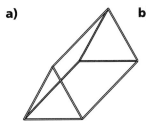 **b)**

11. Sketch each real-life object. Identify which polyhedron it most resembles and draw its net.

a) an ice cube
b) a mailbox
c) a doorstop
d) a six-sided teepee

12. How many pieces of straw do you need to build a skeleton to model each real-life object in question 11?

13. Use sketches, or a polyhedron set, to draw two different nets for a triangular pyramid.

Chapter Problem

14. Build a model of the skeleton that could be used to frame a skateboard ramp.

15. a) What three-dimensional figure has 12 edges of equal length? Build a model or draw a representation of it. Record the number of faces and vertices.
   b) Try to give a second answer for part a).

Extend

16. a) Use the models you have built for earlier questions. Copy and complete the table.

Polyhedron	Number of Faces, *F*	Number of Vertices, *V*	Number of Edges, *E*
Triangular pyramid			
Square-based pyramid			
Pentagonal pyramid			
Triangular prism			
Rectangular prism			
Pentagonal prism			

b) Examine the data in your table. Find a pattern that relates the number of faces, vertices, and edges in a polyhedron. Try building more polyhedra to test your hypothesis.

17. If you are given the number of faces, vertices, and edges of a polyhedron, can you identify the polyhedron? Provide an illustrated paragraph or model demonstration to answer.

Making Connections

The Many Faces of Euler

The relationship among faces, vertices, and edges of polyhedrons was discovered by Swiss mathematician Leonhard Euler (1707–1783). Euler (pronounced *Oiler*) is perhaps the most productive mathematician of all times. He published over 800 books and papers. Even though he lost sight in one eye at age 28 and became totally blind at age 59, he had an amazing memory and continued to dictate discoveries until his death. He was interested in all areas of mathematics, as well as related topics such as engineering and astronomy. He loved doing math puzzles

One classic puzzle, that led Euler to develop a whole new branch of mathematics called topology, is the seven bridges of Königsberg problem. Königsberg has seven bridges across the river that passes through the city. The challenge is to find a path that a person could take to walk around the city crossing each bridge exactly once. Trace the map and see if you can solve the problem.

To find out more about topology go to **www.mcgrawhill.ca/links/math8** and follow the links.

Surface Area of a Triangular Prism

This tent is made of canvas, including a canvas floor. How do the manufacturers determine the area of canvas needed to make the tent?

Discover the Math

Materials
• linking polygons

Alternative:
• straws and modelling clay

How can you find the surface area of a triangular prism?

1. What geometric figure is the tent in the photo? Make a model of the tent using linking polygons or make its skeleton using straws.

2. In order to find out how much material was used to make the tent, you need to know the surface area of all of its faces. Sketch a net for the tent.

3. How many faces are there in total? Which faces are congruent? What are their shapes? How many are there of each shape?

4. **Reflect** Describe how to find the surface area of any triangular prism. What area formulas do you need to use?

Example 1: Find Surface Area

Find the surface area of the triangular prism.

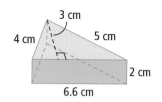

Solution

The triangular prism has two congruent triangular bases and three rectangular faces.

Find the area of each different-shaped face.

Area of one triangular base = $\frac{1}{2}$ × base × height

$$A = \frac{1}{2} \times b \times h$$

$$A = \frac{1}{2} \times 6.6 \times 3$$

$$A = 9.9$$

Strategies

Choose a formula

Area of the front rectangular face = length × width

$$A = l \times w$$
$$A = 6.6 \times 2$$
$$A = 13.2$$

Area of the left side rectangular face = $l \times w$

$$A = 4 \times 2$$
$$A = 8$$

Area of the right side rectangular face = $l \times w$

$$A = 5 \times 2$$
$$A = 10$$

Total surface area = 2 × 9.9 + 13.2 + 8 + 10

= 51.0

The surface area of the triangular prism is 51 cm².

There are two triangular bases, so I need 2 × 9.9.

Literacy Connections

Area is a measure of two-dimensional space covered. When lengths are given in centimetres, the area is in square centimetres (cm²).

Example 2: Use Surface Area and Convert Units

Gary has 2 m² of plywood and wants to make a small skateboard ramp. If he makes each right triangular face 1 m long and 40 cm high, how much plywood is left for the three rectangular faces?

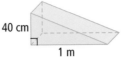

Solution

The problem involves a mixture of units of measure. Choose whether to work in metres or in centimetres.

Method 1: Work in Metres
Area of one triangular face: base is 1 m, height is 40 cm or 0.4 m

$$A = \frac{1}{2} \times b \times h$$

$$A = \frac{1}{2} \times 1 \times 0.4$$

$$A = 0.2$$

The area of the two side faces is 2×0.2 m², or 0.4 m².
Amount of plywood left = 2 − 0.4
                        = 1.6

After making the triangular end faces, Gary has 1.6 m² of plywood left to make the three rectangular faces.

Method 2: Work in Centimetres
Area of one triangular face: base is 1 m or 100 cm, height is 40 cm

$$A = \frac{1}{2} \times b \times h$$

$$A = \frac{1}{2} \times 100 \times 40$$

$$A = 2000$$

The area of the two side faces is 2×2000 cm², or 4000 cm².

To find the area of plywood left, convert 2 m² to square centimetres.
2 m² = 2 × 100 cm × 100 cm
     = 20 000 cm²
Amount of plywood left = 20 000 − 4000
                        = 16 000

After making the triangular end faces, Gary has 16 000 cm² of plywood left to make the three rectangular faces.

> 1 m = 100 cm
> 1 m² = 100 cm × 100 cm

> The answers are the same:
> 1.6 m² = 1.6 × 100 cm × 100 cm
>   = 16 000 cm²

Key Ideas

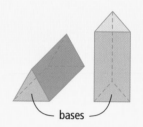

- The surface area of a triangular prism is the sum of the areas of its faces.

- A triangular prism has two congruent triangular faces and three rectangular faces. The two triangular faces are often called the bases, even though they may not be horizontal.

bases

Communicate the Ideas

1. In an equilateral triangular prism, the two bases are equilateral triangles. What is true about the three rectangular faces?

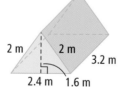

2. Describe the faces of a right isosceles triangular prism. How would you find its surface area?

Check Your Understanding

Practise

For help with questions 3 and 4, refer to Example 1.

3. A small doorstop is in the shape of a right triangular prism.

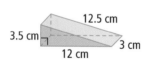

   a) What is the area of one triangular face?
   b) What is the total area of the rectangular faces?
   c) What is the surface area of the doorstop?

4. A tent, with attached ground sheet, is an isosceles triangular prism.
   a) What is the area of one triangular face?
   b) What is the total area of the rectangular faces?
   c) What is the surface area of the tent?

For help with questions 5 to 7, refer to Example 2.

5. A triangular prism has a surface area of 450 cm². What is the total area of the rectangular faces if the total area of the triangular bases is 86 cm²?

6. A triangular prism has a surface area of 200 cm². What is the area of one triangular face if the total area of the rectangular faces is 120 cm²?

7. A triangular prism has a surface area of 1.8 m². If each triangular face has an area of 2500 cm², what is the total area of the rectangular faces, in square metres?

Apply

8. Ellen built a storage shed in the shape of a triangular prism. What area of plywood did she need? The shed has a wooden floor but is open at the front (no front triangular face).

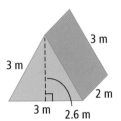

9. a) Which triangular prism do you think has a greater surface area?

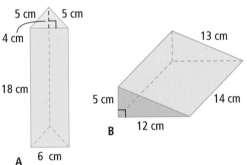

b) Determine the surface area of the two triangular prisms. Was your prediction correct?

Chapter Problem

10. A steel ramp is a right triangular prism.

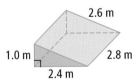

a) What is the total area of sheet metal needed to make the ramp?

b) What assumptions did you make in part a)?

---

11. A company makes bicycle seats from metal triangular prisms covered with rubber padding. How much padding is required to cover the seat's entire surface area?

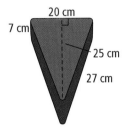

12. The diagram shows the dimensions of a slice of carrot cake. Icing is spread on the top and back of the slice.

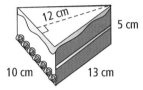

a) What is the surface area of the iced portion of the slice of cake?

b) What is the entire surface area of the slice of cake?

c) What percent of the slice of cake is covered with icing?

13. Dan sketched the tree house he wants to build using scraps of wood. How many square metres of wood will Dan need to build the roof of the tree house, including the gable ends? Round your answer to the nearest square metre.

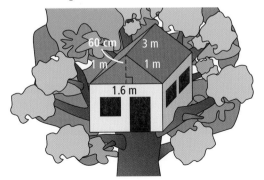

14. A company specializes in producing magazine holders for business offices, schools, and homes. Each magazine holder is made out of cardboard.

8 cm
22 cm
25 cm

a) What area of cardboard is used to make one magazine holder?

b) The company makes 2000 of these holders each day. How many square metres of cardboard do they need each day?

 15. a) If the area of one triangular face is 9 m², what is the total area of all the triangular faces of this triangular prism?

b) The area of one triangular base of an equilateral triangular prism is 500 cm². The area of one of its rectangular faces is 0.25 m². What is the total surface are of the prism?

c) If all dimensions of an equilateral triangular prism are doubled, how does the surface area change? Justify your answer.

Extend

16. Lisa is preparing food for a picnic. She plans to pack a wedge of cheese and will put plastic wrap around it.

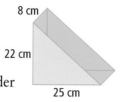

7.8 cm
3.5 cm
4 cm
7 cm

a) How much plastic wrap will she need to cover the cheese's entire surface area?

b) Why would Lisa find it difficult to keep the cheese fresh using only the amount of wrap calculated in part a)?

17. How much plywood is needed to build a ramp to a portable classroom? Justify your answer.

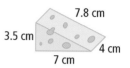
Making Connections

Euler Lines

Leonhard Euler explored networks of edges to try to find a rule for when a complete path can be drawn. A path that starts at one vertex and travels along each edge exactly once before returning to the starting point is called an **Euler line**.

1. Trace each of the following diagrams. For which can you draw an Euler line?

a)   **b)**   **c)**

2. Explore more networks. Can you find a rule that tells when a network has an Euler line?

3. Describe some possible applications for this concept.

Volume of a Triangular Prism

Focus on...
- finding the volume of a triangular prism

Most Canadian cheddar cheese is made in 18-kg rectangular blocks, which are cut into four and sealed in plastic for shipping to grocery stores. Each store then cuts and shrink-wraps individual pieces of various sizes and shapes for their customers. The world's largest cheese was made in Granby, Quebec, in 1995. This huge block of cheddar had a mass of 26 085 kg (about the same as four African elephants).

Discover the Math

How can you find the volume of a triangular prism?

1. What geometric figure is created when a rectangular block of cheese is cut diagonally in half?

2. How does the volume of one part compare with the volume of the rectangular block?

3. Compare the wedge of cheese with the original block of cheese. How are the two shapes the same? How do they differ?

4. If you put one wedge of cheese directly on top of the other, how would the volume of this shape compare to the original block of cheese? Which dimension has changed to make this true?

5. What two factors does the volume of a triangular prism depend on?

6. **Reflect** Describe how to find the volume of a triangular prism in terms of its base and its height.

Example 1: Find Volume

Find the volume of the triangular prism.

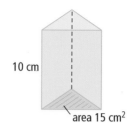

10 cm

area 15 cm²

Literacy Connections

Volume is a measure of the amount of space occupied. It is a three-dimensional concept and so its units are cubic units.

volume 1 cm³

1 cm

area 1 cm²

Solution

Volume of triangular prism = area of base × height

$$V = 15 \times 10$$
$$V = 150$$

The volume of the triangular prism is 150 cm³.

Example 2: Solve a Volume Problem

The school cafeteria offers sandwiches for lunch. Each sandwich is diagonally sliced into triangular halves and placed into a plastic box. Calculate the volume of each sandwich box, to the nearest cubic centimetre.

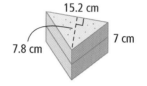

15.2 cm

7.8 cm

7 cm

Solution

The base is a triangle. Use $A = \frac{1}{2} \times b \times h$.

Volume = area of base × height

$$V = \left(\frac{1}{2} \times 15.2 \times 7.8\right) \times 7$$

Estimate: Half of 15 × 8 is 15 × 4 or 60. 60 × 7 = 420

$$V = 414.96$$

©0.5 ×15.2 ×7.8 ×7 = 414.96

The volume of each sandwich box is 415 cm³.

Example 3: Use Volume Concepts

When Trisha pours 1 L of water into a triangular vase, the depth of water is 20 cm. What is the area of the triangular base of the vase? Hint: 1 cm³ = 1 mL.

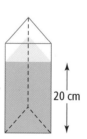

20 cm

Solution

First, express the volume in cubic centimetres.

1 L = 1000 mL
   = 1000 cm³

Then, use the formula.

Volume = area of base × height

$$1000 = \text{area of base} \times 20 \quad \textbf{Solve by inspection.}$$
$$1000 = 50 \times 20$$

The area of the triangular base of the vase is 50 cm².

5 × 20 = 100
So, 50 × 20 = 1000

Key Ideas

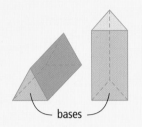

- The bases of a triangular prism are the surfaces that are triangles.

- The volume of a triangular prism can be found by multiplying the area of one triangular base by the height of the prism.

- The formula for the volume of a triangular prism is
  Volume = area of triangular base × height of prism

bases

Communicate the Ideas

1. Consider this triangular prism.
h is the height of the triangular base
w is the width of the base
l is the length (or height) of the prism

a) What is the area of one base of the triangular prism?
b) What is the formula for the volume of the triangular prism in terms of h, w, and l?

Check Your Understanding

Practise

For help with questions 2 and 3, refer to Example 1.

2. Find the volume of each triangular prism.

a)

6 m

area of base 9 m²

b)

5 cm

area of base 4 cm²

3. Find the volume of each triangular prism.

a)

6.2 cm

area of base 5.5 cm²

b)

2.5 m

area of base 8.6 m²

For help with questions 4 and 5, refer to Example 2.

4. Calculate the volume of each triangular prism.

a)

45 cm
27 cm
15 cm
36 cm

b)

26 m
10 m
16 m
4 m

5. Calculate the volume of each triangular prism. Round your answers to the nearest tenth.

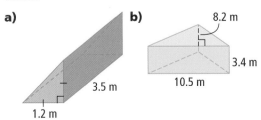

a)

3.5 m
1.2 m

b)

8.2 m
3.4 m
10.5 m

For help with questions 6 and 7, refer to Example 3.

6. A triangular prism has a volume of 100 cm^3 and a height of 20 cm. What is the area of one of its bases?

7. A triangular prism can hold 2 L of water. If the area of one of its bases is 250 cm^2, what is the height of the prism?

Apply

8. Each triangular tile in a board game has a thickness of 8 mm. What is the volume of one tile if the area of its base is 3.5 cm^2?

9. A standard pool table comes with a triangular rack to hold the 15 billiard balls. The rack has three equal sides, each 28.6 cm long. It is 5.7 cm deep. The shortest distance from the tip of the triangle to the opposite side is 24.8 cm.

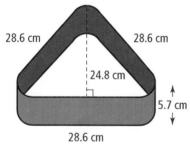

a) What is the amount of space (volume) within the rack? Round your answer to the nearest cubic centimetre.

b) The 15 billiard balls fit exactly into the rack. What is the approximate diameter of each ball? What do you notice about the answer? Hint: Draw a diagram to see how many balls fit on each side of the rack.

10. Mel kneaded a lump of dough into a ball with a volume of 2000 cm^3. How many cookies can she make with this cookie cutter? What assumption(s) do you need to make?

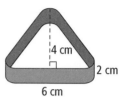

11. The Patels own an A-frame cottage and want to install air conditioning. One air-conditioning unit says it will cool up to 500 m^3. Will one of these units be enough to cool the cottage? Justify your answer.

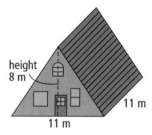

12. Jimmy is preparing for a camping trip with two of his friends. He is not sure if there will be enough room for the three of them in his tent.

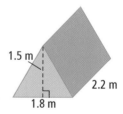

a) How much space is there inside the tent?
b) Will this be enough room for the three of them to fit comfortably? Give reasons for your answer.

13. The diagram shows the dimensions of a closed paper bag.

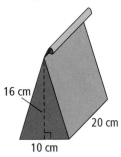

16 cm
20 cm
10 cm

a) Identify the base and determine its area.
b) How much space is available within the closed paper bag?
c) What assumption did you make in answering part b)? Is this a fair assumption? Explain.

14. Determine the volume of space available for storage in this under-the-stairs closet.

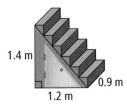

1.4 m
0.9 m
1.2 m

15. a) Which triangular prism do you
Try This! think has a greater volume?

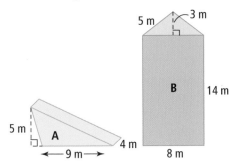

5 m 3 m
B 14 m
5 m A
9 m 4 m 8 m

b) Calculate the volume of each to check.
c) What would the height of prism B need to change to for its volume to be the same as that of prism A? Explain.

Extend

16. A chocolate maker sells chocolate bars in the form of triangular prisms for $1.25. A salesperson expects the selling price of a new bar with double the dimensions of the $1.25 bar to be $2.50. Is the salesperson correct in charging twice the amount of money? If not, what do you think is a fair price for the new size? Explain your reasoning.

17. The diagram shows four right triangular prisms. Notice that the dimensions of prisms B, C, and D are exactly twice, three times, and four times, respectively, the dimensions of prism A.

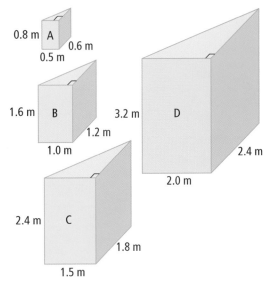

0.8 m A
0.6 m
0.5 m

1.6 m B 3.2 m D
1.2 m
1.0 m
2.4 m

2.4 m C
1.8 m
2.0 m
1.5 m

a) Calculate the volume of each prism.
b) Compare the volumes of prisms B, C, and D with the volume of prism A. Is there a pattern relating the volumes and the ratio of their dimensions? Why do you think this happens?
c) Can you devise a rule for finding the volume of triangular prisms whose dimensions have been doubled, tripled, quadrupled, and so on?

Surface Area or Volume of Triangular Prisms

The photo shows the world's largest indoor wave pool, in the West Edmonton Mall. It is 94 m long and holds 12.3×10^6 L of water.

Discover the Math

How can you find the surface area or the volume of a triangular prism?

1. Imagine that the wave pool is empty for repairs. It is a triangular prism.

   a) The inside of the pool needs painting. What do you need to calculate to find the amount of paint needed, surface area or volume? Explain why.

   b) How can you work out the amount of water needed to refill the pool?

2. Suppose you are a purse designer. You need to know how much leather is needed to make the purse you have sketched.

   a) What concept is this, surface area or volume? Explain why.

   b) What dimensions would you need to find?

3. Concrete is being poured to fill a space in the shape of triangular prism. The engineer needs to figure out how much concrete is needed. What concept is this, surface area or volume? Explain why.

4. **Reflect** How do you decide whether a problem about a triangular prism is about surface area or volume?

Example: Find Surface Area or Volume

The diagram shows the dimensions of a wave
pool. It has been emptied so it can be painted.

a) Determine the amount of paint needed.
The paint coverage rate is 10 m²/L.

b) How much water is needed to fill the pool?
Hint: 1000 L = 1 m³.

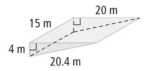

Literacy Connections

Solving Problems
Stuck on a problem?
Try the following:
• Reread it.
• Read it aloud.
• Refer back to an
  example.
• Reread the part of
  the textbook that
  relates to the topic.

Solution

a)

Surfaces get painted, so
this is an area problem.

There are four faces to be painted: the two triangular side faces,
the rectangular back wall, and the rectangular slanting floor.

Area of one triangular face = $\frac{1}{2}$ × base × height

$$A = \frac{1}{2} \times b \times h$$

$$A = \frac{1}{2} \times 20 \times 4$$

$$A = 40$$

Area of the back rectangular face = length × width

$$A = l \times w$$
$$A = 15 \times 4$$
$$A = 60$$

Area of the rectangular slanting face = $l \times w$

$$A = 20.4 \times 15$$
$$A = 306$$

There are 2 triangular side
faces, so I need 2 × 40.

Total area to be painted = 2 × 40 + 60 + 306
= 446

The surface area to be painted is 446 m².
10 m² is painted using 1 L of paint.
The amount of paint needed is about 45 L.

$$\frac{446 \text{ m}^2}{10 \text{ m}^2} = 44.6$$

b) Volume = area of base × height

$$V = \left(\frac{1}{2} \times 20 \times 4\right) \times 15$$

$$V = 600$$

Water fills the space in
the pool, so this is a
volume problem.

The volume of the pool is 600 m³.
1 m³ = 1000 L. So, it will take 600 000 L of water to fill the pool.

Key Ideas

- The surface area of a triangular prism is the sum of the areas of its faces.

- Volume of a triangular prism = area of base × height of prism

Communicate the Ideas

1. Carl says the size of the piece of cheese shown is 20 cm². Explain what mistake he is making.

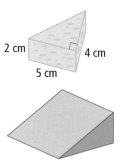

2. Bob wants to know how much foam is needed to fill a wedge-shaped pillow. What does he need to calculate, surface area or volume? Justify your response.

Check Your Understanding

Practise

For help with questions 3 and 4, refer to the Example.

3. The dimensions of a right triangular prism are given.

   15 cm, 9 cm, 12 cm, 5 cm

   a) Determine its surface area.
   b) Calculate its volume.

4. The diagram shows the dimensions of an isosceles triangular prism.

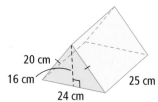

20 cm, 16 cm, 24 cm, 25 cm

   a) Determine its surface area.
   b) Calculate its volume.

5. The scoop on a backhoe is an equilateral triangular prism.

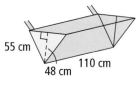

55 cm, 48 cm, 110 cm

   a) What area of sheet metal was used to make the scoop?
   b) How much liquid can the scoop hold?
   c) How much earth might the scoop hold? Explain your answer.

6. One type of chocolate is packaged in a box that is a triangular prism.

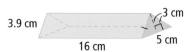

3.9 cm, 3 cm, 16 cm, 5 cm

   a) Find the least amount of cardboard needed to package each chocolate bar. Round your answer to the nearest unit.

b) The manufacturer needs to allow for the overlapping part that makes up the seams. How much cardboard is needed for each box if 10% more is added for the seams?

c) If 1.2 g of chocolate fills 1 cm³, how many grams of chocolate fit in each box?

7. Decide whether the following statements are always, sometimes, or never true. Justify your answers using pictures and words. Then, change each statement that is sometimes true to make a similar statement that is always true.

a) The surface area of a triangular prism can be found by adding half the area of the triangular faces to the area of the rectangular faces.

b) The volume of a triangular prism can be found by multiplying the area of the base by the height.

c) The base area of a triangular prism is calculated by dividing the base area of a rectangular prism by two.

Apply

8. Samantha is preparing a project for her science class. She has decided to demonstrate the nature of white light as it passes through solid glass prisms. Her teacher asks her to show some related calculations.

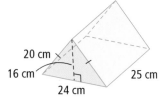

Using the dimensions provided, help Samantha determine the amount of glass used to make the triangular prism.

 9. The school has hired construction workers to build a wheelchair ramp to the entrance.

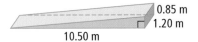

a) How much concrete is needed to make the ramp?

b) The exposed surfaces of the the ramp are to be painted blue. How many cans of paint are needed? One can covers 20 m².

Extend

10. Three triangular prisms, A, B, and C, are shown.

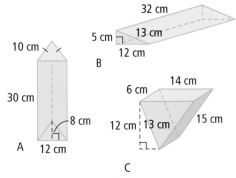

a) Which do you think is the biggest? Define what you mean by the biggest.

b) Which triangular prism has the greatest volume?

c) Which has the greatest surface area?

d) If a triangular prism has a large volume, does it also have a large surface area? Justify your answer.

11. A triangular prism has a height of 8 cm and a volume of 400 cm³.

a) What is the area of a base of the triangular prism?

b) Sketch two possible triangular prisms, with dimensions, that match the description given.

Key Words

For questions 1 to 3, copy the statement and fill in the blanks. Use some of these words: cube, edges, faces, net, prism, pyramid, triangular, rectangular, skeleton, vertices

1. A ▪▪▪▪⊙▪▪▪▪ ▪▪▪▪▪ has two faces that are congruent triangles and three faces that are rectangles.

2. A ▪▪▪▪▪⊙▪▪ is a framework made of the ▪▪▪▪▪ of a three-dimensional figure.

3. The surface area of a three-dimensional figure is the sum of the areas of its ▪▪▪⊙▪.

4. Rearrange the circled letters in questions 1 to 3 to make a key word. Define this word.

8.1 Recognize and Sketch Three-Dimensional Figures, pages 244–247

5. Name the three-dimensional figure that has each set of three views.

a)

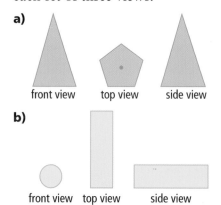

front view   top view   side view

b)

front view   top view   side view

6. Draw the front, top, and side views of this object.

8.2 Build Models of Three-Dimensional Figures, pages 248–252

7. Which of the following nets will not fold to form a triangular pyramid? Check your prediction. Draw the nets on paper, and then cut them out and fold to see.

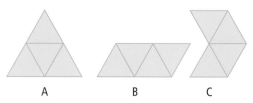

A   B   C

8. How many edges and vertices are in the skeleton of this house?

9. Draw the skeleton for a hexagonal prism. State the number of faces, vertices, and edges it has.

8.3 Surface Area of a Triangular Prism, pages 253–258

10. Calculate the surface area of this large ramp.

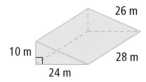

11. Yolanda has three vases that are triangular prisms. She wants to spray-paint the outside of the vases. Determine the surface area of each vase to be painted, given the following information.

Vase A: The area of the triangular base is 20 cm^2, and the total area of the rectangular faces is 150 cm^2.

Vase B: The triangular base has an area of 5 cm², and each rectangular face has an area of 25 cm².

Vase C: The triangular base has an area of 11 cm², and each rectangular face measures 5 cm by 20 cm.

8.4 Volume of a Triangular Prism, pages 259–263

12. What is the height of this triangular prism if its volume is 1200 cm³?

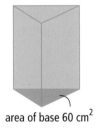

area of base 60 cm²

13. Find the volume of this wooden doorstop.

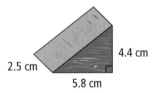

4.4 cm
2.5 cm
5.8 cm

14. The two houses in the diagram are on the same street and they are both for sale. Henry wants to buy the house with the most attic space. Which house should he buy?

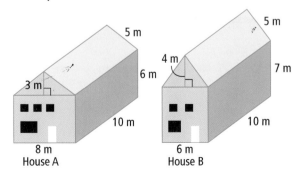

5 m
6 m
3 m
10 m
8 m
House A

4 m
5 m
7 m
10 m
6 m
House B

8.5 Surface Area or Volume of Triangular Prisms, pages 264–267

15. Helen is building a triangular corner shelving unit to display pictures and awards. The unit resembles a triangular prism and is made using five pieces of wood.

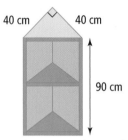

40 cm   40 cm
90 cm

a) Calculate the area of wood needed to make the shelving unit.
b) Calculate the amount of space taken up by the shelving unit.

16. Pierre is packing sandwiches into his lunch box. Each sandwich has been sliced diagonally into halves.

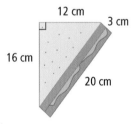

12 cm
3 cm
16 cm
20 cm

a) How much plastic is required to wrap each sandwich to keep it fresh? Justify your answer.
b) How many sandwiches can fit in the lunch box if its volume is 1625 cm³?
c) What assumptions did you make in part b)?

CHAPTER
8

Practice Test

Strand	NSN	MEA	GSS	PA	DMP
Questions	1–5, 7–11	1–11	1, 6	1	

Multiple Choice

For questions 1 to 5, choose the best answer.

1. The number of edges in the skeleton is

   A 6
   B 7
   C 10
   D 12

2. The total area of the rectangular faces of a triangular prism is 320 cm². The total area of its triangular faces is 100 cm². The surface area of the prism is

   A 120 cm² **B** 220 cm²
   C 320 cm² **D** 420 cm²

3. The volume of this triangular prism is

   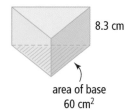

   8.3 cm

   area of base
   60 cm²

   A 7.2 cm³
   B 51.7 cm³
   C 68.3 cm³
   D 498 cm³

4. The rectangular faces of a triangular prism are equal in size. If the total area of all the rectangular faces is 17 m², what is the approximate area of one of the rectangular faces?

   A 4 m² **B** 6 m²
   C 51 m² **D** 68 m²

5. The area of a base of a triangular prism is 6 m². Its volume is 24 m³. The height of the prism is

   A 3 m **B** 4 m
   C 12 m **D** 18 m

Short Answer

6. Draw the front, top, and side views of this building.

7. How much sheet metal is used to make each small dustpan, not including the handle?

   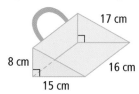

   17 cm

   8 cm   16 cm

   15 cm

8. What is the surface area of this fold-out tent with attached groundsheet?

   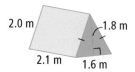

   2.0 m   1.8 m

   2.1 m   1.6 m

9. Hedda is making a cake for the school bake sale. After mixing all the ingredients, she has about 1 L of batter. Will there be enough batter to fill this triangular cake pan to a depth of 4 cm? Explain and justify your answer. Hint: 1 L = 1000 cm³.

   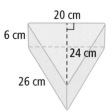

   20 cm

   6 cm

   24 cm

   26 cm

Extended Response

10. A company makes D-ring binders. The front and back rectangular sides of a binder each measure 30 cm by 24.5 cm, and the spine is 10 cm thick. When each binder is empty, it resembles a triangular prism. The company shrink-wraps the binders in plastic and packs them in boxes of 20 for shipping to retailers.

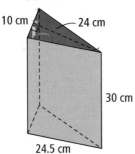

a) How much plastic is required to shrink-wrap each binder?

b) What size of boxes does the company need?

11. Greg is buying groceries. He wants to buy some cheese, but he is not sure which size to get. The supermarket sells wedges of cheese in three sizes. Cheese wedge A costs $3.50, B costs $4.75, and C costs $6.50. Which is the best buy? Explain and justify your answer.

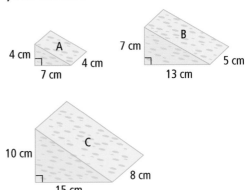

Chapter Problem Wrap-Up

Design a skateboard ramp. Your ramp should include at least one triangular prism.

1. a) Sketch your triangular prism ramp and label the dimensions you will use.

   b) Draw a net of the ramp or build a skeleton of it.

   c) Calculate the area of plywood needed to build it. Explain your solution.

   d) How much space does your ramp fill?

2. Build a model of your design. You may work full size or choose a suitable scale. If you choose to use a combination of three-dimensional shapes to build a more complex ramp, explain your choices.

Measurement at Work

There are many work environments in which very precise measurements are important. Machine parts must be exactly sized for the item to work properly. In the medical field, exact amounts of medications must be measured.

Research and describe one precision measuring instrument. Make a poster telling about the tool you chose.

What is the instrument used for?

What type of person/career uses it?

What type of training does the person need to use the measuring tool?

What does math have to do with the human body?

The human body contains trillions of cells.

We rarely think about the large numbers that describe our own bodies. For example:

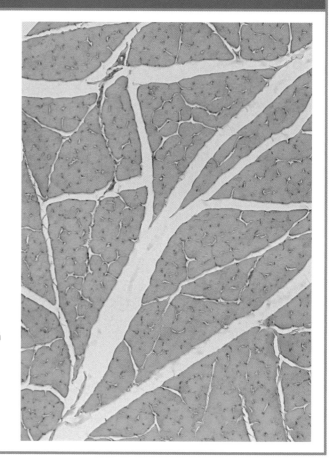

- There are over 100 000 hairs on a full head of hair.
- The heart pumps about 300 000 000 L of blood in a lifetime.
- The human body makes over 100 000 000 000 red blood cells in a day.

1. Each of these examples shows a number in standard form. Write each number in scientific notation.

2. Use your research skills to find other large numbers that describe the human body. Express each number in standard form and in scientific notation.

3. Compare numbers found by the whole class. What is the greatest number?

Design a Runway

To raise money for a spring trip, your school will host a fashion show in the gym. Design a sloping runway so that the models can walk through the audience and up on to the stage.

Your research suggests that:
- the stage should be 1 m high
- the area of the stage should be 36 m^2
- the runway must be wide enough for two models to pass each other
- the runway must be centred on the stage
- the runway must be painted
- the surface of the runway must have slip-proof matting
- the runway needs to be packed with material to reduce vibrations

1. Draw labelled diagrams of your design.

2. Calculate the materials needed.

3. How much money do you think you can raise? Justify your answer.

Chapter 5 Ratios, Rates, and Percents

1. Ron is threading beads to make a friendship bracelet. He creates a pattern.

   a) What is the ratio, in lowest terms, of the number of red beads to the number of yellow beads?

   b) Ron completes the bracelet. He uses five greens beads. How many red beads does he use?

   c) There are 55 beads altogether in the finished bracelet. How many of them are yellow?

2. Selena runs 450 m in 90 s at a fairly constant speed.

   a) Express her speed as a unit rate.

   b) At this rate, how long will it take Selena to run 1 km?

3. Which is the better buy? What assumption did you make?

4. The regular price for a computer is $850. The store offers a 20% discount. The computer is subject to both PST and GST. Find

   a) the amount of the discount

   b) the sale price

   c) the total taxes

   d) the amount you have to pay the store

Chapter 6 Patterning and Algebra

5. Josh takes mushrooms, green peppers, and tomatoes out of the refrigerator. Use Pascal's triangle to find how many different ways Josh can make a pizza with up to three toppings.

6. Examine the pattern of equilateral triangles.

inside line

   a) Describe the relationship between the number of triangles and the number of inside lines.

   b) Model the relationship with an equation.

   c) How many inside lines are in a row of 32 triangles?

7. The value of the nth term of a sequence is $3.5 + 2n$. Write the first four terms of the sequence. Explain how you found the terms.

8. Franka is a salesperson at a health club. She earns $500 per week, plus $80 for each memberships he sells.

   a) Copy and complete the table for 0 to 6 memberships sold in a week.

Number of Memberships Sold	Weekly Earnings ($)

   b) Plot the ordered pairs on a grid.

   c) Describe the pattern of points.

   d) What will Franka earn if she sells 10 memberships in one week? Justify your method.

9. Your school holds a table tennis tournament. A player who wins a match advances to play against another winner in the next round. A player who loses a match is eliminated. How many players can enter a tournament that needs five rounds to find the overall winner?

Chapter 7 Exponents

10. Are 2^5, 3^5, 6^5, and 10^5 all powers of 5? Explain your thinking.

11. The sum of the digits in the number 63 is a perfect square. How many other natural numbers up to 100 have this property?

12. The number of bacteria in a culture doubles every 6 h. There are 1000 bacteria in the culture at noon today. How many bacteria will be in the culture at noon in 2 days?

13. Which numbers is closest in value to 8.9×10^6? Explain your reasoning.

5.3×10^6 6.1×10^6 1.1×10^7 8.9×10^7

14. Estimate the height, in metres, of a stack of ten million pennies.

Chapter 8 Three-Dimensional Geometry and Measurement

15. The front views of some objects are shown. Name two possible three-dimensional figures each might be.

a)

front view

b)
front view

16. Sketch the skeleton for each three-dimensional shape. How many pieces of straw would you need to build each polyhedron?

a) cube
b) square-based pyramid
c) triangular prism

17. The tent shown has an attached groundsheet. The entire outside surface is to be sprayed with waterproofing. The can of waterproofing says it will cover up to 8 m². How many cans are needed for this tent?

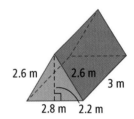

2.6 m   2.6 m   3 m

2.8 m   2.2 m

18. Gordon has a ruler that is an equilateral triangular prism. Find the volume of the ruler.

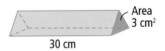

Area 3 cm²

30 cm

19. The dimensions of a scalene triangular prism are given.

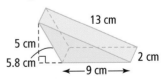

13 cm

5 cm

5.8 cm

2 cm

9 cm

a) Determine its surface area.
b) Calculate its volume.

Data Management and Probability

- Collect, read, organize, interpret, discuss, and present data in tally charts and frequency tables.

- Understand the relationship between a census and a sample.

- Understand the difference between a bar graph and a histogram.

- Construct line graphs, comparative bar graphs, circle graphs, and histograms.

- Use numeric data from databases and in spreadsheets to solve problems.

- Use technology to examine, interpret, and display data.

Key Words

census

population

sample

comparative bar graph

histogram

database

spreadsheet

CHAPTER 9

Data Management: Collection and Display

You live in the age of information. With advances in technology, you can find data on just about any topic, including sports, music, movies, health, and business.

But did you know that you can find data on how teens feel about everyday topics such as friends and school?

By the end of this chapter, you will have
- collected your own data on one of these topics
- organized and displayed it in a variety of ways
- compared your results with the population

Chapter Problem

When you have a problem, it often helps to talk to someone about it. Who would you turn to—a friend, a family member, or perhaps a teacher or other adult that you respect? Do you think other teens deal with their problems in the same way?

Tally Charts and Frequency Tables

Tally charts are used to record collected data. A frequency table is formed when you count up all the tallies.

Marta organized her book collection by category.

Category	Tally	Frequency
Science fiction	‖‖‖ ‖‖‖ ‖	
Teen romance	‖‖‖ ‖	
History	‖‖‖	
Biography	‖‖‖	

1. Copy and complete the frequency table for Marta's book collection.

2. How many books does Marta have?

Bar Graphs and Circle Graphs

Bar graphs are used to compare categories. For example, the bar graph shows that Marta has four times as many science fiction books as biographies.

Circle graphs are used to compare each category to the whole. For example, the circle graph shows that half of Marta's books are science fiction.

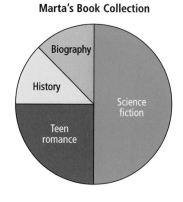

Marta's Book Collection

3. Use the bar graph and then the circle graph to answer these questions.

a) Which category is Marta's favourite?

b) Describe the relationship between the number of teen romance books and the number of history books.

c) What fraction of her books are teen romance?

4. For each part of question 3, which graph made it easier to answer the question? Explain why.

5. Which graph do you think best displays the data on Marta's books? Explain.

Find a Percent of a Number

Marta now has 60 books. 15% are history books. How many history books does she have?

$15\% = \dfrac{15}{100}$

$\quad = 0.15$ **Write the percent as a decimal.**

History books = $0.15 \times$ total number of books
$\qquad\qquad\quad = 0.15 \times 60$
$\qquad\qquad\quad = 9$

There are 9 history books in Marta's collection.

6. Calculate.

  a) 50% of 40   **b)** 75% of 24

7. Calculate.

  a) 10% of 35   **b)** 6% of 25

Mean and Median

Pierre's last 6 golf scores were 83, 82, 86, 77, 80, and 84.
Find the **mean** or average score.
Find the **median** or middle score.
To calculate the mean, find the sum of the values. Then divide by the number of values.

Mean = $(83 + 82 + 86 + 77 + 80 + 84) \div 6$ **Do brackets first.**
$\qquad = 492 \div 6$
$\qquad = 82$

Pierre's mean golf score is 82.

To find the median, arrange the values in order from least to greatest.

77   80   82   83   84   86   82.5 is halfway between 82 and 83.

Pierre's median score is 82.5.

8. Calculate the mean of each set.

  a) 12, 15, 14, 16, 13
  b) 80, 65, 75, 90, 60, 50

9. Find the median of each set.

  a) 12, 15, 14, 16, 13
  b) 80, 65, 75, 90, 60, 50

9.1

Collect, Organize, and Use Data

Focus on...

- collecting sample data
- comparing a sample to a population
- circle graphs

Do you like to listen to music? Think of all the ways that you can obtain and play recorded music. Piracy is the illegal sharing of music. This is a serious issue today. Some artists feel that they are not receiving fair payment for their work.

How can you find out if these artists have a valid claim? One way is to conduct a **census** and ask *everyone* who listens to music. Is there an easier way?

census

- a survey in which everyone participates

Discover the Math

How can you use survey data to draw conclusions about a large group?

1. Design a survey to find out how grade 8 students in your school obtain and listen to music (e.g., CDs, radio, Internet, TV videos, and so on).

2. Carry out the survey with your class. Record your data using a frequency table.

population

- the entire group of people you want to learn about

3. Display the data using a graph of your choice.

4. What can you say about your community's grade 8 **population** based on your **sample** data?

sample

- a small group that represents a population

5. **Reflect** Explain how you can make predictions about a population using sample data. How accurate do you think predictions like these are?

Example 1: Compare a Sample to a Population

One grade 8 class is surveyed about how they obtain music. The sample survey results show that the Internet is the most popular source of music.

The entire grade 8 population of the school is 90 students. Predict how many prefer to use the Internet.

Format	Tally	Frequency
Radio	|||||	5
TV videos	|||||	5
CDs	|||| |||	8
Internet	|||| ||||	10
Other	||	2

Solution

First, find the total number of students in the class.
$5 + 5 + 8 + 10 + 2 = 30$
There are 30 students in the class.

Method 1: Use Ratios

10 out of 30 prefer to use the Internet. This ratio can be written in fraction form as $\frac{10}{30}$.

Write a proportion comparing the sample to the population.

$$\frac{10}{30} = \frac{?}{90}$$

Multiply the numerator and denominator by 3.

$\times 3$

$$\frac{10 \times 3}{30 \times 3} = \frac{30}{90}$$

Based on the sample data, 30 grade 8 students at the school prefer to use the Internet.

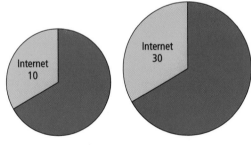

Sample Size = 30   Population Size = 90

Method 2: Use Percents

10 out of 30 prefer to use the Internet. Convert the fraction to a percent.
$$\frac{10}{30} = 33.\overline{3}\%$$
Find $33.\overline{3}\%$ of the population.

$33.\overline{3}\%$ of 90
$= 0.\overline{3} \times 90$
$= 30$

Based on the sample data, 30 grade 8 students at the school prefer to use the Internet.

Literacy Connections

Population and Sample
A population refers to every person in a group being surveyed or studied.

A sample refers to a relatively small number of people chosen from the population. A sample should reflect the same characteristics as the population from which it is drawn.

Population

Sample

Strategies
What other strategy could you use to solve this question? Which one is the most efficient?

Making Connections

You applied ratios and percent in Chapter 5.

Example 2: Use a Circle Graph to Display Data

A grade 9 class of 24 students is surveyed about how they obtain music.

Draw a circle graph to display the data.

Format	Number of People
Radio	3
TV videos	4
CDs	6
Internet	8
Other	3

Solution

To do this,
- express each category as a fraction
- write as a decimal
- since there are 360° in a circle, multiply each decimal value by 360 to find the section angle

Strategies
Make a table or chart

Format	Number of People	Fraction	Decimal	Section Angle
Radio	3	$\frac{3}{24}$	$3 \div 24 = 0.125$	$0.125 \times 360° = 45°$
TV videos	4	$\frac{4}{24}$	$4 \div 24 = 0.1\overline{6}$	$0.1\overline{6} \times 360° = 60°$
CDs	6	$\frac{6}{24}$	$\frac{6}{24}$ is the same as $\frac{1}{4}$. I can show $\frac{1}{4}$ of a circle. It is 90°.	
Internet	8	$\frac{8}{24}$	$8 \div 24 = 0.\overline{3}$	$0.\overline{3} \times 360° = 120°$
Other	3	$\frac{3}{24}$	$\frac{3}{24}$ is the same as $\frac{1}{8}$. This is half of $\frac{1}{4}$ of a circle. It must be 45°.	

$\frac{1}{6}$ of 360° is 60°. This is correct.

$\frac{1}{4} \times 360° = \frac{360°}{4} = 90°$

Draw a circle. Use a protractor to measure each section.

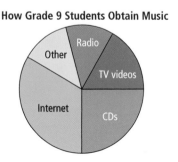

How Grade 9 Students Obtain Music

Shade or colour the sections if you want to. Then, label the sections and write a title.

- A census is a survey of an entire population.

- A sample is a small group taken from a population. A sample is often surveyed to make predictions about the whole group.

Population   **Sample**

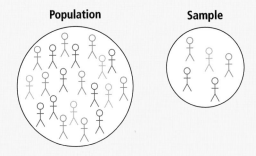

- To create a circle graph:
  - Express each category as a fraction or a decimal.
  - Multiply to find the section angle.
  - Use a protractor to measure and draw each section angle.

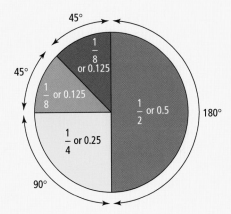

Communicate the Ideas

1. a) Use an example to explain the difference between a sample and a population.
   b) Describe two reasons why you might use a sample instead of a population.

2. What's wrong? Leanne is checking her section angle calculation for TV videos.

> I know that $\frac{4}{24} = \frac{1}{6}$. So, the section angle is $\frac{1}{6} \times 360° = 60°$.
> Why did my calculation give me 57.6° instead of 60°?

Format	Number of People	Fraction	Decimal	Section Angle
Radio	3	$\frac{3}{24}$	$3 \div 24 = 0.125$	$0.125 \times 360° = 45°$
TV videos	4	$\frac{4}{24}$	$4 \div 24 = 0.1\overline{6}$	$0.16 \times 360° = 57.6°$

Practise

For help with questions 3 and 4, refer to Example 1.

A group of grade 8 students were surveyed about their favourite type of television program. Use this data set for questions 3 and 4.

Type of Program	Tally	Frequency
Reality TV	ⅢⅢ ⅢⅢ	10
Sports	ⅢⅢ Ⅰ	6
Cartoons	ⅢⅢ	5
Educational programs	ⅢⅠ	4
Situation comedies	ⅢⅢ ⅢⅢ	10
Other	ⅢⅢ	5

3. Suppose there is a population of 120 grade 8 students at the school. Use ratios to predict how many would pick

a) reality TV

b) sports

4. Suppose there is a population of 200 grade 8 students at the school. Use percents to predict how many would pick

a) educational programs

b) situation comedies

For help with questions 5 to 7, refer to Example 2.

5. A group of teens were surveyed about how often they use a computer.

a) Copy and complete the table.

How Often	Number of Teens	Fraction	Decimal	Section Angle
Daily	55			
1 to 6 days a week	40			
Less often	5			
TOTAL				

b) Draw a circle graph to show the data.

6. A group of teens were surveyed about how often they use a cellular phone.

a) Copy and complete the table.

How Often	Number of Teens	Fraction	Decimal	Section Angle
Daily	5			
1 to 6 days a week	10			
Less often	15			
Do not use	70			
TOTAL				

b) Draw a circle graph to show the data.

7. A group of teens were surveyed about how often they use the Internet. Draw a circle graph to show the data.

How Often	Number of Teens
Daily	20
1 to 6 days a week	30
Less often	6
Do not use	4

Apply

8. Identify the population from which each sample is taken.

a) A group of model car collectors are surveyed about the most popular models.

b) A group of lacrosse players are asked what their favourite type of lacrosse stick is.

c) Students at a high school are questioned about what type of music they want to hear at the school dance.

d) A group of teens are asked how many times a year they go to the beach.

9. The circle graph shows sample survey data about the types of video games that members of a computer gaming club like to play.

Grade 8 Students: Favourite Type of Video Game

a) The club has 300 members in total. Based on this sample, predict how many members prefer each type of game.

b) What strategy did you use to solve part a)? What other strategy might you use? Which strategy is more efficient? Explain.

Chapter Problem

10. Use this survey question.

> **Who would you talk to if you had a problem choosing courses for grade 9?**

a) Conduct your survey with at least 20 grade 8 students. Try to ask the same number of boys and girls. Record the data for boys separately from the data for girls.

b) Display your combined data for boys and girls using both a bar graph and a circle graph.

c) Which graph do you prefer for your data? Explain why.

Try This!

11. Alvin, a market researcher, has presented the following bar graph to his boss.

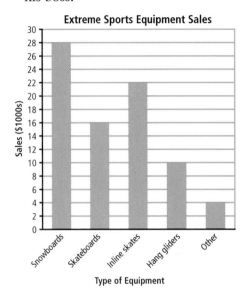

Alvin's boss tells him that she would prefer to see the data in the form of a circle graph.

a) Draw a circle graph for the data.

b) Explain the steps you took to do this.

c) Suggest a reason why Alvin's boss asked for a circle graph.

Extend

12. A survey asked Canadians what their favourite pastime is. The results were extended to the entire population.

Canadians' Favourite Pastimes	
Camping	🍁🍁🍁
Playing Sports	🍁🍁🍁🍁
Watching TV	🍁🍁🍁
Surfing the Internet	🍁🍁
Shopping	🍁🍁
Other	🍁🍁

🍁 represents 2 million people

Suppose that 200 people in the sample picked camping.

a) Find the number of people in the sample.

b) Construct a frequency table for the sample.

Comparative Bar Graphs

Are teens less active today than in the past? Some say that television, video games, and the Internet have replaced outdoor activities such as sports. Do data support these claims?

Discover the Math

How can you compare data for different groups using a single graph?

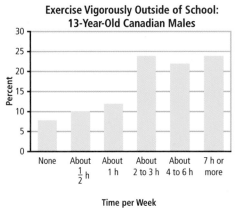

Exercise Vigorously Outside of School: 13-Year-Old Canadian Males

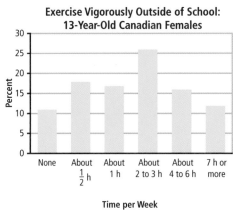

Exercise Vigorously Outside of School: 13-Year-Old Canadian Females

1. List three things these graphs tell you.

2. a) Approximately what percent of 13-year-old males spend no time exercising vigorously outside of school?

 b) Approximately what percent of 13-year-old males spend 7 h or more exercising vigorously outside of school?

 c) What is the most common amount of time spent exercising vigorously by 13-year-old males?

3. Repeat step 2 for 13-year-old females.

4. Reflect

   a) Compare the two bar graphs. What differences can you see between males and females regarding exercise habits? Justify your observations.

   b) How could you make it easier to compare the two sets of data? Describe your ideas using pictures and words.

Example 1: Read a Comparative Bar Graph

This **comparative bar graph** shows a store's movie sales for a given month. Each movie category is divided into two formats: VHS and DVD.

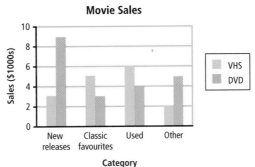

Movie Sales

   a) What were the sales in the Used category in VHS format? DVD format?

   b) In which categories were DVD sales greater than VHS sales? In which categories were VHS sales greater than DVD sales?

   c) Which category had the greatest sales? Which had the least sales?

comparative bar graph

• a bar graph in which two or more groups of data are shown side by side

Solution

a) Read the values for each bar in the Used category. VHS sales were $6000. DVD sales were $4000.

b) Compare the heights of the bars in each pair. DVD sales were greater than VHS sales for New Releases and Other. VHS sales were greater than DVD sales for Classic Favourites and Used.

c) Find the total sales in each category by adding the VHS and DVD sales figures.

Strategies
Make a table or chart

Category	VHS Sales ($1000s)	DVD Sales ($1000s)	Total Sales ($1000s)
New releases	3	9	12
Classic favourites	5	3	8
Used	6	4	10
Other	2	5	7

New Releases had the greatest sales. Other had the least sales.

Example 2: Draw a Comparative Bar Graph

Fifty students in a junior high school were surveyed to find what their preferred mode of transportation is.

Girls	
Mode of Transportation	**Number**
Bicycle	15
Skateboard	6
Walking	9

Boys	
Mode of Transportation	**Number**
Bicycle	9
Skateboard	8
Walking	3

50 people were surveyed. There are more girls than boys. To compare results, I'll find percents for each data set.

a) Draw a comparative bar graph to show the data.
b) What conclusions can you draw from the graph?

Solution

a) The total number of girls surveyed is $15 + 6 + 9 = 30$.
The total number of boys surveyed is $9 + 8 + 3 = 20$.

Girls		
Mode of Transportation	**Number**	**Fraction**
Bicycle	15	$\frac{15}{30}$
Skateboard	6	$\frac{6}{30}$
Walking	9	$\frac{9}{30}$

I can do the data set for girls mentally. $\frac{15}{30}$ is $\frac{1}{2}$. This is 0.5 or 50%.

$\frac{6}{30}$ is $\frac{1}{5}$. This is 0.2 or 20%. $50\% + 20\% = 70\%$. So the last one is 30%.

I'll use a table to organize my calculations for the boys.

Boys				
Mode of Transportation	**Number**	**Fraction**	**Decimal**	**Percent**
Bicycle	9	$\frac{9}{20}$	$9 \div 20 = 0.45$	$0.45 \times 100\% = 45\%$
Skateboard	8	$\frac{8}{20}$	$8 \div 20 = 0.4$	$0.4 \times 100\% = 40\%$
Walking	3	$\frac{3}{20}$	$3 \div 20 = 0.15$	$0.15 \times 100\% = 15\%$

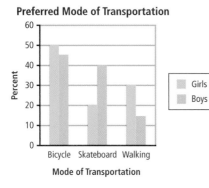

Preferred Mode of Transportation

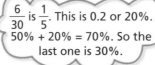

Use two different colours for the bars. Connect the bars in each pair for each category.

Add a legend.

Making Connections

You used percents for circle graphs in Section 9.1. Now, you are using them for comparative bar graphs.

b) Bicycling is the most popular among girls and boys. A greater percent of boys than girls prefer skateboarding. A greater percent of girls than boys prefer walking.

Key Ideas

- A comparative bar graph shows how two or more groups of data compare.

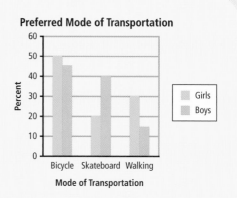
Preferred Mode of Transportation

- You can compare groups of data that have different sizes by using percents.

15 out of 30 girls prefer bicycles. 9 out of 20 boys prefer bicycles. If I compare the original numbers, it looks like almost twice as many girls prefer bicycles as boys.

Looking at the comparative bar graph, I see that they're closer, 50% to 45%.

Communicate the Ideas

1. a) Explain the difference between the bar graph and the comparative bar graph.

b) Describe two situations in which you would use a comparative bar graph to display data.

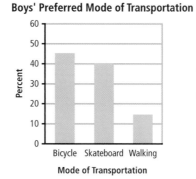
Boys' Preferred Mode of Transportation

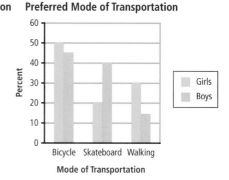
Preferred Mode of Transportation

2. Sheila surveyed 10 girls and 20 boys about their favourite activity.

She states, "A greater percent of girls than boys prefer inline skating." Is she correct? Explain.

Activity	Girls	Boys
Inline skating	5	6

Practise

For help with questions 3 to 5, refer to Example 1.

The comparative bar graph shows grade 9 course selection for a community. Use this data set for questions 3 to 5.

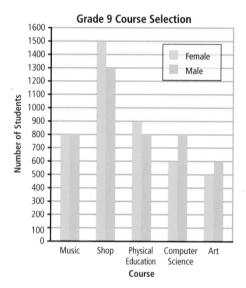

Grade 9 Course Selection

3. **a)** Which course did the greatest number of females choose?
   b) Which course did the least number of males choose?
   c) Which course did the same number of males and females choose?

4. **a)** How many female students chose Computer Science?
   b) How many male students are chose Shop?
   c) How many students chose in Art?

5. **a)** Which courses did more female students choose than male students?
   b) Which courses did more male students choose than female students?

For help with questions 6 to 8, refer to Example 2.

6. Kiana and Rose are in the same math class. They decide to compare scores on their first four tests.

Test	Kiana	Rose
1	58%	70%
2	63%	66%
3	66%	61%
4	71%	52%

a) Draw a comparative bar graph to show the data.
b) What does the graph tell you about the students' performance?

Apply

Grades 7 and 8 students were asked what their favourite subjects are. Use this data set for questions 7 and 8.

Grade 7 Students		
Subject	**Tally**	**Frequency**
Physical Education	|||| |||| |||| |||| ||||	
Art	|||| |||| |||| |||	
Science	|||| |||| ||	
Other	||||		

Grade 8 Students		
Subject	**Tally**	**Frequency**
Physical Education	|||| |||| |||| ||||		
Art	|||| ||||	
Science	|||| |||| ||||	
Other	||||	

7. **a)** Copy and complete both tables.
   b) Draw a comparative bar graph using frequencies.
   c) According to your graph, is Physical Education more popular with grade 7 or grade 8 students? Explain.

8. a) Add three columns to your tables in question 7a). Use the headings "Fraction," "Decimal," and "Percent." Complete these three columns in both tables.

b) Draw a comparative bar graph using percents.

c) According to your graph, is Physical Education more popular with grade 7 or grade 8 students? Explain.

d) Compare your answer to part c) with your answer to question 7c). Which do you think is more accurate? Justify your answer.

9. Sales data for a music store over a 15-year period are shown.

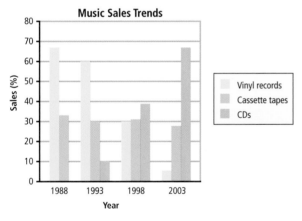

Music Sales Trends

Legend:
- Vinyl records
- Cassette tapes
- CDs

a) The sales data for each year are divided into groups. How many groups are there? What are they?

b) There appears to be a bar missing. Why do you think this is?

c) What conclusions can you draw from this graph?

Chapter Problem

10. Do boys choose different people to talk to about their problems than girls? Use the survey data you collected in question 10 on page 285. Draw one or more comparative bar graphs to answer this question.

11. The daily behaviour patterns of two koala bears are shown in the two circle graphs.

Rocco's Daily Activities

5 h, 3 h, 2 h, 4 h, 10 h

Biff's Daily Activities

3 h, 3 h, 2 h, 7 h, 9 h

Legend:
- Eating eucalyptus
- Sleeping
- Playing
- Personal bear care
- Socializing

a) Draw a comparative bar graph to show the data.

b) Did you use percents to construct your graph? Explain why or why not.

c) Who sleeps more? How many hours more per day?

d) Who do you think is the more active bear? Explain why.

e) Explain how the comparative bar graph makes it easier to answer questions like part d).

f) Make up a question that can be answered by your graph. Answer your question.

Extend

12. Fifty students in a junior high school were surveyed to find what their preferred mode of transportation is.

Mode of Transportation	Girls		Boys	
	Number	Percent	Number	Percent
Bicycle	15	50%	8	40%
Skateboard	6	20%	9	45%
Walking	9	30%	3	15%

The school population is 400 students, in the same boy-to-girl ratio as the sample. Based on the sample, predict the total number of boys and girls in the school that prefer each mode of transportation.

9.3 Histograms

Focus on...
• histograms

How tall are grade 8 students? Are they all nearly the same height? Or are the heights spread out?

Discover the Math

Materials
• metre stick
• chalk or masking tape
• ruler

How can you display large groups of data?

Work in groups of 3 or 4.

1. Set up a station as shown in the photograph. Record the height of each member of your group.

2. a) Record the results of the entire class.
   b) Can you present the data using a frequency table? If so, describe how. If not, explain why not.

3. a) Organize the data into 5 or 6 groups. Explain how you formed the groups.
   b) Does this make it easier to construct a frequency table? Explain.

4. a) Choose one method to display the data. Graph the data.
   b) Describe two things that your graph tells you about the data.
   c) Compare your display with those of other groups.

5. Reflect Describe some effective ways to display large amounts of different data.

Example 1: Read a Histogram

A class of students measured their heights and displayed the data using a **histogram**.

a) Describe the set of data.

b) Which height interval has the greatest number of students?

c) How many students are at least 150 cm tall?

Student Heights

histogram

• a connected bar graph that shows data organized into intervals

Solution

a) Student heights range from 120 cm to 170 cm. More students are near the middle than at either end.

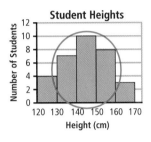

Student Heights

Most of the student heights are in the middle area. Their heights are between 130 cm and 160 cm.

b) The greatest number of students is in the interval 140 cm to 150 cm.

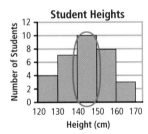

Student Heights

Ten students have heights in this interval.

c) Eleven students are at least 150 cm tall.

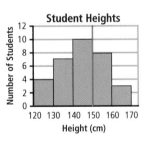

Student Heights

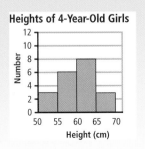

Add the frequencies for the last two intervals. 8 + 3 = 11

Literacy Connections

Describing Data

A line graph shows trends in data over time. For example, this line graph shows Lucy's height on each of her first six birthdays. Her height is increasing with her age.

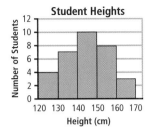

Lucy's Height

A histogram could be used to show the heights of a group of girls all of the same age. This histogram shows the heights of 20 girls at age 4. Most girls at age 4 are between 60 cm and 65 cm in height.

Heights of 4-Year-Old Girls

How tall was Lucy at age 4?

How does her height compare to the heights for other girls at age 4?

Example 2: Draw a Histogram

Mr. Ibrahim marks a major project for his class. The scores are shown as percents.

78	62	83	88	57	70	78	69	71	90
68	81	87	73	66	79	84	95	72	58
85	75	74	64	50	97	73	91	80	77

a) Organize the scores into intervals of 10.

b) Draw a histogram to show the data. Use intervals of 10.

c) What percent of the students achieved 70% or higher?

d) Redraw the histogram using intervals of 5. What additional information does this provide?

Solution

a)

Score (%)	Tally	Frequency
50–59	III	3
60–69	IIIII	5
70–79	IIIII IIIII I	11
80–89	IIIII II	7
90–99	IIII	4

b)

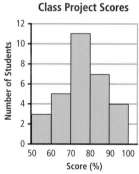

Class Project Scores

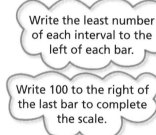

Write the least number of each interval to the left of each bar.

Write 100 to the right of the last bar to complete the scale.

I draw a histogram in the same way as a bar graph, except I join the bars to show how the intervals connect to each other.

c) The number of students that scored 70% or higher is 11 + 7 + 4 = 22.

The total number of students is 3 + 5 + 11 + 7 + 4 = 30.

So, $\frac{22}{30}$, or about 73%, of the students achieved 70% or higher.

d)

Score (%)	Tally	Frequency
50–54	I	1
55–59	II	2
60–64	II	2
65–69	III	3
70–74	⊪ I	6
75–79	⊪	5
80–84	IIII	4
85–89	III	3
90–94	II	2
95–99	II	2

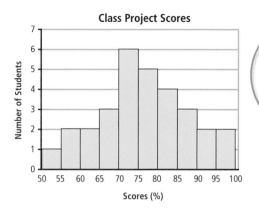

Class Project Scores

The smaller intervals show more detail about the data. For example, now I can see that 5 students scored in the high 70s. The first graph didn't tell me this.

Key Ideas

- A histogram is used to display a large set of data by organizing the data into intervals.

- The intervals of a histogram must be of equal size and include all data in the set. There are usually between 5 and 10 intervals in a histogram.

- Drawing a histogram is similar to drawing a bar graph. The bars in a histogram are connected to show a continuous set of data divided into intervals.

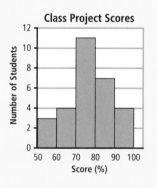

Class Project Scores

Communicate the Ideas

1. a) How are a histogram and a bar graph similar?
b) How are they different?
c) Explain when you would use each type. Provide an example to support your answer.

2. Identify the error in each histogram. How can it be corrected?

a) Ages of People at a Picnic

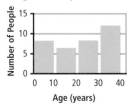

b) Ages of People at a Picnic

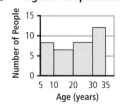

c) Ages of People at a Picnic

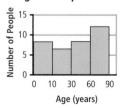

Practise

For help with questions 3 and 4, refer to Example 1.

The histogram shows class results for a quiz. Use this data set for questions 3 and 4.

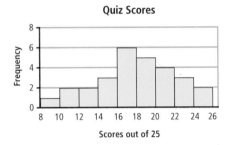

Quiz Scores

3. a) What is the size of the intervals?
   b) What is the greatest score interval? How many scored in this interval?
   c) Which interval has more scores than any other? How many scored in this interval?

4. a) How many students wrote this quiz?
   b) Explain how you found this.

For help with questions 5 to 7, refer to Example 2.

A group of test scores, as percents, are shown. Use this data set for questions 5 to 7.

67	72	81	70	54	93	65	77	60	59
76	89	71	63	68	57	90	82	78	

5. Organize the scores into intervals. Copy and complete the table.

Score (%)	Tally	Frequency
50–59		
60–69		
70–79		
80–89		
90–99		

6. Draw a histogram to show the data.

7. a) Organize the scores into intervals of 5.
   b) Draw a histogram to show the data.

Apply

8. Ola has kept track of her bowling scores.

122	134	156	140	155	181	173
148	113	139	114	189	166	152
147	191	144	152	160	133	174
150	145	136				

   a) Draw a histogram to show the data.
   b) Explain and justify your choice of intervals.

9. Suppose one of your friends missed today's class. Write a brief e-mail to him or her that explains the difference between a bar graph and a histogram. Include an example of when you would use each type of graph.

Try This!

10. The heights of basketball players are given, in metres.

2.22	2.30	2.41	1.89	1.92	2.25	2.05
2.31	2.11	2.15	2.28	2.18	1.95	2.11
2.20	2.09	2.07				

   a) Organize the data into intervals.
   b) Explain and justify your choice of intervals.
   c) Draw a histogram to show the data.
   d) Find another way to present the data. Explain your thinking.

Extend

11. The stem-and-leaf plot shows the weekly earnings, in dollars, of several babysitters.

0	8
1	2 6
2	0 2 4 4 5 8
3	0 2 5
4	0 4

   a) Draw a histogram to show the data.
   b) Rotate the stem-and-leaf plot counterclockwise 90° by turning your book. Compare it to your histogram. Describe how they compare, visually.

Create Histograms Using Fathom™

Focus on...

- creating and manipulating histograms

Use technology to create histograms. This is another way of doing Example 2 on page 294.

Materials

- Fathom™ software
- computers

Optional:

- TECH 9.3A Histograms Using Fathom™

Mr. Ibrahim marks a major project for his class. The grades are shown as percents.

78 62 83 88 57 70 78 69 71 90 68 81 87 73 66
79 84 95 72 58 85 75 74 64 50 97 73 91 80 77

1. Start Fathom™. Enter the data.
- From the **Tool shelf** of icons across the top, click the **Case Table** ▥ icon. Drag the icon into the workspace.
- Click the attribute **<new>**. Type Grades and press **Enter**.
- To enter the grades from Mr. Ibrahim's class, type each value and press **Enter**. You should have 30 grades in total.

2. Create a histogram.
- From the **Tool shelf**, click the **Graph** ▦ icon. Drag the icon into the workspace.
- Click the heading Grades in the table you created. Hold the mouse button down and drag to **Drop an attribute here** in the Graph Box. Let go of the mouse button.
- Click **Dot Plot** in the upper right of the Graph Box. From the pop-up menu, select **Histogram**.

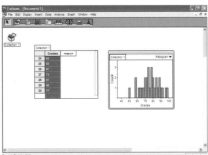

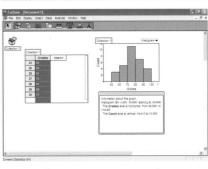

3. Organize the scores into intervals of 10.
- Double click the values along the horizontal axis. A new window will appear. Anything in blue can be changed.
- Change **Histogram: Bin width** to 10.000 and **Starting at** to 50.000. Change the **Grade** axis values to 40.000 and 110.000. Change the **Count** axis value to 12.000.

4. **Reflect** What advantages do you see in using technology to create a histogram?

Use Databases to Solve Problems

How comfortable are young teens in discussing problems with friends? Does this change with age? Is there a difference between girls and boys?

database

• an organized collection of information
• often stored electronically

You may be surprised to know that there is a large **database** that contains this type of information. The database is called CANSIM: the Canadian Socio-economic Information Management System. It contains information about Canada's people and resources that has been collected and organized by Statistics Canada. E-STAT is the Internet link between you and the CANSIM database.

What other questions do you have about Canadian teens?

Discover the Math

Materials

• TECH 9.4A Access the CANSIM Database

Optional:

• TECH 9.4B Print Graphs From CANSIM

Alternative:

• BLM 9.4A Databases Without Technology

How can you access information in a database to solve problems?

1. Go to **www.mcgrawhill.ca/links/math8** and follow the links to access E-STAT.

• Click **English**.
• On the next Web page, click **Accept and enter**.

2. Find data about teen students from the Table of Contents Web page.

- Under People, select **Education**.
- On the next Web page, click **Data**.
- Then, under CANSIM, select **Students**.

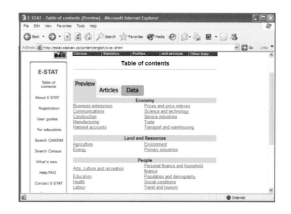

3. Quickly scan the list of tables. Briefly describe some of the data that look interesting to you.

4. Find data on how Canadian teens feel about discussing problems with friends.

- Select table 110-0011.
- Next, select **Canada**, **Males** or **Females**, **13 years**, and **Friend(s) of same sex**.
- Then, for **Response**, click **Select all**.
- Finally, click **Retrieve as a Table**.

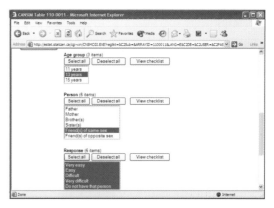

5. Select a type of graph to display the data.

- Choose **Bar graph (vertical)**, **Bar graph (horizontal)**, or **Pie chart**.
- Then, click **Go**.

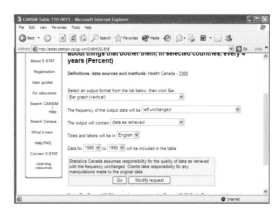

6. a) Analyse the data. What does the graph tell you?

b) Use the Internet browser's **Back** button to return to the previous page. Select a different type of graph to present the data, and then click **Go**. Does this new graph give you any more information? Which type of graph do you prefer? Why?

7. Go back and look at data on how adolescents feel about discussing problems with friends of the *opposite* sex. Produce a graph for this data set and compare it to your original data.

8. Use the Internet browser's **Back** button to return to the Table of Contents Web page.

a) Pose a problem or a question that you think you might be able to find data for.

b) Find data and produce graphs related to your problem.

c) Describe two or three answers or conclusions that you see.

9. Reflect Trade your problem with a classmate. Explore and solve each other's problem. Describe your process for finding the information in the CANSIM database.

Technology Tip

• To compare graphs, you could print them or copy and paste them into a word-processing document.

Example: Read a Database

A telephone directory, printed or electronic, is a database.
How is the database organized?

Cold Springs

S

Name	Address	Phone
Smith A	123 First	555-1234
Smith Allan	149 Rowanwood Rd	555-8963

Solution

A database is organized into records. Records consist of fields of data. This database lists records in alphabetical order, by name.

Cold Springs

S

Name	Address	Phone
Smith A	123 First	555-1234
Smith Allan	149 Rowanwood Rd	555-8963

There are three fields: Name, Address, and Phone.

There is a record for each person. This record is for A Smith, who lives at 123 First, and whose phone number is 555-1234.

- A database is an organized collection of information. For example, a telephone directory is a database. It lists information about people in alphabetical order.

Cold Springs

S

Name	Address	Phone
Smith A	123 First	555-1234
Smith Allan	149 Rowanwood Rd	555-8963

- A database is organized into records. Records consist of fields. The sample telephone directory shows the records for two people that live in Cold Springs. Each record consists of three fields. The fields contain a person's name, address, and telephone number.

- Electronic databases allow you to select specific information or sort the information in different ways.

- You can use data that you obtain from a database to answer questions and solve problems.

Communicate the Ideas

1. Describe three things you discovered about how young teens feel about discussing problems with friends.

2. Identify one other topic that you used E-STAT to find data on. Describe three things you discovered about this topic.

3. Suggest an application at home or at school for which you could use a database to store and retrieve information. Describe how the database might be organized.

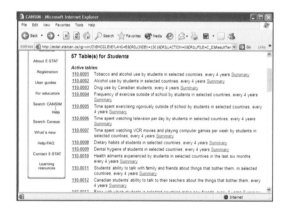

Our school administration uses a database for student enrolment and information. This makes it easy to locate a student while at school.

The video store uses a database for movies and customers. This makes it possible to find out which movies are rented and by whom.

Practise

For help with questions 4 to 6, refer to the Example.

Use the sample telephone directory for questions 4 and 5.

Blue Canyon		
H		
Name	**Address**	**Phone**
Hager Gene	561 Front Rd	555-3645
Haley Andrea	182 Rock Rd	555-4332
Hall Julie	1025 Hill Top	555-9001
Halls Roger	1114 Valley St	555-0047

4. a) How many records does the telephone directory have?

b) Copy one record from the directory.

5. How many fields does each record have? What piece of data is in each field?

6. A cell phone's memory contains several databases. One of these is similar to a telephone directory. The screen shows three records.

a) How many fields does each record contain?

b) What data are contained in the first field?

c) What data are contained in the second field?

d) Are these records displayed in alphabetical or numerical order?

7. This screen shows a list of databases stored in the cell phone's memory. What information do you think might be stored in each database?

Apply

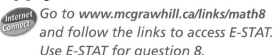 Go to *www.mcgrawhill.ca/links/math8* and follow the links to access E-STAT. Use E-STAT for question 8.

8. Use E-STAT to find data about how teens in other countries feel about discussing problems with friends. Follow these steps:

- From the People section of the Table of Contents Web page, select **Education**.
- On the next Web page, click **Data**.
- Then, under CANSIM, select **Students**.
- Finally, select table **110-0011**.

Choose a country of interest in the **Geography** section of table 110-0011. Compare the data you find with what you learned about Canadian youths in Discover the Math. Write a brief report on your findings.

9. Search the Internet and choose a database on a subject that interests you.

a) Pose two problems or questions that you think the database will be able to answer. Record the Web address of the database.

b) Search the database and try to solve your problems. Describe what you discovered.

Chapter Problem

10. How does your survey data compare with those of other Canadian teens?

Compare your findings from Discover the Math with the data you collected in question 10 on page 285. Comment on any similarities or differences that you observe.

11. Go to the school or public library.

a) What kind of database do they use to store information?

b) Search for five books or articles on a topic of your choice. Explain how you did the search. Copy the record for each of the five items you found.

c) Look at your five records. Identify at least three fields in these records.

d) How easy is it to find library materials using a database? Explain.

e) Write an information paragraph describing what you learned about the library database.

Literacy Connections

Writing an Information Paragraph
- Start with a topic sentence. This provides the main idea. For example, you may have learned how to use fields to find books in the database.
- Provide some supporting details. For example, you may provide examples of the fields you used and what you found.
- End with a concluding sentence. For example, you may decide that using a database is easier than you thought.

Extend

You can use E-STAT to access Census data.

 Go to **www.mcgrawhill.ca/links/math8** and follow the links to access E-STAT.

- From the Table of Contents Web page, click **Search Census** on the left side of the page.
- Explore the Census database to answer questions 12 and 13.

12. a) When was North America's earliest Census conducted? Who conducted it?

b) What kind of data are available from this time period?

c) Briefly describe the other available Census data.

13. a) Search the most recent Census to find socio-economic data for your community. Follow these steps:
- Under **Search for a geographic area**, select 2001 Census. Type the name of your community. Click **Search!**.
- On the next Web page, select a topic of interest.
- Display the data using the choices that appear at the bottom of the page.
- Use your Internet browser's **Back** button to explore other data that interest you.

b) Write a brief report on a topic of interest that you learned about.

Use a Spreadsheet to Present Data and Solve Problems

Focus on...
• spreadsheets

Suppose you are the host of a reality television show called *Eliminator*. In your show, three teams compete in various outdoor events. After each event, teams are awarded a score out of 10. The results for the first five events are shown.

Event	Event Name	Team		
		Hot Diggity Dogs	Nasty Bunch	Fancy Dancers
A	Obstacle Course	9	8	3
B	Mud Pit Mash	7	7	4
C	Search and Rescue	5	8	6
D	Splash-Fest	6	7	7
E	Leap-Frog Relay	4	7	8

A **spreadsheet** is a useful tool for displaying data and performing calculations. How could a spreadsheet help you to determine who should be eliminated and who should go on?

spreadsheet

• a software tool for organizing and displaying numeric data
• software packages include AppleWorks, ClarisWorks, Microsoft® Excel, and Quattro® Pro

Discover the Math

Materials

• TECH 9.5A Using AppleWorks 6.2

Optional:
• TECH 9.5B Using AppleWorks 5.0
• TECH 9.5C Using Quattro® Pro 10
• TECH 9.5D Using Microsoft® Excel 2002

Alternative:
• BLM 9.5A Spreadsheets Without Technology

How can you use a spreadsheet to display data and solve problems?

1. Look at the event scores for the teams competing in *Eliminator*.

a) Which team appears to be improving overall? Justify your choice.

b) Which team appears to be the best overall? Explain why.

2. Open a new spreadsheet in AppleWorks 6.2. Enter the data as shown.

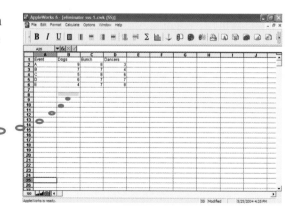

Column B intersects row 8 here. This is cell B8.

3. Look at trends in performance. Create a time series (line graph) for each team.

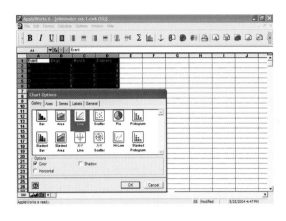

- Select the data. Click cell A1 and drag to cell D6.
- From the **Options Menu**, select **Make Chart....**
- From the **Chart Options** window, under the **Gallery** tab, select **Line**. Click the **Labels** tab. In the **Title** box, type **Team Performance**. Click the **Axis** tab. Select the **X axis** button. In the **Axis Label** box, type Event. Select the **Y axis** button. In the **Axis Label** box, type Score.
- Click **OK**.

4. a) Click and drag the graph so that it is underneath the data.

b) Describe the performance trend of each team.

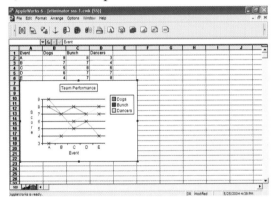

5. Analyse the data. First, clear the graph from the spreadsheet.

- Click on the graph.
- From the **Edit** menu, choose **Clear**, or press the **Delete** key.
- Type Mean, Median, and Sum at the bottom of column A.

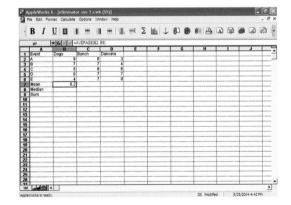

6. a) Calculate the mean score for the Hot Diggity Dogs.
- Click cell B7.
- Type **=AVERAGE(B2..B6)**.

b) Calculate the mean score for the other two teams. Use this shortcut:
- Click cell B7 and drag to cell D7.
- From the **Calculate** menu, select **Fill Right**.

Literacy Connections

Trends in Graphs
A trend is the general direction that a time series (line graph) is going. For example, the graph shows the scores of a different team competing in Eliminator. The team's performance trend increased until event C. Then, the team's performance trend decreased.

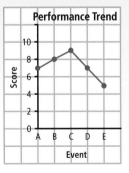

7. Find the total number of points for each team. Repeat step 6 using the =SUM( ) function.

8. a) Find the median score for the Hot Diggity Dogs.
- Click cell B2 and drag to cell B6.
- From the **Calculate Menu,** select **Sort….**
- In the dialogue box, select **Vertical**. Then, click **OK**.
- In the Dogs column, there are five data values. The middle one, or the third value, is the median. Make a note of the value in cell B4.
- From the **Edit** menu, select **Undo Sort**.
- Click cell B8. Type the value you noted.

b) Repeat part a) for the other two teams. Remember to undo the sort each time!

9. Which team has the greatest mean score? greatest total overall score? greatest median score?

10. Create a comparative bar graph for all five events.
- Click cell A1 and drag to cell D6.
- From the **Options Menu,** select **Make Chart….**
- From the **Chart Options** window, under the **Gallery** tab, select **Bar**. Enter an appropriate title and labels for the two axes as you did in step 3.
- Click **OK**.

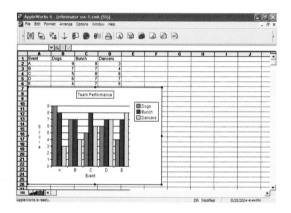

11. a) Describe how this graph makes it easy to tell which team won each event.
b) How many events did each team win?
c) Explain how the comparative bar graph also provides information about the performance trends of each team.

12. Reflect
a) List various ways you can display data using a spreadsheet.
b) List various ways you can use a spreadsheet to answer questions or solve problems.

Databases and spreadsheets organize data in different ways. The information in a database is organized into records. Each record consists of one or more fields. The fields contain the data.

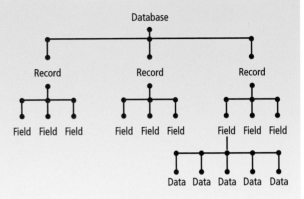

A spreadsheet is a table organized into rows and columns. The intersection of a row and a column is called a cell.

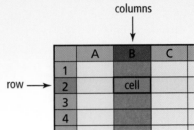

Key Ideas

- A spreadsheet is a software tool used to organize and display numeric data.

- A spreadsheet can be used to develop various types of graphs.

- The best choice of graph depends on the type of data and the types of comparisons you wish to focus on.

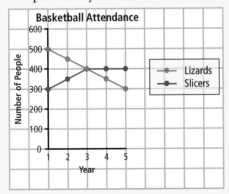

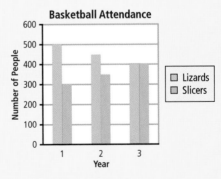

– Use a line graph to show how data are changing over time.

– Use a comparative bar graph to show how different sets of data compare to each other.

- A spreadsheet can be used to perform calculations quickly and accurately.

Communicate the Ideas

1. a) What types of graphs would you use to display the set of data? Explain why.
b) Describe what the graph would show about Cassie's math scores.
c) Explain how you could use a spreadsheet to calculate Cassie's mean test score.

Cassie's Math Scores	
Test	Percent
1	62
2	66
3	70
4	72
5	77

2. a) Can a comparative bar graph be used to show trends? Explain, with an example.
b) How is a line graph similar to a comparative bar graph?
c) How are they different?
d) Describe two advantages of each type of graph.

3. Who is right, Leanne or Brian? Explain.

A spreadsheet and a database are organized in the same way.

No, they aren't. A database is organized into records and fields. A spreadsheet is organized into rows and columns.

Check Your Understanding

Practise

4. Three friends worked together on an English project. Matt worked 7 h. Adam worked 5 h. Cindy worked 6 h. The data set is displayed as a bar graph and as a circle graph.

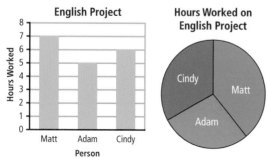

Which graph do you think clearly identifies each person's contribution? Explain.

5. Two friends record the time they spend studying one week.

Trina		Liane	
Day	Time (h)	Day	Time (h)
Monday	3	Monday	2
Tuesday	2	Tuesday	3
Wednesday	2	Wednesday	3
Thursday	2	Thursday	3
Friday	2	Friday	1

Display the data set as a comparative bar graph and a line graph. Which graph do you think clearly identifies each person's studying trends? Explain.

Apply

Three teams compete in various outdoor events. After each event, teams are awarded a score out of 10. The results for the first five events are shown. Use this data set for questions 6 to 8.

Event	Team		
	Lizards	Cats	Amazons
A	5	9	8
B	6	7	8
C	6	6	7
D	7	6	7
E	8	5	8

6. a) Which team do you think deserves to win the competition? Justify your choice using data, statistics, graphs, and mathematical reasoning.

 b) Pick a different team. Write a convincing argument that suggests why this team should win.

7. Suppose there are two more events. Each team is convinced that they can win the overall competition, based on total points. Is this possible? Explain why or why not.

8. Suppose you are interviewing the captain of the Amazons team. What do you think he or she will say to convince you that the Amazons will win the competition?

9. Describe some advantages of using a spreadsheet to create graphs for data.

Chapter Problem

10. Use technology to investigate different ways to display your findings in question 10 on page 285.

 a) Enter some of the data that you gathered earlier into a spreadsheet.

 b) Create the same graph that you produced with paper and pencil.

 c) Experiment with different graph types and options. Which types of graph are effective for displaying your data? Which are not effective? Explain.

11. The table shows game attendance for two basketball teams.

Game	Attendance	
	Twisters	Gliders
1	500	300
2	450	350
3	350	500
4	400	400
5	500	350

 a) Enter the data into a spreadsheet.

 b) Create a graph to display the data set.

 c) Calculate the mean, median, and mode.

 d) Ask a question about the data. Answer your own question.

Extend

12. Use the team results on page 304. Suppose 10 bonus points are awarded for each event won in *Eliminator*. Suppose also that an additional 5 points are awarded to the team that has won the most events.

 a) Based on this, determine the total score for each team after the first five events.

 b) Explain how you found your answers.

 c) Which team benefits the most from the bonus system? Which team benefits the least? Explain.

Key Words

Use the clues to help you solve the puzzle.

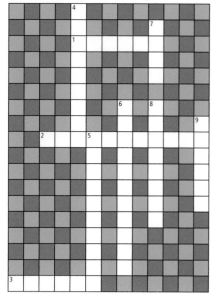

Across

1. a small group that represent a population

2. a type of bar graph in which two or more groups of data are shown side by side

3. middle value of a set of data

Down

4. a connected bar graph that shows data organized into intervals

5. the entire group of people you want to learn about

6. a software tool for organizing and displaying numeric data.

7. average

8. an organized collection of information; often stored electronically

9. a survey in which everyone participates

9.1 Collect, Organize, and Use Data, pages 280–285

A group of grade 8 students are surveyed about the type of movie they prefer to rent. Use this information for questions 10 and 11.

Type of Movie	Tally	Frequency
Drama	⊮	
Action	⊮ ⊮	
Comedy	⊮ IIII	
Science fiction	⊮ I	

10. a) Copy and complete the frequency table.

 b) Draw a bar graph to show the data.

 c) Draw a circle graph to show the data.

 d) Describe one advantage of each graph for displaying the data.

11. Suppose there is a population of 120 grade 8 students at the school.

 a) Predict how many prefer comedy.

 b) Predict how many prefer action.

9.2 Comparative Bar Graphs, pages 286–291

12. Anya compared her test scores to the class average.

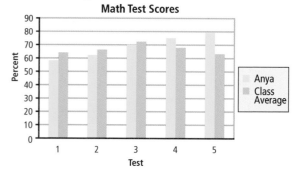

a) On which tests did Anya score higher than the class average?

b) Compare the trend in Anya's scores to the trend in the class average.

13. The following data show the favourite sport to watch among a group of students.

Girls	
Sport	**Number**
Basketball	3
Figure Skating	6
Football	3
Hockey	12

Boys	
Sport	**Number**
Basketball	9
Figure Skating	3
Football	6
Hockey	12

a) Draw a comparative bar graph to show the data.

b) Which sport is the most popular among boys?

c) Which sports are more popular among girls than boys?

9.3 Histograms, pages 292–297

14. The histogram shows the masses of 17 cats.

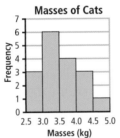

Masses of Cats

a) Estimate the greatest mass of these cats. Estimate the least mass of these cats.

b) Why is it not possible to accurately determine the masses in part a)?

c) What is the most common mass interval? How many cats are in this interval?

15. The final scores, out of 50, for a bicycle rodeo competition are shown.

37 24 41 34 32 29 27 33 39 40
43 26 44 19 36 35 31 27 33 46

a) Organize the data into intervals.

b) Explain how you chose the interval size.

c) Draw a histogram to show the data.

9.4 Use Databases to Solve Problems, pages 298–303

 Go to *www.mcgrawhill.ca/links/math8* and follow the links to access *E-STAT.*

Use E-STAT for question 16.

16. a) Find data about how healthy Canadian teens think they are.

b) Display the data for 13-year-old females or males as a pie chart. What does the graph tell you?

9.5 Use a Spreadsheet to Present Data and Solve Problems, pages 304–309

Weekly income, in dollars, for three friends is shown. Use the data for question 17 or 18.

	A	B	C	D
1	Week	Sadia	Kizzy	Pete
2	1	150	210	160
3	2	180	200	200
4	3	200	225	190
5	4	250	195	150

17. a) Whose weekly income appears to be increasing? Explain.

b) Which friend has the greatest mean weekly income?

18. Use a spreadsheet to answer the questions.

a) For each friend, calculate the mean weekly income.

b) For each friend, calculate the total income for the month.

c) Display the data. Explain why you chose the type of graph you did.

19. a) Use examples to explain the differences between how databases and spreadsheets are organized.

b) Describe a situation in which you would use a database.

c) Describe a situation in which you would use a spreadsheet.

Multiple Choice

For questions 1 to 5, select the best answer.

A sample of 20 boys and 20 girls were surveyed to see which candidate they plan to choose for student council president. The results are shown. Use the information for questions 1 to 3.

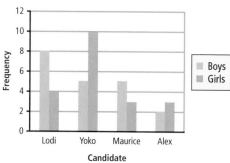

Candidates for Student Council President

1. Which candidate has twice as many votes from girls as from boys?

   A Lodi   **B** Yoko
   C Maurice   **D** Alex

2. Which candidate has the least votes, overall?

   A Lodi   **B** Yoko
   C Maurice   **D** Alex

3. Suppose the student population is 400, with an equal number of boys and girls. How many votes do you expect the winner to get in total, based on this sample?

   A 50   **B** 100
   C 150   **D** 200

4. Which of the following statements is false?

   A A good sample will have similar characteristics to the population from which it is taken.
   B In a census, the entire population is surveyed.
   C A sample is always larger than the population from which it is taken.
   D The Internet can be used to access several databases.

5. Which of the following statements is false?

   A A spreadsheet can be used to produce several types of graphs.
   B You can perform calculations with a spreadsheet.
   C You can use a database to store and retrieve data.
   D All databases require the use of spreadsheets.

Short Answer

6. Both graphs show the results of a survey on favourite chicken restaurants.

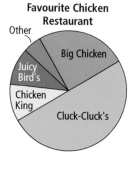

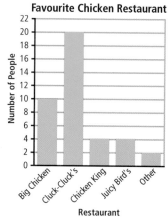

Describe one advantage each graph has in displaying the data.

7. a) Describe a problem you could solve using a database.

b) Describe a problem you could solve using a spreadsheet.

Extended Response

8. The final marks, as percents, for a grade 8 English class are shown.

75 71 68 82 89 60 55 73 81

66 58 71 83 68 88 90 57 74

73 67 68 75 95 86 48 92

a) Draw a histogram to display the data.

b) Explain how you chose the intervals.

9. Hair colour for students in a class is shown.

Boys	
Hair Colour	Number
Black	2
Blond	2
Brown	5
Red	1

Girls	
Hair Colour	Number
Black	4
Blond	9
Brown	5
Red	2

a) Draw a comparative bar graph to display the data.

b) Which hair colour is the most common for boys?

c) Which hair colour are as common for girls as for boys?

Chapter Problem Wrap-Up

In question 10 on page 285, question 10 on page 291, question 10 on page 303, and question 10 on page 309, you collected, organized, and displayed data about how your classmates feel about discussing problems with different people in their lives.

Ask your own question about something that interests you.

1. What are two different ways that you could collect information about this question? Explain the advantages and disadvantages of each.

2. Use one of your ways from question 1 to collect information about your question.

3. Display the information in at least two different ways.

4. Discuss your findings. Explain how each display helps you analyse the information.

Data Management and Probability

- Read, discuss, and interpret displays of data and present the information using mathematical terms.

- Determine trends and patterns by making inferences from graphs.

- Understand and apply the concept of the best measure of central tendency.

- Determine the effect on a measure of central tendency of adding or removing a value.

- Assess bias in data-collection methods.

- Make and evaluate arguments that are based on data analysis.

- Discuss trends in graphs to clarify understanding and draw conclusions about the data.

- Explain the choice of intervals or symbols used in graphs.

Key Words

mean

median

mode

measures of central tendency

sample

population

random sample

majority

CHAPTER 10

Data Management: Analysis and Interpretation

Soon you will be entering high school and a whole new world of choices. Which courses will you take? Where will you go after you graduate: college, university, an apprenticeship, or the workplace? How can your knowledge of data management help you make important decisions like this?

By the end of this chapter, you will be able to analyse and interpret data on a career of your choice.

Chapter Problem

Rachel is interested in becoming a radio broadcaster. She makes a list of questions to research.

> What courses should I take in high school?
>
> Is the program I'm interested in offered at college, university, or both?
>
> How much can I expect to earn when I graduate?

What other questions might Rachel research?

How might she use the data she collects to decide if this career is right for her?

Get Ready

Stem-and-Leaf Plots

A group of grade 8 students are asked how many minutes per night they usually spend doing homework. The results are shown in a **stem-and-leaf plot**.

Stem (tens)	Leaf (ones)
①	⑤
2	0 5 5 5
3	0 0 5
4	0 5

The stems represent the tens digit. The leaves represent the ones digit. So, this entry represents 15 min.

1. Use the stem-and-leaf plot to answer each question.

   a) What is the greatest amount of time spent on homework?

   b) What is the most common amount of time spent on homework?

   c) Describe three other things the data tell you.

2. The number of baskets of pears picked by a group of workers is shown.

28	24	32	41	18	29
33	26	19	31		

Create a stem-and-leaf plot to organize the data.

Measures of Central Tendency

Find the **mean**, **median**, and **mode** for the time, in minutes, Dillion spent doing homework.

25 30 30 20 15 30

$$\text{Mean} = \frac{\text{sum of values}}{\text{number of values}}$$
$$= (25 + 30 + 30 + 20 + 15 + 30) \div 6$$
$$= 150 \div 6$$
$$= 25$$

The mean study time is 25 min.

To find the median, arrange the values in order from least to greatest.

1̸5 2̸0 25 30 3̸0 3̸0

The median study time is 27.5 min, halfway between 25 min and 30 min.

The mode is the most common value, or 30 min. It appears three times.

3. Find the mean, median, and mode for each set of data.

   a) 11 16 17 16 18

   b) 55 60 85 65 60

4. Find the mean, median, and mode for each set of data.

   a) 22 27 22 27 28 27

   b) 75 74 81 92 77 75

Samples and Populations

How will Canadians vote in the next federal election? You could find out by asking every eligible voter in Canada. You can also collect information by asking a group of 100 Canadian voters. This is a **sample** of the voting **population**.

5. Match each sample with the population it is taken from.

Sample

a) a group of teens try a new video game

b) a group of people taste-test a new flavour of cheesecake

c) a group of teens at a school are asked if their school is safe

Population

A all teens in the school

B all teens who play video games

C all people who eat cheesecake

6. What population does each sample represent?

a) a group of driver education students evaluate a driving course

b) some teens are asked to try out a new skateboard

c) a group of students are asked what their favourite cafeteria meal is

d) a group of people are asked if they like a rock band's new lead singer

Pictographs

A group of students are asked about their favourite kind of pizza. The results are shown in a **pictograph**.

Favorite Pizza

Cheese	🍕🍕🍕🍕🍕🍕
Pepperoni	🍕🍕🍕🍕
Veggie	🍕🍕◺
Other	🍕

🍕 represents 2 students

7. Use the Favourite Pizza pictograph to answer these questions.

a) Which pizza is the most popular?

b) How many students chose veggie?

c) Explain how you used the pictograph to answer parts a) and b).

8. Marta's book collection is organized by category.

a) Draw a pictograph to display the data.

b) Explain why you chose the symbol you did.

Category	Number of Books
Science fiction	16
Teen romance	8
History	4
Biography	3
Other	1

Analyse Data and Make Inferences

Focus on...
- analysing data and trends in data
- making inferences based on data analysis

Preparing for high school can involve planning for your future. What kinds of careers interest you? What type of education will you need?

Discover the Math

How can you analyse data to solve problems and make predictions?

The line graphs show the educational trends of working Canadians.

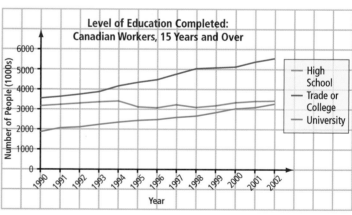

1. Describe one trend that you see in the graph.

2. Do you expect this trend to continue? Explain why or why not.

3. Look at the trends for university and high school. Predict what will happen in the mid-2000s.

4. **Reflect** How can you use trends in data to help you plan for your future?

Example 1: Analyse a Trend

Analyse the line graph for Canadian workers that have completed trade school or college.

a) How many Canadian workers had completed trade school or college in 2001?

b) When did the number of Canadian workers that had completed trade school or college reach 5 million?

c) Predict how many Canadian workers will have completed trade school or college in 2005.

Solution

a) Locate the year 2001 on the horizontal axis. Go straight up to the graph. Then, go straight left to read the number of people on the vertical axis.

$5400 \times 1000 = 5\ 400\ 000$

The vertical scale is measured in 1000s. Multiply by 1000 to find the correct value.

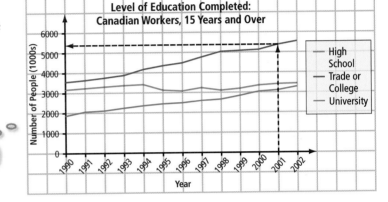

In 2001, about 5 400 000 or 5.4 million Canadian workers had completed trade school or college.

b) Locate 5 million on the vertical axis. Go straight right to the graph. Then, go straight down to read the year.

$5000 \times 1000 = 5\ 000\ 000$. I need to locate 5000 on the vertical axis.

The number of Canadian workers that had completed trade school or college reached 5 million around 1998.

c) Extend the graph to predict a trend. This trend suggests that about 6.2 million Canadian workers will have completed trade school or college in 2005.

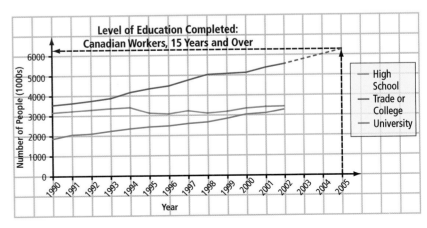

Example 2: Analyse a Set of Data

Rachel is thinking about becoming a radio broadcaster. She does some research and finds that she would have to go to college for three years. She also finds data that list starting salaries for radio broadcasters. Describe the data Rachel found. Estimate how much she might expect to earn.

Salaries ($)

Stem (thousands)	Leaf (hundreds)
30	5 8
31	2 5 5 8
32	0 3

Solution

Method 1: Analyse the Range of Data

Salaries ($)

Stem (thousands)	Leaf (hundreds)
(30)	(5) 8
31	2 5 5 8
(32)	0 (3)

The least salary is $30 500. The greatest is $32 300.

Rachel can expect to start earning anywhere between $30 500 and $32 300.

Method 2: Calculate the Measures of Central Tendency

To get a better estimate, find the mean, median, and mode.

$$\text{Mean} = \frac{\text{sum of values}}{\text{number of values}}$$

$= (30\ 500 + 30\ 800 + 31\ 200 + 31\ 500 + 31\ 500 + 31\ 800 + 32\ 000 + 32\ 300) \div 8$

$= 251\ 600 \div 8$

$= 31\ 450$

The mean starting salary is $31 450.

The median is the middle value.

Salaries ($)

Stem (thousands)	Leaf (hundreds)
30	5̶ 8
31	2̶ 5 5 8̶
32	0̶ 3̶

The two middle values are the same.

The median starting salary is $31 500.

The mode is $31 500. It appears twice.

The three measures of central tendency are very close to each other. Rachel could expect to earn approximately $31 500.

● You can analyse sets of data using various displays.
  – Line graphs can be used to analyse trends.

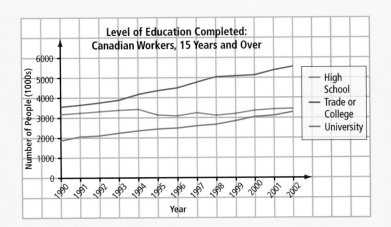

Level of Education Completed: Canadian Workers, 15 Years and Over

Number of People (1000s) vs Year

Legend: — High School, — Trade or College, — University

  – A stem-and-leaf plot can be used to analyse the range of data and to find the measures of central tendency.

Salaries ($)

Stem (thousands)	Leaf (hundreds)
30	5 8
31	2 5 5 8
32	0 3

● You can make inferences based on data analysis. For example, you analysed a trend to predict the number of Canadian workers that will have completed trade school or college in 2005. You also used data analysis to find an expected starting salary.

Communicate the Ideas

1. Describe each sales trend.

a)

b)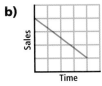

c)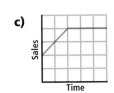

d)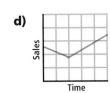

2. The stem-and-leaf plot shows the top 10 scores for a video game. Describe three things the data tell you.

Video Game Scores

Stem (thousands)	Leaf (hundreds)
4	2 6 8
5	0 2 2 3 5
6	2 7

Practise

For help with questions 3 to 6, refer to Example 1.

The trend in hard rock fans for a small town is shown.

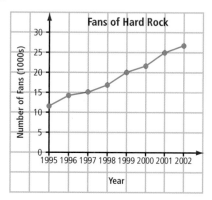

Use the line graph for questions 3 to 6.

3. Describe the trend.

4. a) Estimate the number of fans in 1996.
   b) Estimate the number of fans in 2000.

5. When did the number of fans reach 25 000?

6. Predict the number of listeners in 2005.

For help with questions 7 and 8, refer to Example 2.

The high temperatures for several Ontario cities are shown in the stem-and-leaf plot.

Temperatures (°C)

Stem (tens)	Leaf (ones)
1	9
2	0 1 3 6 7 7
3	0 1 2

Use the stem-and-leaf plot for questions 7 and 8.

7. a) What is the coldest temperature?
   b) What is the warmest temperature?

8. Find the mean, median, and mode temperatures.

Apply

9. Claudette is practising her figure-skating routine for a tournament. Her coach records the number of errors Claudette makes in each practice.

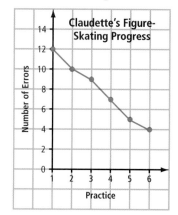

a) Describe the trend in Claudette's performance.
b) Claudette has four more practices before the tournament. Do you think she has a chance of an error-free performance at the tournament? Justify your answer.
c) What other factors might affect her performance?

10. Suppose you measured the outside temperature for 24 h.

a) Sketch a line graph to show what the trend in temperature might look like.
b) Describe and explain the features of your graph.

11. The line graph shows Julie's findings on the use of the Internet to obtain music.

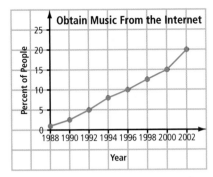

a) Describe the trend.
b) Some musical artists complain that illegal music sharing on the Internet has had a negative effect on CD sales. Do you think the artists' claim is justified? Explain.

Chapter Problem

12. Rachel finds data on unemployment rates.

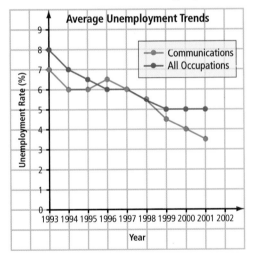

a) Describe each trend.
b) When did the unemployment rate for communications drop to 4%?
c) Do you think these trends will continue? Explain.

Try This! **13.** Two classes are given two different geometry tests on the same material. The scores, out of 50, are shown.

Test A Scores

Stem (tens)	Leaf (ones)
1	7 9 9
2	2 4 5 5 6 8 9
3	0 1 1 2 3 5 6 8
4	1 3

Test B Scores

Stem (tens)	Leaf (ones)
1	9
2	2 6 9
3	1 4 5 5 6 8 9
4	0 2 3 3 4 5 5 6 8

a) Describe each set of scores.
b) Compare the overall performance of the two classes. Justify your reasoning.

Extend

14. The graph shows average earnings for different education levels, by age.

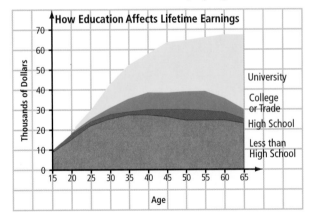

a) Describe each earnings trend.
b) Estimate the maximum average earnings for each level of education.
c) How could you use this graph to determine the total expected lifetime earnings of a university graduate? Estimate this amount.

Understand and Apply Measures of Central Tendency

Download Time (min)
10
12
2
10
15
11

Radek wants to download one more piece of software from the Internet before his dad uses the computer. How can you use data to estimate download times?

Discover the Math

mean
- $\dfrac{\text{sum of values}}{\text{number of values}}$

median
- middle value when a set of data is arranged in order

mode
- most common value in a set of data

measure of central tendency
- a value that a data set tends to be centred around
- the mean, median, or mode

How can you pick the best measure of central tendency when an unusual value occurs?

1. How long should Radek tell his dad the download will take? Justify your answer.

2. Draw a bar graph to show the data.

3. a) Find the mean , median , and mode . Use a horizontal line to show the mean and median on your bar graph.
   b) Which measure of central tendency best describes a typical download time for Radek?

4. a) One of the download times is quite different from the others. Suppose you remove it. Predict how this will change each of the measures of central tendency.
   b) Test your prediction. Recalculate the measures of central tendency for the remaining five download times.

5. **Reflect** Describe the effect an unusual value has on each measure of central tendency in a set of data.

Example: Measures of Central Tendency With an Unusual Value

Eliana is training for a 100-m race. Her coach records her practice times.

a) Find the mean, median, and mode.

b) Which measure of central tendency best describes Eliana's performance? Explain.

c) What happens to her mean time when Trial 3 is not included?

Trial	Time (s)
1	10.8
2	10.6
3	15.4
4	10.5
5	10.7
6	10.4

Solution

a) Mean = $\dfrac{\text{sum of all values}}{\text{number of values}}$

$= (10.8 + 10.6 + 15.4 + 10.5 + 10.7 + 10.4) \div 6$

$= 68.4 \div 6$

$= 11.4$

The mean time is 11.4 s.

To find the median, arrange the values in order from least to greatest.

~~10.4~~   ~~10.5~~   10.6   10.7   ~~10.8~~   ~~15.4~~

The median time is 10.65 s, halfway between 10.6 s and 10.7 s.

There is no mode for this set of data.

> The mode is the most common value. In this case, every value occurs only once.

b)

> Eliana's mean time is 11.4 s. She ran faster in five of the trials. I would not choose this value.

> Her median time is 10.65 s. She ran faster than this in half of the trials. She ran slower than this in half of the trials. I would choose this value.

> There is no mode. So, I would not choose this value.

c) Calculate the mean without Trial 3.

Mean = $\dfrac{\text{sum of all values}}{\text{number of values}}$

$= (10.8 + 10.6 + 10.5 + 10.7 + 10.4) \div 5$

$= 53 \div 5$

$= 10.6$

> This is a much better choice for describing her typical performance than the original mean of 11.4 s.

The mean time, without Trial 3, is 10.6 s. This is close to Eliana's median time for all trials.

- When a small set of data has a very high or very low value:
  - The mean is not a good measure of central tendency.
  - The median is usually a good choice for describing the data.
  - The mode may not exist, or may not be reliable.

  For example, the table shows Eliana's practice times for running 100 m.

Trial	Time (s)
1	10.8
2	10.6
3	15.4
4	10.5
5	10.7
6	10.4

The mean time is 11.4 s. The median time is 10.65 s. There is no mode.

- Removing an unusual value from a small set of data can cause the mean to change significantly. For example, Eliana's mean time goes from 11.4 s to 10.6 s when Trial 3 is not included.

Communicate the Ideas

Anna's golf scores are 82, 85, 83, 106, and 80.

Use this set of data for questions 1 and 2.

1.

The median is the best measure of central tendency for Anna's golf scores.

If you don't include her worst score of 106, then the mean is the best measure of central tendency.

Both Matt and Maria are correct. Explain why.

2. Why is the mode not a good choice to describe Anna's typical golf score?

Check Your Understanding

Practise

For help with questions 3 and 4, refer to the Example.

3. Biko wrote five math tests. His scores, in percent, are shown.

81   83   56   79   80

a) Find the mean, median, and mode.

b) Which measure of central tendency best describes Biko's typical performance?

4. Sierra bowled six games. Her scores are shown.

123 130 128 132 126 123

a) Which two measures of central tendency best describe a typical bowling score for Sierra?

b) Explain why the other measure of central tendency is not a good choice.

Apply

5. Joel hopes to improve his next test score. His previous test scores, in percent, are 64, 60, 64, and 72.

a) Find the mean and the median.

b) Joel thinks that he will score 90% on the next test. Find the mean and median of Joel's scores with a fifth score of 90% included.

c) Explain why the 90% score does not have the same impact on both the mean and the median.

6. A shoe store owner keeps track of shoe sales, by size, for a popular women's brand.

Shoe Size	Number of Pairs Sold
6	2
7	8
8	6
9	1
10	1

a) Which measure of central tendency is most important to the store owner? Explain.

b) Explain why the other measures of central tendency are not important.

7. In what kind of situation is the median often a better measure of central tendency than the mean? Use examples to support your explanation.

Chapter Problem

8. Suppose you are applying to a university or college program. To be accepted, you must have at least a 70% mean for your best six grade 12 marks. Here are your grade 12 marks.

72 80 66 63 74 60 68 70

Will you get accepted into the program? Explain why or why not.

9. Mr. Shanechi gave his math class a quiz worth 20 points. The marks for the class are shown.

15 16 14 14 15 16
17 15 14 13 15 14
15   6 14 15 16 17

a) Find the mean, median, and mode.

b) One of the marks is unusual. Recalculate the mean without this mark.

c) How much has the mean changed in this case? Explain why.

Extend

10. Three students are applying to a university to study science. Their grade 12 marks are shown.

Course	Alysia	Laurie	Ahmed
Biology	88	84	61
Chemistry	86	82	82
Physics	80	62	88
Calculus	82	80	90
Geometry	81	60	87
English	85	90	65
Computers	90		
Data management	87		
Geography		85	
History		90	

a) Calculate the mean for each student.

b) A student must have at least an 80% mean to be accepted. Based on your calculations, who will be accepted?

c) The university has a policy of using the mean of a student's *best six* final marks for determining acceptance. This is called the student's "graduation average." Find each student's graduation average.

d) Based on graduation average, who will be accepted?

e) Who will benefit the most from the university's acceptance policy? Explain.

Bias in Samples

You and your friends believe that most students use the school's computer lab for school work. How could you use survey data to back up your argument?

Discover the Math

How can you make sure that a sample is not biased?

Example 1: Sample Size

Ms. Santino gave her class a quiz worth 20 points. After marking the first three quizzes, she is concerned that the class did not understand the lesson.

a) Find the mean, median, and mode for Ms. Santino's **sample**.

b) Here are all the scores.

11	12	11	18	17	15
15	12	14	19	16	16
13	18	15	16		

Find the mean, median, and mode for the entire class **population**.

c) What is wrong with Ms. Santino's sample?

sample
• a small group that represents a population

population
• the entire group of people you want to learn about

Well, it looks like I may have to go over this lesson again. The marks aren't very good.

Solution

a) Sample

$$\text{Mean} = \frac{\text{sum of all values}}{\text{number of values}}$$
$$= (11 + 12 + 11) \div 3$$
$$= 34 \div 3$$
$$= 11.\overline{3}$$

The mean is about 11.

To find the median, order the values from least to greatest.

~~11~~   11   ~~12~~

The median is 11.

The mode is 11.

The mean, median, and mode for the sample are all around 11.

b) Population

$$\text{Mean} = \frac{\text{sum of values}}{\text{number of values}}$$
$$= (11 + 12 + 11 + 18 + 17 + 15 + 15 + 12 + 14 + 19 + 16 + 16 + 13 + 18 + 15 + 16) \div 16$$
$$= 238 \div 16$$
$$= 14.875$$

The mean is about 15.

To find the median, order the values from least to greatest.

~~11~~ ~~11~~ ~~12~~ ~~12~~ ~~13~~ ~~14~~ ~~15~~ 15
15 ~~16~~ ~~16~~ ~~16~~ ~~17~~ ~~18~~ ~~18~~ ~~19~~

The median is 15.

> The two middle values are the same.

There are two modes, 15 and 16. Both values appear three times.

The mean, median, and mode for the population are all around 15.

c) The results for Ms. Santino's sample are much lower than the results for the entire class.

Measure of Central Tendency	Sample	Population
Mean	$11.\overline{3}$	14.875
Median	11	15
Mode	11	15 and 16

> I guess my sample size was too small. The class average was almost 75 %.

Example 2: Random Sample

Trina is investigating how the grade 8 student population at her school uses computers. She surveys some of her friends and graphs her results. Trina concludes that students use computers mainly for schoolwork. What is wrong with Trina's sample? Describe a better sampling method.

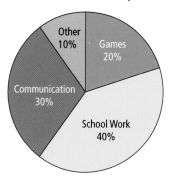

How Students Use Their Computer Time

Other 10%
Games 20%
Communication 30%
School Work 40%

random sample

- a sample in which everyone in a population has an equal chance of being selected

Solution

Trina's sample is biased. She only surveyed friends. Other students may have different computer habits. To avoid this bias, Trina should use a **random sample** .

Example 3: Sample Characteristics

The student population at Slava's school were asked for suggestions on how the activity budget might be spent. Slava would like the money to be spent on baseball equipment. He decides to randomly survey students at a baseball game to get their opinions.

What is wrong with Slava's sample?

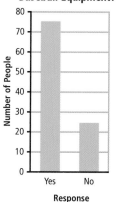

Should Our School Buy New Baseball Equipment?

Solution

Slava's sample is biased. He surveyed a random sample of students at a baseball game. This sample does not represent the entire school population. Not all students attend baseball games.

- An unbiased sample
  - is randomly drawn
  - reflects the characteristics of the population from which it is drawn
- A sample may be biased if it is too small.

Communicate the Ideas

1. Ron received this e-mail from his friend. Write his response.

FROM: Harry
TO: Ron
SUBJECT: Joan's samples

I missed the lesson on bias in samples. Would you please explain why the sample that Joan chose is a good one?

"Joan is interested in how grade 8 students get to school. She decides to randomly survey a group of grade 8 students."
Thanks,
Harry

2. Use the cartoon to explain how sample size can cause biased results.

Check Your Understanding

Practise

For help with questions 3 to 5, refer to Example 1.

3. A hockey coach asks two players whether the team should spend more time practising the power play. Do you think this sample will reflect the overall opinion of the team? Explain why or why not.

4. The school secretary asks three teachers whether they would prefer cookies or ice cream as the school picnic dessert. Do you think this sample will reflect the overall opinion of the school staff? Explain why or why not.

5. A school study was conducted to determine typical earnings for grade 8 students who did part-time work last summer. Weekly earnings for the four students that were surveyed are shown.

$25 $30 $20 $90

Do you think this sample contains bias? Explain why or why not.

For help with questions 6 to 8, refer to Example 2.

6. A hockey coach surveys the entire team to find out if there is too much violence in the game. Is this a random sample? Explain.

7. The names of all students at a school are put into a large drum. Names are picked without looking. Is this a random sample? Explain.

8. Leo is interested in how the students at his school use their computer lab time. He surveys every third student working in a computer lab. Is this a random sample? Explain.

For help with questions 9 to 11, refer to Example 3.

Use the survey question for questions 9 to 11.

> Do you think students should be required to take Physical Education in school?

9. A group of school athletes are randomly surveyed. Is this sample biased? Explain.

10. A group of school coaches are randomly surveyed. Is this sample biased? Explain.

11. A group of students from the school population are randomly surveyed. Is this sample biased? Explain.

Apply

12. A group of fans at a Toronto Blue Jays game are asked who they think will win the World Series. The results are in the next day's newspaper as a prediction. Why is this survey biased? Suggest how the bias could be removed.

13. Kelly thinks that the music selection in his school cafeteria's jukebox is boring. He asks six of his friends, who all agree. He presents his findings to the student council.

   a) Is this a random sample? Explain why or why not.
   b) Identify the bias in Kelly's sample.
   c) Describe how Kelly could conduct an unbiased survey.

Chapter Problem

14.

Rachel is now a college student studying radio broadcasting. Part of the college program requires her to work for a term at a radio station. She gets a placement at a local hard rock station. The station manager asks Rachel to perform an on-air survey to find the most popular song of all time. Rachel invites listeners to call in with their all-time favourite. Do you think Rachel's sample contains bias? Explain why or why not.

15. How many siblings does a typical grade 8 student have?

a) Randomly pick two classmates and ask them. Find the mean. Do you think this sample represents the entire class? Why or why not?

b) Randomly pick two more classmates and find the mean for all four students. Do you think this is closer to or farther from the mean for the whole class? Explain.

c) Find data for the whole class. Explain what you notice.

d) Why does the size of a sample affect how well it describes the population?

16. In karate, a kata is a sequence of self-defence movements against imaginary opponents. In tournaments, kata performances are given a score out of 10. Miya received the following scores from 10 judges for her kata.

Judge	1	2	3	4	5	6	7	8	9	10
Score	6.5	6	8.5	7	6.5	6.5	6	6.5	4.5	7

a) Calculate Miya's mean score based on all 10 judges.

b) Use the first three judges' scores as a sample. Find the mean.

c) Use the last three judges' scores as a sample. Find the mean.

d) Compare your answers for parts b) and c) to the mean from part a).

e) In karate tournaments, the highest and lowest scores are often not included when calculating the mean. Why do you think this is done?

17. In Example 1, Ms. Santino gave her class a quiz worth 20 points. She marked three quizzes. The marks were 11, 12, and 11. She thought her class did not understand the lesson.

Measure of Central Tendency	Sample	Population
Mean	$11.\overline{3}$	14.875
Median	11	15
Mode	11	15 and 16

a) Suppose Ms. Santino marked the quizzes in reverse order. The last three quiz marks are 18, 15, and 16. Would this sample provide accurate measures of central tendency for overall class performance? Explain why or why not.

b) Would a combined sample of the first three scores and the last three scores provide a good sample? Why or why not?

Extend

18. Test scores, in percent, are recorded.

55	62	88	72	78	94	42	71	68
66	70	85	48	57	72	83	74	60
91	38	68	70	71	64	87	73	72

a) Find the mean, median, and mode for this population.

b) Write each score on a slip of paper. Put the slips into a hat or paper bag. Shuffle the slips. Randomly draw three scores. Calculate the mean, median, and mode of the sample. Record your results.

c) Replace the slips of paper. Repeat part b) four times.

d) Repeat parts b) and c) using a sample size of 5.

e) Repeat parts b) and c) using a sample size of 10.

f) Note any patterns you see. Write a brief report on your findings.

Make and Evaluate Arguments Based on Data

Focus on...
- evaluating arguments based on data
- making arguments based on data

Rachel has just graduated from college with a diploma in radio broadcasting. At Rachel's first job interview, the station manager claims that the typical starting salary of the station's employees is around $40 000. Should Rachel expect to earn this much if she gets the job?

Discover the Math

How can you make and evaluate arguments based on data?

Rachel uses the employee directory to make a table of the job positions and number of employees in each.

Then, Rachel searches the Internet to find typical salaries for each job.

Radio Station		
Job	Number of Employees	Typical Starting Salary
Secretary	2	$24 000
Salesperson	3	$28 000
Radio broadcaster	6	$31 000
Station manager	1	around $80 000
President	1	around $120 000

1. Based on the data she found, how much do you think Rachel should expect to earn if she gets the job? Justify your answer.

2. Use measures of central tendency to find out how the station manager arrived at a "typical" starting salary of $40 000. Explain your thinking.

3. **Reflect** Explain why the manager's statement about the station's typical salary is misleading. How could the statement be changed so that it is not misleading?

Example 1: Evaluate an Argument Based on Data

The teachers at Midtown Junior High agree to organize a school trip. They ask Ishmail, the student council president, to conduct a random survey to find which of three options students prefer.

Ishmail claims that the **majority** of students prefer the Québec City trip. He presents the data to the teachers.

How has Ishmail distorted data to make a convincing argument?

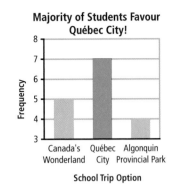

majority
- more than $\frac{1}{2}$
- more than 50%

Solution

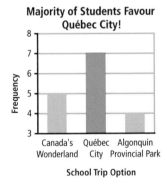

If I stack the two blue bars together, they are shorter than the red bar. This is because the vertical scale doesn't start at 0.

Why is the Quebec bar red? It should be blue, like the others.

The title contains bias! It should just say what the graph is about.

Compare Ishmail's graph to the undistorted graph.

Distorted Graph

Undistorted Graph

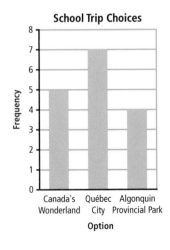

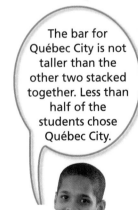

The bar for Québec City is not taller than the other two stacked together. Less than half of the students chose Québec City.

The undistorted graph shows that, while Québec City was the most popular choice, it did not get a majority of votes. 7 out of 16 is less than half.

Example 2: Make an Argument Based on Data

An auto-racing team must decide which of its two best drivers will enter a major race. Data for the recent performances of both drivers are shown.

	Finish Position				
Driver	Race 1	Race 2	Race 3	Race 4	Race 5
Funokoshi	5	3	3	2	2
McDowell	1	2	8	4	3

Make an argument based on data that supports each driver.

Solution

Argument to Support Funokoshi
Look at the performance trend for each driver.

Funokoshi's performance has continued to improve over the past five races. McDowell's trend has not been consistent.

Also consider the mean finish position of each driver. Add the finish positions and divide by 5.

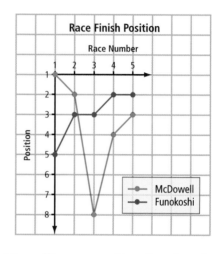

Funokoshi's mean = $(5 + 3 + 3 + 2 + 2) \div 5$
= $15 \div 5$
= 3

> Funokoshi usually finishes in around third place.

McDowell's mean = $(1 + 2 + 8 + 4 + 3) \div 5$
= $18 \div 5$
= 3.6

> McDowell usually finishes in third or fourth place.

Funokoshi's performance is improving. His mean finish position of 3 is better than McDowell's mean of 3.6. The team should go with Funokoshi in the big race.

Argument to Support McDowell
McDowell had a bad performance in Race 3. If this race is not included, McDowell's mean finish position changes.
McDowell's mean (without Race 3) = $(1 + 2 + 4 + 3) \div 4$
= $10 \div 4$
= 2.5

> McDowell usually finishes second or third.

If Race 3 is not included, McDowell's mean finish position is better than Funokoshi's. Also notice that McDowell has won a race. The team should go with McDowell in the big race.

Key Ideas

- It is important to evaluate claims that are based on data.

- Graphs may be distorted to support claims.

- Data can be used to build convincing arguments.

Communicate the Ideas

1. In Example 1, Ishmail drew a distorted bar graph that favoured Québec City for the school trip. His friend, Maya, draws this bar graph for the same data.

   a) What argument do you think Maya's graph supports?

   b) How does her choice of interval for the vertical scale help her argument?

   c) How does her choice of graph title distort the data?

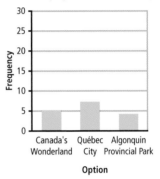

2. The recent sales performance of two salespeople is shown.

   a) Use the sales trends to argue that Benson is the better salesperson.

   b) Use the sales trends to argue that Cheng is the better salesperson.

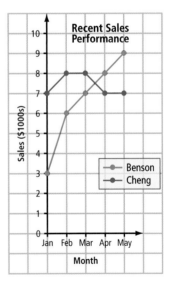

Practise

For help with questions 3 to 5, refer to Example 1.

3. The graph in this advertisement shows the results of a taste test.

Move over Bonzo, The Big Cheese is in town!

The Big Cheese: 56%   Bonzo Burger: 44%

a) Which burger maker do you think created this advertisement? Explain why.
b) What impression is achieved by using a distorted graph?

One day of sales at a small bookstore is shown. The store owner claims that the majority of books sold at his store are non-fiction books. Use the bar graph for questions 4 to 6.

Majority of Customers Prefer Non-fiction Books

4. How have the data been distorted to support the store owner's claim?

5. a) Draw an undistorted bar graph of the data.
  b) Did non-fiction books make up the majority of books sold? Explain.

6. Should the store owner make claims based on data from one day? Explain.

For help with questions 7 and 8, refer to Example 2.

7. Monthly sales figures for two salespeople are shown.

Cheng		Benson	
Month	**Sales ($1000s)**	**Month**	**Sales ($1000s)**
January	7	January	3
February	8	February	6
March	8	March	7
April	7	April	8
May	7	May	9

a) Use mean sales to argue that Cheng is the better salesperson.
b) Suppose that Benson just started in January. Use mean sales for February to May to argue that Benson is the better salesperson.

8. Andrea has written five geography tests. Each test was worth 40 points.

30   18   33   33   29

a) Calculate Andrea's mean score for the five tests.
b) Andrea claims that her mean score is over 75%. Make an argument to support her claim.

Apply

9. An investment broker shows a client this pictograph. Clients tend to invest in companies that are successful.

Annual Earnings

AAA Mutual

Tri-Gold Investors

Leading Edge Limited

represents $2 million

a) Explain the choice of symbol used for this graph.
b) Is this graph misleading? Explain.
c) Describe three things this graph tells you.

10. A random sample of Toronto residents are surveyed. Decide if each headline is appropriate or not, based on the results. Explain why.

More Money Should Be Spent on Public Transit

Percent of People (vertical axis, 0 to 80)
Agree: 70
Disagree: 30
Response (horizontal axis)

a) "70% of Ontario people unhappy with current spending on public transit"

b) "$\frac{3}{4}$ of Toronto residents dissatisfied with public transit funding"

c) "Survey shows majority of Toronto residents agree that more money should be spent on public transit"

d) "Over $\frac{2}{3}$ of Toronto residents feel that more money should be spent on public transit"

11. A random sample of 100 Canadians were surveyed about their favourite pastime.

Favourite Pastime	Frequency
Television	20
Playing sports	25
Internet/video games	20
Outdoor recreation	15
Reading	8
Other	12

a) Pose three questions that can be answered with this set of data.

b) Answer each question.

c) Write an argument about the pastimes of Canadians.

Chapter Problem

12. Rachel finds that the average hourly wage for broadcasters is $12.50. The average hourly wage for all occupations combined is $11.

a) Draw a distorted bar graph that Rachel could use to argue that she will be making more than twice the average hourly wage of all other occupations.

b) Draw a distorted graph that Rachel's parent or guardian could use to argue that Rachel will be making about the same.

Try This!

13. Three sales representatives are being interviewed for a promotion to sales manager. Part of each interview will focus on recent sales performance.

	Monthly Sales ($1000s)				
Candidate	January	February	March	April	May
Lenora	7	8	9	8	8
Joseph	8	3	10	9	9
Suni	4	6	7	8	11

Make an argument for each candidate to support why he or she should get the promotion.

Extend

14. Search newspapers, magazines, or the Internet for data about a controversial topic.

a) Pick a position on that topic. Use the data you found to write an argument to support your position. Use measures of central tendency, graphs, or other data management techniques.

b) Reverse your position. Use the same data, or find new data, to write an argument to support your new position.

c) Show your data to a parent, guardian, or older sibling. Can you convince the person that you are right in both cases?

Key Words

For questions 1 to 7, copy the statement and fill in the blanks. Use some of these words:

mean	median	mode
sample	majority	population
random sample		

measures of central tendency

1. Ty surveys a sample of the grade 8 ▖▖▖▖▖.

2. 19 is the ▖▖▖▖▖ of 14, 20, 25, 14, 22.

3. Marlene picks names from a hat to choose who to survey. This is a ▖▖▖▖▖.

4. 20 is the ▖▖▖▖▖ of 14, 20, 25, 14, 22.

5. More than half of the grade 8 students like video games. This is a ▖▖▖▖▖.

6. 14 is the ▖▖▖▖▖ of 14, 20, 25, 14, 22.

7. Mean, median, and mode are all ▖▖▖▖▖.

10.1 Analyse Data and Make Inferences, pages 318–323

8. Science project scores, in percent, for a class are shown. Describe three things the set of data tells you.

Stem (tens)	Leaf (ones)
4	7
5	5 9
6	4 4 6 8
7	1 1 1 3 5 5 9
8	2 4 5 8
9	1 3

A book club tracks its sales to determine trends in popularity.

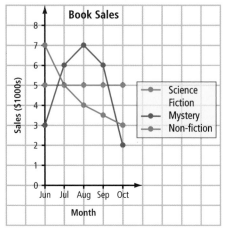

Use the line graph for questions 9 and 10.

9. Describe the sales trend for each category of book.

10. **a)** In which month were science fiction sales greater than the other two categories?
    b) Predict the sales for each category in November.

10.2 Understand and Apply Measures of Central Tendency, pages 324–327

11. Ashley is in charge of ordering jeans at a clothing store. Sales data from last week for their most popular brand are shown. Which measure of central tendency is the most important to Ashley? Explain why.

Size	Pairs Sold
26	1
28	2
30	9
32	7
34	3
36	1

12. Goals scored for two hockey players over the past five seasons are shown.

Susana	
Season	**Goals Scored**
1	32
2	30
3	56
4	33
5	31

Layla	
Season	**Goals Scored**
1	35
2	38
3	36
4	14
5	40

a) Calculate the mean number of goals for each player. Based on this measure, who is the better scorer?

b) Each player has had one unusual season. Recalculate the mean for each player without the unusual number of goals. By how much has the mean changed?

10.3 Bias in Samples, pages 328–333

13. At a National Basketball Association (NBA) game, a group of fans were randomly surveyed about whether or not there should be another sports specialty channel on cable TV. Do you think the results of this survey are biased? Explain why or why not.

14. A grade 6 to 8 school principal is wondering whether or not to cancel a school dance due to lack of interest. She randomly asks four students if they plan to go to the dance. Do you think this sample will reflect the overall opinion of all students? Explain why or why not.

10.4 Make and Evaluate Arguments Based on Data, pages 334–339

15. A record company is deciding which of their two top artists to promote as the main artist for a major concert. CD sales data for each artist's last four releases are shown.

Artist	CD Sales ($millions)			
	Release 1	**Release 2**	**Release 3**	**Release 4**
Chukaboomerang	8.5	9	8	7
Serentrippity	3.5	4.5	6	7

a) Make an argument based on the data that supports choosing Chukaboomerang.

b) Make an argument based on the data that supports choosing Serentrippity.

16. In a survey conducted over the Internet, teens were asked how many hours per day they typically spend online. A newspaper article about the survey results has the headline "Today's youth no longer active: $\frac{2}{3}$ of all teens spend over 2 h a day surfing the Internet!"

Hours Online	Frequency
0 to 1	4
1 to 2	6
2 to 3	11
3 to 4	8
more than 4	1

a) Show how the reporter arrived at "$\frac{2}{3}$ of all teens."

b) List three reasons why the headline is biased.

Multiple Choice

For questions 1 to 3, choose the best answer. The line graphs show the population trends for three towns.

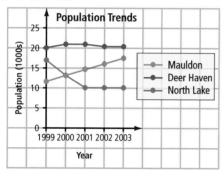

Use the data set for questions 1 to 3.

1. Which phrase best describes the population trend of North Lake?

A did not change

B increased steadily

C decreased steadily

D decreased and then levelled off

2. Three of the following statements are true. Identify the *false* statement.

A Deer Haven has the greatest population for the time period shown.

B The population of North Lake was 10 000 by 2003.

C The population of Mauldon is steadily decreasing.

D The population of Mauldon was the same as the population of North Lake in 2000.

3. Predict the population of Mauldon in 2005 based on the trends shown.

A about the same as Deer Haven

B about the same as North Lake

C about 10 000

D about 15 000

Short Answer

4. Identify the bias in each sample. Suggest how the bias could be removed.

a) A number of dog owners at the park are randomly surveyed about new park rules for pets.

b) A school is considering changing the colours of their school uniforms. The student council president asks three of her friends for their opinions.

5. A group of fans were randomly selected at a National Hockey League (NHL) game. They were asked who they thought would win the Stanley Cup: the Canadiens, the Maple Leafs, or the Senators. The results are shown.

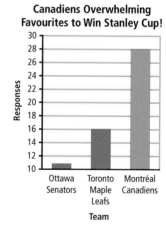

a) List three ways that the results have been distorted.

b) Suggest how you could change the graph to show undistorted results.

Extended Response

6. Starting salaries for engineers are shown in the stem-and-leaf plot.

Salaries ($)

Stem (thousands)	Leaf (hundreds)
38	8
39	0 6 7
40	0 0 4 6
41	0
42	
43	
44	
45	6

a) Find the mean, median, and mode.

b) One of these salaries is unusual. Describe what happens to the three measures of central tendency if this salary is not included.

7. An academic award is given to the student who shows the most promise for future studies. Recent averages, in percent, are shown for the two finalists.

Student	Average (%)		
	Term 1	Term 2	Term 3
Anthony	89	90	87
Hermia	85	88	92

Make a convincing argument for each student to support why he or she should win the award.

Use measures of central tendency, graphs, or other data management tools as part of your argument.

Chapter Problem Wrap-Up

Which career is more appealing?

Actor

At Work: perform in theatre, film, TV, or radio
Education: university degree or college diploma
Work Prospect:

Randomly Selected Sample Salaries from 2004 ($1000)
30
32
29
34
257
35

Bus Driver

At Work: transport people along scheduled routes
Education: high school diploma, special driver's licence
Work Prospect:

Randomly Selected Sample Salaries from 2004 ($1000)
35
41
35
55
38
39

1. Analyse the data for each career.

2. Choose one of the careers. Write a convincing report about why the career you choose is better than the other one.

3. What other factors might influence your decision about which career is better?

Making Connections

What does math have to do with crash tests?

Safety is an important factor when choosing a car to buy. Crash data collected by the Insurance Institute for Highway Safety show the overall improvement in crash ratings. About half of the vehicles tested in 1995 earned "marginal" or "poor" ratings. By 2002, most vehicles earned "good" ratings.

This type of graph is called a stacked bar graph. It is similar to a comparative bar graph. Instead of the bars being displayed side by side, the same bars are stacked on top of each other.

Why do you think a stacked bar graph was used to display the data?

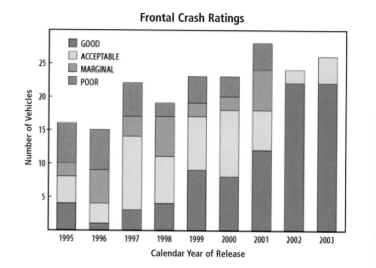

Frontal Crash Ratings

Making Connections

What does data analysis have to do with driving?

A Statistics Canada research paper called *Driving Characteristics of the Young and Aging Population* contains an analysis of the Canada Vehicle Survey data for the year 2000.

The report states that the youngest age group drives the greatest number of kilometres during the weekends (Fridays, Saturdays, and Sundays, 48%).

Do you think the graph is misleading? Explain.

How does the scale on the vertical axis emphasize the differences in daily driving distances?

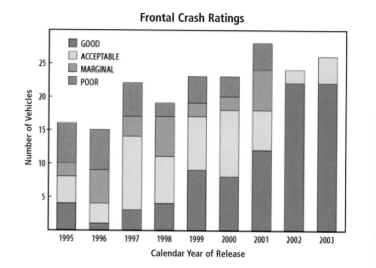

Chart 5: Percentage of Kilometres Driven by Age Group and Day of Week, 2000

 Go to **www.mcgrawhill.ca/links/math8** and follow the links to find out more about the driving habits of Canadians.

What Interests You?

Pick a topic that interests you.

Use the Internet, books, magazines, and other sources to find data on your topic. You can survey people, too. Form an argument that can be supported by your data.

Henri Richard was the best hockey player of all time, and I have the data to prove it!

What is the most popular sport among grade 8 students? I'll develop a survey to find out.

The book Anne of Green Gables has attracted more tourists to Prince Edward Island than anything else.

Who is our best bet for a gold medal at the next Olympics?

1. Research your topic.

2. State a point of view that can be supported by your data.

3. Create a presentation to support your point of view. Your presentation should include
   • tables and graphs
   • an analysis of trends
   • calculations of various measures of central tendency
   • a discussion of any possible bias and how you dealt with it

4. Present your findings to your class.

Number Sense and Numeration

- Add and subtract integers with and without the use of manipulatives.

- Discover and demonstrate an understanding of the rules for the multiplication and division of integers through patterning.

- Multiply and divide integers.

- Understand and apply the order of operations with brackets for integers.

Patterning and Algebra

- Describe and justify a rule in a pattern.

- Find and describe patterns using words.

Data Management and Probability

- Know that a pattern on a graph may indicate a trend.

Key Words

opposite integers

zero principle

CHAPTER 11

Integers

Ocean water gets colder as you go farther down. So, an animal that requires cold water lives in deeper water than one needing warmer water.

Eleanor is a marine biologist at an aquarium. She must know what water temperatures the various sea creatures she looks after need to survive.

By the end of this chapter, you will be able to calculate the temperature of ocean water at various depths, and determine what types of sea animals can survive at those temperatures.

Chapter Problem

Describe the pattern of temperature changes on this graph.

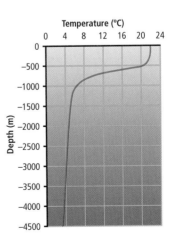

Get Ready

Order Integers

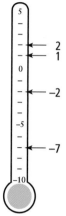

The table gives the high temperatures, in degrees Celsius, for one day in January, for four Ontario cities.

The temperatures can be recorded on a thermometer or on an integer number line.

City	High Temperature (°C)
Leamington	2
North Bay	–7
Brockville	–2
Hamilton	1

The temperature in North Bay is colder than the temperature in Brockville. So, –7 is less than –2. This can be written as –7 < –2.

1. Compare the integers in each pair using < or >.

a) –6, 8   **b)** 1, –3

2. Use < or > to compare the integers in each pair.

a) –10, –15   **b)** –16, –11

Points on a Coordinate Grid

This coordinate grid represents locations on a map. Rick's home (H), his school (S), the library (L), the community centre (C), and the grocery store (G) are marked.

The locations of the points can be shown using ordered pairs. The school is at (2, –2).

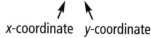

x-coordinate   y-coordinate

Each number indicates distance in blocks and direction.
For example, the school is 2 blocks east and 2 blocks south of home.

3. Write the ordered pair for each place. Identify the distance and direction of each from home.

a) the library   **b)** the community centre
c) the grocery store

4. a) Plot the following points in order.
(1, 0), (0, 1), (–1, 1), (–2, 0), (–2, –2), (–1, –3), (0, –3), (1, –2), (1, –1), (0, –1)

b) Join the points with a smooth curve. What letter is formed?

Mean

Rick's scores in a game of Scrabble® are recorded as follows:

12, 28, 7, 10, 12, 8, 5, 21, 33, 14, 8, 12, 4, 6

Calculate his mean score per turn.

$$\text{Mean} = \frac{\text{total score}}{\text{number of turns}}$$
$$= (12 + 28 + 7 + 10 + 12 + 8 + 5 + 21 + 33 + 14 + 8 + 12 + 4 + 6) \div 14$$
$$= 180 \div 14$$
$$\doteq 12.9$$

Rick's mean score per turn was approximately 12.9 points.

5. Find the mean for each set of data.

a) weekly pay: $230, $125, $200, $125, $187, $160

b) heights of students: 120 cm, 132 cm, 165 cm, 123 cm, 189 cm, 154 cm, 140 cm

6. Barb's mean score per question on a math contest was 9.5. There were 8 questions. What was her total score? Explain your steps.

Order of Operations

To evaluate expressions, follow the order of operations.

$2 + 3(12 - 9)$	**Brackets.**
$= 2 + 3(3)$	**Multiply.**
$= 2 + 9$	
$= 11$	

$4^2 - (8 + 3)$	**Exponent and brackets.**
$= 16 - 11$	
$= 5$	

B   Brackets
E   Exponents
D } Division and Multiplication,
M } from *left* to *right*
A } Addition and Subtraction,
S } from *left* to *right*

You may sometimes do two operations in the same step.

7. Evaluate.

a) $15 + 5(17 - 12)$
b) $24 \div (10 - 4)$
c) $(8 - 7)^2$

8. Evaluate.

a) $18 - 3 \times 5 + 2$
b) $8^2 - 7^2$
c) $25 - 2(3^2 + 1)$

11.1

Add Integers

Focus on...
- representing integer addition using manipulatives
- adding integers without manipulatives

Waterfalls are measured by the height of their initial drop. After most waterfalls, there is a sequence of rapids, which can add many metres to the total drop. Angel Falls in Venezuela initially drops 815 m and then another 82 m. Niagara Falls, Ontario, initially drops 47 m and then another 33 m. What is the total drop of each set of waterfalls?

Discover the Math

How can you add integers?

Example 1: Interpret Integer Chips

Literacy Connections

When a negative integer is written at the beginning of a sum, you can write it without brackets. When it follows a plus or a minus sign, you must use brackets to separate the negative sign from the operation sign.

Each red chip represents +1. Each blue chip represents –1. Interpret each set of integer chips. Then, write and solve the addition statement.

a)

b)

Solution

a)

When all the chips are the same colour, you can just count the number of chips.

There are 8 blue chips.
–3 + (–5) = –8

b)

There are 6 blue chips left.
$-8 + 2 = -6$

One red chip and one blue chip together represent zero. This is the **zero principle**. Cancel zero pairs. The remaining chips give the final answer.

zero principle
• the sum of **opposite integers** is zero
• $3 + (-3) = 0$ is an example

opposite integers
• two integers with the same numeral but different signs
• 5 and –5 are opposite integers

Example 2: Add Integers

Find each sum in two ways:
• using integer chips
• using a number line
a) $3 + 6$
b) $-2 + (-6)$
c) $5 + (-5)$
d) $7 + (-3)$

Literacy Connections

A positive integer can be written without the plus sign in front.

Solution

Method 1: Use Integer Chips

a)

$3 + 6 = 9$

b)

$-2 + (-6) = -8$

c)

$5 + (-5) = 0$

d)

$7 + (-3) = 4$

Method 2: Use a Number Line

a)

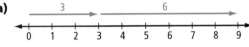

$3 + 6 = 9$

b)

$-2 + (-6) = -8$

c)

$5 + (-5) = 0$

d)

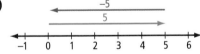

$7 + (-3) = 4$

Example 3: Find Sums Mentally

Many sports use a plus/minus rating system to rate their players. Each goal scored by the team while a player is on the field is recorded as 1 and each goal against is recorded as −1. Use mental math to determine each player's plus/minus rating on a field hockey team. Justify your answer.

Player	Goals For	Goals Against
Kelly	7	8
Husnia	5	3
Yan	5	10

Solution

Player	Goals For	Goals Against	Plus/Minus Rating	Justification
Kelly	7	8	$7 + (−8) = −1$	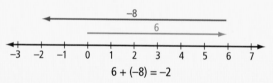
Husnia	5	3	$5 + (−3) = 2$	There are 2 more goals for than goals against, so the result is 2.
Yan	5	10	$5 + (−10) = −5$	There are 5 more goals against than goals for, so the result is −5.

Key Ideas

- You can use integer chips to show the sum of integers. This textbook uses red for positive and blue for negative.

- You can also use an integer number line to show the sum of integers.

  $$6 + (−8) = −2$$

- If two integers in a sum have the same sign, add the two numerals and keep the sign the same.

  $5 + 3 = 8$

  > I have 5 positives and then 3 more positives. That's 8 positives altogether.

  $−4 + (−1) = −5$

  > I have 4 negatives and then 1 more negative. That's 5 negatives altogether.

- If two integers in a sum have opposite signs, the result depends on the relative sizes of the integers.

  $−4 + 7 = 3$

  > There are 3 more positives than negatives. The result is 3.

  $6 + (−8) = −2$

  > There are 2 more negatives than positives. The result is −2.

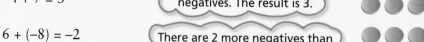

Communicate the Ideas

1. During the field hockey season, Andre was on the field when his team scored 15 goals. While he was on the field, the opposing team scored 17 goals. Explain how you would figure out Andre's plus/minus rating.

2. Explain how the zero principle was used to find this sum.
   −5 + 4 = −1

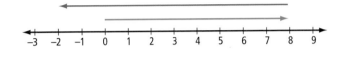

3. Explain how the number line models this sum.
   8 + (−10) = −2

4. What sum is modelled here? Explain how you know.

Check Your Understanding

Practise

For help with questions 5 and 6, refer to Example 1.

5. What integer sum is shown? Give each result.

   a)

   b)

6. Find the sum represented by the integer chips.

   a)

   b)

For help with questions 7 to 9, refer to Example 2.

7. Use integer chips or a number line to model each sum.

   a) 4 + (−9)   b) −3 + (−5)
   c) −4 + (−4)   d) 2 + (−3)

8. What integer sum is shown? Give each result.

   a)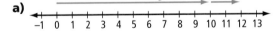

   b)

   c)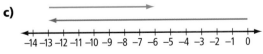

   d)

9. What integer sum is shown? What do you notice about the results? Explain why this happens.

a)

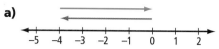

b)

For help with questions 10 to 12, refer to Example 3.

10. Decide whether each sum is positive, negative, or zero. Do not evaluate.

a) 6 + (−6)   **b)** 7 + 19
c) −4 + (−25)   **d)** −7 + 4
e) −10 + 15   **f)** 123 + (−789)

11. Use mental math to find each sum.

a) 4 + 10   **b)** 3 + (−9)
c) −3 + (−6)   **d)** −2 + (−7)
e) 7 + (−4)   **f)** −5 + (−3)

12. Find the plus/minus rating for the captains of the boys' and girls' hockey teams.

Player	Goals For	Goals Against
Surjeet	7	8
Elizabeth	8	6

13. Calculate each sum.

a) 11 + 4   **b)** −20 + 15
c) 25 + (−65)   **d)** −41 + (−52)
e) 73 + (−83)   **f)** −50 + 24

14. Calculate each sum.

a) 6 + 5 + 1
b) 6 + (−10) + 3
c) 10 + (−12) + (−8)
d) −13 + 7 + (−15)
e) −40 + (−60) + (−50)
f) 7 + (−14) + (−10) + 12

Apply

15. In golf, *par for the course* means the average number of strokes needed by an expert golfer to complete the round. People who score less than this get a score under par. For example, 2 under par is a score of −2. Jeannie's scores in four games of mini-putt golf were −4, −6, 2, and −3. Cameron's scores were −2, −3, −1, and −3. How did Jeannie's total score for the four games compare to Cameron's?

16. The table shows the performance of two stocks on the Stock Exchange over 5 days last week. ExMac started the week at $23, and MaxLine started at $25. Which company ended the week with a higher price?

Stock	Mon	Tues	Wed	Thurs	Fri
ExMac	+5	−1	+2	−3	+4
MaxLine	−2	+1	−5	0	+7

17. The kelvin temperature scale starts with absolute zero. This is the temperature at which there is no energy left. It cannot get any colder. To get the kelvin temperature from the Celsius temperature, add 273. Write each Celsius temperature in kelvin (symbol K).

a) 0°C
b) −40°C
c) −100°C
d) −273°C

> ### Did You Know?
>
> The kelvin temperature scale was designed by Lord Kelvin (William Thompson, 1824–1907), a British inventor and scientist. To learn more about Lord Kelvin, go to www.mcgrawhill.ca/links/math8 and follow the links.

Try This!

18. Bryce's bank statement for July shows his deposits and withdrawals. When he pulled the statement out of the envelope, he tore off part of it.

a) Calculate Bryce's balance after each transaction.

b) Write an integer expression to show Bryce's deposits for July.

c) Write an integer expression to show Bryce's withdrawals for July.

d) What is Bryce's balance at the end of the month?

e) In August, Bryce had a total of four transactions. His final balance was $62. What could the four transactions have been? Can you answer this question in more than one way?

Bryce Brown
125 Main St.
Bank Balance for July 2004
Opening Balance: $124

Date	Transaction	Amount	Balance
July 2	Withdrawal	$28	
July 5	Withdrawal	$48	
July 8	Deposit	$32	
July 21	Withdrawal	$89	
July 23	Withdrawal	$33	
July 24	Deposit	$20	
July 29	Deposit	$15	
July 31	Withdrawal	$49	

Did You Know?

A bank may allow you to have a negative balance in your account. A negative balance is called an overdraft. The bank may charge a fee for this service.

Extend

19. On October 1, Bryce's bank balance was $130. During October, he made two withdrawals and one deposit. At the end of the month, his bank balance was $95. List two withdrawals and one deposit that would give this final balance. Give three other answers.

20. The table shows the change in population, in thousands, between the 1996 and 2001 censuses.

Province or Territory	Change in Population (1000s)
Newfoundland & Labrador	−39
Prince Edward Island	0
Nova Scotia	−1
New Brunswick	−9
Québec	98
Ontario	656
Manitoba	6
Saskatchewan	−11
Alberta	278
British Columbia	183
Yukon	−2
Northwest Territories	−3
Nunavut	2

a) What was the total decrease in population for the provinces and territories whose populations decreased?

b) What was the total increase in population for the provinces and territories whose populations increased?

c) What was the total increase or decrease in population in Canada?

d) Illustrate the changes in population on a bar graph.

Subtract Integers

Focus on...
- representing integer subtraction using manipulatives
- subtracting integers without manipulatives

If the CN Tower in Toronto or the Skylon Tower in Niagara Falls were standing at the bottom of each of the Great Lakes, would it be submerged? If not, how much would be visible above the surface? What information do you need to know to answer this question?

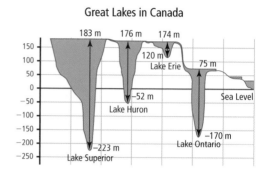

Great Lakes in Canada

Discover the Math

How can you subtract integers?

Example 1: Subtract Using Integer Chips

Model each expression using integer chips. Then, subtract.

a) $7 - 2$ **b)** $-5 - (-3)$ **c)** $2 - 7$

Solution

a)

$7 - 2 = 5$

To subtract 2, remove 2 red chips.

b)

$-5 - (-3) = -2$

To subtract −3, remove 3 blue chips.

c)

$2 - 7 = -5$

There are not enough red chips to take away 7 of them. Add 5 zero pairs.

To subtract 7, remove 7 red chips.

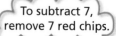

Example 2: Subtract by Adding the Opposite

a) $3 - (-2)$
b) $-4 - (-2)$
c) $-3 - 5$
d) $2 - 7$

Making Connections

You worked with subtracting integers in grade 7. Remember to use the zero principle:
$(+1) + (-1) = 0$

Solution

a)

> Start with 3 red chips for 3.

> Add 2 red chips and 2 blue chips using the zero principle.

> Take away 2 blue chips to subtract −2.

> The integer chips represent the sum 3 + 2. The answer is 5. You can subtract an integer by adding its opposite.

$3 - (-2)$
$= 3 + 2$
$= 5$

b)

> Start with 4 blue chips for −4.

> Add 2 blue chips and 2 red chips using the zero principle.

> Take away 2 blue chips to subtract −2.

> The integer chips represent the sum −4 + 2. The answer is −2. You can subtract an integer by adding its opposite.

$-4 - (-2)$
$= -4 + 2$
$= -2$

c) $-3 - 5$
$= -3 + (-5)$
$= -8$

> Add the opposite.

d) $2 - 7$
$= 2 + (-7)$
$= -5$

> Add the opposite.

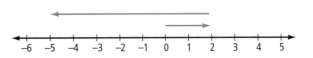

Example 3: Find Temperature Differences

The overnight low temperatures for four cities are given.

Find the temperature change from the first city to the second city in each pair.

a) Québec City to Gander   **b)** Québec City to Winnipeg
c) Leamington to Gander

Location	Low Temperature (°C)
Leamington, Ontario	5
Winnipeg, Manitoba	−14
Gander, Newfoundland & Labrador	−2
Québec City, Québec	−9

Solution

	Cities	Temperature Difference	Solution
a)	Québec City to Gander	$-2 - (-9)$ $= 7$	From −9 to −2 is 7 steps to the right.
b)	Québec City to Winnipeg	$-14 - (-9)$ $= -5$	This can be done on a vertical number line. The answer is −5. From −9, it is 5 steps down to −14. −9°C −14°C
c)	Leamington to Gander	$-2 - 5$ $= -7$	From 5 to −2 is 7 steps to the left.

Key Ideas

- Subtraction of integers can be modelled using integer chips or a number line.
  For example, $-4 - 1 = -5$.

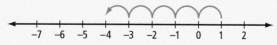

On a number line, the difference is the distance and direction from the second integer to the first.

- Subtraction of integers can be done by adding the opposite integer.
  For example, $-4 - 1$
  $$= -4 + (-1)$$
  $$= -5$$

Communicate the Ideas

1. Explain how you would subtract 2 − (−7) using integer chips. What do you do when there are not enough chips to subtract?

2. In an investment board game, Sarah earned $5 on her first turn, but then lost $7 on her next turn. Illustrate this situation on a number line.

3. Show 3 − 6 in at least three different ways.

Check Your Understanding

Practise

For help with questions 4 and 5, refer to Example 1.

4. Illustrate each subtraction using integer chips. Then, give the result.

   a) 5 − 9   **b)** −3 − 7
   c) −5 − (−1)   **d)** 4 − (−3)

5. Evaluate using integer chips.

   a) 10 − 3   **b)** 5 − (−4)
   c) −2 − 8   **d)** −6 − (−11)

6. State whether each difference is positive, negative, or zero. Do not evaluate.

   a) −6 − (−6)   **b)** 7 − 15
   c) 3 − (−25)   **d)** −7 − (−4)
   e) −10 − (−15)   **f)** 103 − 438

For help with questions 7 and 8, refer to Example 2.

7. Subtract by adding the opposite.

   a) 1 − 7   **b)** 3 − (−12)
   c) −2 − 10   **d)** −5 − 8
   e) 8 − (−4)   **f)** −10 − (−3)

8. Find each difference by adding the opposite.

   a) −3 − 6   **b)** −8 − (−6)
   c) 15 − (−17)   **d)** −45 − (−32)
   e) 44 − 71   **f)** −30 − 15

For help with questions 9 to 11, refer to Example 3.

9. Subtract using a number line.

   a) 5 − 7   **b)** −3 − (−4)
   c) 2 − (−6)   **d)** −8 − 1

10. Find each difference using a number line.

    a) 11 − 10   **b)** −5 − 3
    c) −7 − (−7)   **d)** 8 − (−3)

11. Use a number line to evaluate each expression. Which have the same result? Explain.

    a) 3 − 8   **b)** 3 + (−8)
    c) 3 − (−8)   **d)** −3 + 8
    e) 8 − 3   **f)** −3 − 8

Apply

12. Copy each equation. Replace each ▮ with the correct integer.

    a) 6 − ▮ = −10
    b) −4 − ▮ = −5
    c) 5 − ▮ = 7
    d) ▮ − 12 = −2
    e) ▮ − 3 = −10
    f) ▮ − (−7) = −4

13. Evaluate each expression.

a) 10 – 15 – 9
b) 5 – 17 – (–3)
c) –4 – (–2) – 7
d) –13 – 12 – (–15)
e) –40 – (–20) – (–10)
f) 9 – 6 – 8 – 12

14. Express each of the following using integer subtraction. Then, evaluate and interpret the results.

a) Wendy gained 10 points then lost 15 points.
b) While on a training routine, you lost 3 kg one month. Then, you lost another 4 kg.
c) Jose owed $10. His friend paid $5 of that debt for him.
d) The high temperature on Friday was 3°C. The low temperature was –6°C.

15. Mount Everest is the tallest mountain in the world, measured from sea level.

Mount Mauna Kea, in Hawaii, U.S.A., is the tallest mountain when measured from its base. It rises from 5854 m below sea level to 4349 m above sea level.

How tall is Mount Mauna Kea?

16. On the Space Shuttle, liquid oxygen is stored at –183°C. The oxygen is heated to a temperature of 260°C, and then it is mixed with hydrogen. Hydrogen is stored at a temperature of –250°C. The mixture that results burns at a temperature of 3315°C.

a) By how much is the liquid oxygen heated before it is mixed with hydrogen?
b) How much hotter is the temperature at which the mixture burns than the temperature at which the hydrogen is stored?

 Try This!

17. The diagram shows the elevations, compared to sea level, of the surface and deepest points of the four Great Lakes in Canada.

a) How deep is each lake?
b) How much farther below sea level is the bottom of Lake Superior than the bottom of Lake Erie?
c) The CN Tower in Toronto is 553 m tall. If it were standing on the bottom of Lake Ontario, would it be submerged or would it be visible above the surface? By how much?
d) The Skylon Tower in Niagara Falls is 160 m tall. How many Skylon Towers could be stacked in Lake Superior and still be submerged?

Great Lakes in Canada

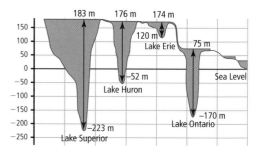

Extend

18. Is the following statement true or false? Explain.

When you subtract two numbers, the difference is always smaller than the first number.

19. You recently checked your bank statement. It said that you have overdrawn your account by $20. This is recorded as –$20. You thought it contained $20.

a) What is the difference in the amounts?
b) Describe the error that could have been made.

11.3

Multiply Integers

Focus on...
• multiplying integers using patterns

Chris, a marine biologist, and his partner, Leslie, are conducting their research on sea trout. They are using a submersible that dives at a rate of 2.5 m every 30 s. How deep will the submersible dive in 2 min? 3 min? 10 min? 25 min? How long will it take to reach a depth of 1 km?

Discover the Math

Materials

Optional:
• BLM 11.3A Multiply Integers Using Integer Chips

How can you multiply integers using patterns?

Part 1: Multiply Opposite Integers

1. Copy and complete the multiplication statements to continue the pattern.

   $4 \times 3 = 12$
   $4 \times 2 = \blacksquare$
   $4 \times 1 = \blacksquare$
   $4 \times 0 = \blacksquare$
   $4 \times (-1) = \blacksquare$
   $4 \times (-2) = \blacksquare$

2. Describe the pattern. Explain how you used it to complete the last two multiplications.

3. **Reflect**

   a) State a rule for multiplying a positive number by a negative number.

   b) Would your rule hold for a negative number times a positive number? Explain.

Part 2: Multiply Two Negative Integers

1. Use your results from Part 1 to copy and continue this pattern.

$-4 \times 3 = -12$
$-4 \times 2 = $ ■
$-4 \times 1 = $ ■
$-4 \times 0 = $ ■
$-4 \times (-1) = $ ■
$-4 \times (-2) = $ ■

2. Describe the pattern. Explain how you used it to complete the last two multiplications.

3. **Reflect** State a rule for multiplying a negative number by a negative number.

Example 1: Find Integer Products

Find each product.
a) -4×3
b) $5 \times (-2)$
c) $-7 \times (-4)$

Solution

a) $-4 \times 3 = -12$ ● ○ ○ ○ ○ ○
> The signs are different, so the product is negative.

b) $5 \times (-2) = -10$ ● ○ ○ ○ ○ ○
> The signs are different, so the product is negative.

c) $-7 \times (-4) = 28$ ● ○ ○ ○ ○ ○
> The signs are the same, so the product is positive.

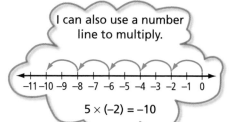
> I can also use a number line to multiply.

$5 \times (-2) = -10$

Example 2: Apply Integer Multiplication

Six students each owe $5 for a field trip. What is the total amount owed? What integer rule does this illustrate?

Solution

$6 \times (-5) = -30$

The six students owe a total of $30. This is −$30. This illustrates that the product of a positive number and a negative number is negative.

> We each owe $5. That's −5. There are 6 of us, so multiply $6 \times (-5)$.

Example 3: Multiply More Than Two Integers

Find each product.

a) $5 \times (-9) \times (-3)$

b) $-2 \times (-4) \times (-7) \times 2$

Solution

a) $5 \times (-9) \times (-3)$

$= -45 \times (-3)$

$= 135$

> I use the order of operations and multiply from left to right.

b) $-2 \times (-4) \times (-7) \times 2$

$= 8 \times (-7) \times 2$

$= -56 \times 2$

$= -112$

Key Ideas

- When you multiply two integers,
  – if the signs are the same, the product is positive
  – if the signs are different, the product is negative

> $5 \times 5 = 25$ and
> $-4 \times (-4) = 16$

> $5 \times (-5) = -25$ and
> $-5 \times 5 = -25$

Communicate the Ideas

1. Which of the following can be represented using integer multiplication, and which cannot? Explain.

a) three losses of $10 each

b) the difference between 200 m above sea level and 40 m below sea level

c) the 3 by 4 shaded area of a coordinate grid

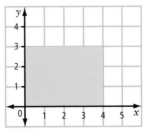

2. Do $2 \times (-3)$ and -3×2 give the same result? Explain, using words and diagrams.

3. What integer multiplication is shown? What is the result? Explain how you know.

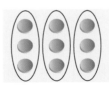

Practise

For help with questions 4 to 8, refer to Example 1.

4. Find each product.

a) 7×6 **b)** $5 \times (-10)$

c) -4×4 **d)** -7×8

5. Multiply.

a) 8×9 **b)** $2 \times (-9)$

c) -5×3 **d)** $11 \times (-3)$

6. What integer multiplication does each number line model? Find the result.

a)

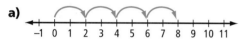

b)

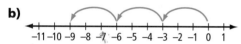

7. Multiply.

a) $-3 \times (-5)$ **b)** $-8 \times (-4)$

c) $-9 \times (-6)$ **d)** $-12 \times (-7)$

8. Find each product.

a) $-7 \times (-2)$ **b)** $-12 \times (-12)$

c) $-6 \times (-11)$ **d)** $-11 \times (-11)$

For help with question 9, refer to Example 2.

9. Write each situation as an integer expression using multiplication. State the result and its meaning.

a) A scuba diver dove down 5 m, then took a rest. She did this 6 times. At what depth was the scuba diver after the 6 dives?

b) Susan withdrew $20 from the bank machine on three different days. Her mom deposited the money back into her account. How much did Susan's mother deposit?

For help with questions 10 to 12, refer to Example 3.

10. Predict the sign of each product. Justify your answer. Do not evaluate.

a) $-21 \times (-18)$

b) $72 \times (-657)$

c) $-2 \times (-3) \times (-1)$

d) $4 \times (-9) \times (-8) \times 5$

e) $-2 \times (-2) \times (-2) \times (-2) \times (-2) \times (-2)$

f) $-5 \times 7 \times (-5) \times 7 \times (-5) \times 7 \times (-5) \times 7$

11. Evaluate each product in question 10.

12. Evaluate each product.

a) $5 \times (-5) \times (-5)$

b) $10 \times 10 \times (-10)$

c) $-2 \times (-2) \times (-2) \times (-2) \times (-2)$

d) $-3 \times (-5) \times (-4)$

e) $7 \times (-3) \times 10$

f) $-3 \times (-2) \times (-1) \times 11$

13. From your results in questions 10 and 12, state a set of rules that helps you predict the sign of any multiplication statement.

14. Use multiplication to evaluate. What strategy did you use?

a) $-7 + (-7) + (-7) + (-7) + (-7) + (-7)$

b) $-2 + (-2) + (-2) + (-2) + (-2)$

c) $-13 + (-13) + (-13) + (-13)$

d) $-15 + (-15) + (-15)$

Apply

15. Use a pattern to explain each result.

a) $3 \times (-5) = -15$

b) $-4 \times (-7) = 28$

16. Write an integer expression using multiplication for each situation. State the result and the meaning of the result.

a) The temperature rises an average of 2°C every hour. How many degrees does it rise in 4 h?

b) In an investment game, Allen lost $50 in each of 4 turns. How much did he lose?

c) A submarine dove at a rate of 25 m/min for 8 min. How far did the submarine dive?

d) In a board game, you lose, in points, 100 times the roll of one number cube. How much do you lose with a roll of 4?

17. Write a problem that has a solution of $12 \times (-4)$.

Chapter Problem

18. In a tropical ocean location, the temperature decreases by about 3°C for every 25 m in depth. The temperature at the surface is 25°C.

a) What is the water temperature 125 m below the surface?

b) The clearnose skate can live in water with temperatures from 6°C to 27°C. How far below the surface can the skate live?

19. Explain how the number line is used to model multiplication of integers.

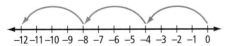

20. Use a number line to model each integer expression.

a) 3×7

b) $2 \times (-5)$

c) $4 \times (-6)$

Try This!

21. On the stock market, the price of one share of High Flier Airlines dropped by an average of 15¢ per day over 30 days.

a) What was the total price change during the first 5 days?

b) What was the total price change over the entire 30-day period?

c) You buy shares on the 10th day. How much money will you lose, per share, if you sell them on the 20th day?

Extend

22. a) List the possible combinations of three different integers that have a product of –12.

b) Find all the possible combinations of three different integers whose product is 30.

23. a) Plot the points A(2, –1), B(–3, –4), and C(–5, 2) on a coordinate grid. Join them to form a triangle.

b) Multiply the x- and y-coordinates of A, B, and C by 2 and graph the results. Describe the resulting triangle.

c) Multiply the x- and y-coordinates of A, B, and C by –2 and graph the results. Describe the resulting triangle.

d) Describe what would happen if you multiplied the x-coordinates by 2 and the y-coordinates by –2.

Divide Integers

To calculate the mean temperature over a day, meteorologists measure the temperature at regular intervals. Explain how they calculate the mean after the data have been collected.

Time	midnight	2 A.M.	4 A.M.	6 A.M.	8 A.M.	10 A.M.	noon	2 P.M.	4 P.M.	6 P.M.	8 P.M.	10 P.M.
Temperature (°C)	−15	−14	−14	−12	−8	−7	−5	−5	−6	−8	−11	−14

Discover the Math

How can you divide integers?

The triangle illustrates the multiplication statement $4 \times 3 = 12$. It also illustrates the related division statements $12 \div 4 = 3$ and $12 \div 3 = 4$.

Part 1: Divide Opposite Integers

  1. Copy the triangle. Add symbols and arrows to show the related multiplication and division statements.

  2. a) Draw a similar triangle to illustrate $-4 \times (-3) = 12$.
   b) Use the triangle to write the related division statements.
   c) What sign does each of your answers have?

  3. a) Draw a triangle to illustrate $-5 \times (-7) = 35$.
   b) Use the triangle to write the related division statements.
   c) What sign does each of your answers have?

  4. Reflect Use your results from steps 2 and 3 to write a rule for dividing a positive integer by a negative integer.

Part 2: Divide Negative Integers by Positive and Negative Integers

1. a) Draw a triangle to illustrate $4 \times (-3) = -12$.
   b) Use the triangle to write the related division statements.
   c) What sign does each of your answers have?

2. a) Draw a triangle to illustrate $-5 \times 7 = -35$.
   b) Use the triangle to write the related division statements.
   c) What sign does each of your answers have?

3. Reflect Use your results from steps 1 and 2 to write rules for
   • dividing a negative integer by a positive integer
   • dividing a negative integer by a negative integer

Example 1: Divide Integers

Jodi has to decrease the temperature of a chemical solution by 20°C.
She can only decrease it 4°C at a time so crystals will not form.
a) How many times must she decrease the temperature?
b) What integer division rule does this show?

Solution

a) Divide the total change by the size of
   each change.
   $-20 \div (-4) = 5$
   Jodi will need to decrease the temperature five times.

> This is the same as asking how many moves of –4 will get you from 0 to –20.

b) This shows that dividing a negative integer by a negative integer
   results in a positive quotient.

Example 2: Find the Mean Point Loss

Tim lost a total of 150 points in five questions on a TV game show.
a) What was his mean point loss per question?
b) What integer division rule does this show?

Solution

a) Divide the total points lost by the number of questions.
   $-150 \div 5 = -30$
   Tim's mean loss per question is 30 points.

> Another way of writing this is $\dfrac{-150}{5} = -30$.

b) This shows that dividing a negative integer by a positive integer results
   in a negative quotient.

Key Ideas

- You can use triangles to illustrate division of integers.

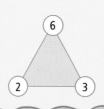

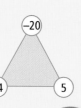

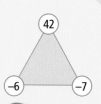

- When dividing two integers,
  - if the signs are the same, the quotient is positive
  - if the signs are different, the quotient is negative

$6 \div 2 = 3$, $6 \div 3 = 2$, and $-20 \div (-4) = 5$

$-20 \div 5 = -4$, $42 \div (-6) = -7$, and $42 \div (-7) = -6$

To multiply and divide integers, follow the same sign rules. But watch out for adding and subtracting! These are different.

Communicate the Ideas

1. Explain why $56 \div (-7)$ and $-56 \div 7$ give the same result.
2. Which is greater,
   a) $45 \div 9$ or $45 \div 5$? **b)** $-45 \div 9$ or $-45 \div 5$?
   Explain why the results differ.
3. Who is correct? Explain.

$\frac{-48}{-3}$ is another way of writing $(-48) \div (-3)$.

No, they don't mean the same thing.

Check Your Understanding

Practise

4. Draw a triangle for each multiplication statement. Then, write the related division statements.
   a) $8 \times (-2) = -16$ **b)** $-7 \times 5 = -35$
   c) $-3 \times (-9) = 27$ **d)** $15 \times (-10) = -150$

For help with questions 5 and 6, refer to Example 1.

5. Find each quotient.
   a) $12 \div 3$ **b)** $-18 \div (-2)$
   c) $56 \div (-7)$ **d)** $-100 \div (-10)$

6. Divide.
   a) $12 \div 3$ **b)** $-20 \div (-4)$
   c) $\frac{-39}{3}$ **d)** $\frac{50}{-10}$

7. Copy each statement. Replace each ■ to make the statement true.
   a) $48 = ■ \times (-6)$
   b) $-25 = ■ \times (-5)$
   c) $■ \times (-6) = -18$
   d) $■ \times 10 = -60$
   e) $-38 = ■ \times 19$
   f) $63 = ■ \times (-9)$

For help with questions 8 to 10, refer to Example 2.

8. A stock decreased in price by $25 over 4 days. What was the mean daily decrease in price?

9. A diver rose a total of 30 m in 6 stages. What was the mean rise per stage?

10. The temperature decreased by 10°C from 6 P.M. to 10 P.M. What was the mean hourly decrease in temperature?

Apply

11. List all the integers that divide evenly into each.
   a) −15   **b)** −24

12. Write an expression involving integer division for each situation. Evaluate each expression and state its meaning.
   a) You owe your parents $35, to be paid in five equal instalments. How much is each instalment?
   b) The temperature dropped a total of 18°C over a 9-h period. What was the mean hourly temperature drop?

13. Make up a question similar to those in question 12. Give it to a classmate to solve. Check to make sure your classmate has answered the question properly.

14. For a science project, Warren researched low temperatures in five Ontario cities.

City	Temperature (°C)
London	−2
Thunder Bay	−12
Brockville	−6
Sudbury	−8
Sarnia	+1

   a) Find the mean low temperature for these cities.
   b) If each temperature were actually 2°C warmer, how would it affect the mean?

15. Eleanor is tracking a whale. It descends at a steady rate of 120 m in 20 min.
   a) What is the whale's unit rate of descent?
   b) How far does the whale descend in 10 min?
   c) How far does the whale descend in 16 min?
   d) The whale needs to come to the surface to breathe after 45 min under water. How deep can it dive if it descends and ascends at the same steady rate?

> ### Making Connections
> You learned about unit rates in Chapter 5.

16. At midnight, the temperature in Iqaluit was −15°C. At noon, it was −5°C. What was the mean hourly increase in temperature from midnight to noon?

 17. Write a related division statement for each product. Then, write an example to go with it.

For example, for $8 \times (-2) = -16$:

$-16 \div (-2) = 8$: A diver dives 2 m/s. How long has she been diving when she is at a depth of 16 m?

   a) $9 \times (-5) = -45$
   b) $-4 \times (-7) = 28$
   c) $-6 \times 6 = -36$

Extend

18. The mean noon temperature during one week was −4°C. Give two examples of what the temperatures might have been each day of the week. Justify your answer.

19. a) Evaluate 5^2 and 6^2. Then, evaluate $(-5)^2$ and $(-6)^2$. What do you notice?
   b) Can the result of squaring a number ever be negative? Explain.

Order of Operations With Integers

The bar graph shows the profit or loss each year to publish the school yearbook.

How would you find the average yearly profit or loss?

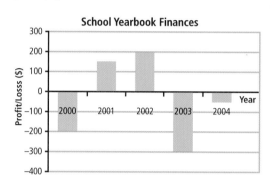

School Yearbook Finances

Discover the Math

How does the order of operations apply to integers?

Example 1: Use the Order of Operations

Evaluate.
a) $6 - 10 + (-2)$
b) $-6 + 5 \times 9 - 50$
c) $-2 + 3(5^2 - 30)$

> The order of operations works the same way with integers as it does with whole numbers.

Solution

B Brackets
E Exponents
D ⎱ Division and
M ⎰ Multiplication, in order from *left to right*
A ⎱ Addition and
S ⎰ Subtraction, in order from *left to right*

a) $6 - 10 + (-2)$ **Subtract.**
$= -4 + (-2)$ **Add.**
$= -6$

ⓒ 6 ⊝ 10 ⊕ 2 ± ⊜ -6.
or ⓒ 6 ⊝ 10 ⊕ (-) 2 ⊜ -6.

b) $-6 + 5 \times 9 - 50$ **Multiply.**
$= -6 + 45 - 50$ **Add.**
$= 39 - 50$ **Subtract.**
$= -11$

ⓒ 6 ± ⊕ 5 ✕ 9 ⊝ 50 ⊜ -11.
or ⓒ (-) 6 ⊕ 5 ✕ 9 ⊝ 50 ⊜ -11.

c) $-2 + 3(5^2 - 30)$ **Exponents.**

$= -2 + 3 \times (25 - 30)$ **Brackets.**

$= -2 + 3 \times (-5)$ **Multiply.**

$= -2 - 15$

$= -17$

Ⓒ 2 ± + 3 × (5 x^2 − 30) = -17.

or Ⓒ (-) 2 + 3 × (5 x^2 − 30) = -17.

Technology Tip

• Calculator keystrokes vary. Check the manual or experiment with a simple calculation that you can answer mentally.

• On computers, the ⌃ key is used to obtain a power. For example, 5 ⌃ 2 = 25.

Example 2: Stock Prices

Stock prices increase and decrease daily. A particular stock showed the following daily changes in price, in cents, over a five-day period: +20, –15, –23, +15, –12. What was the mean daily change in price?

Solution

Mean = $\dfrac{\text{sum of changes}}{\text{number of days}}$

$= [20 + (-15) + (-23) + 15 + (-12)] \div 5$

$= [5 + (-23) + 15 + (-12)] \div 5$

$= [-18 + 15 + (-12)] \div 5$

$= [-3 + (-12)] \div 5$

$= -15 \div 5$

$= -3$

I'll add the numbers in the brackets from left to right.

The stock's mean daily change in price was a loss of 3¢.

Key Ideas

■ The order of operations is the same for integers:

B   Brackets

E   Exponents

D   } Division and Multiplication, in order from *left* to *right*
M

A   } Addition and Subtraction, in order from *left* to *right*
S

Communicate the Ideas

1. The following skill-testing question was given in a contest:

Add 5 and 7.
Multiply by 4.
Subtract 50.

Anna provided this solution:
$5 + 7 \times 4 - 50$
$= 5 + 28 - 50$
$= 33 - 50$
$= -17$

The contest manager gave this solution:
$5 + 7 = 12$
$12 \times 4 = 48$
$48 - 50 = -2$

Which solution do you think is correct? Or are they both correct? Justify your response.

2. List the keystrokes you need to use on your calculator to evaluate the expression $-27 + 31(76 - 43)$.

3. Abby simplified the expression $2 - 5 + 7 - 9 + 4$ in the following way:
$2 - 5 + 7 - 9 + 4$
$= 2 + 7 + 4 - 5 - 9$
$= 13 - 14$
$= -1$
Describe Abby's strategy.

Check Your Understanding

Practise

For help with questions 4 to 7, refer to Example 1.

4. Evaluate without using a calculator.
  a) $4 + (-3) - 9$ **b)** $-2 \times 4 - 1$
  c) $3 + 5 \times (-4)$ **d)** $3 - 5 \times 4$
  e) $6 \div 3 - 7$ **f)** $7 - 6 \div 3$

5. Evaluate. Check your answers with a calculator.
  a) $2(3 - 7)$ **b)** $-3(-6 + 4)$
  c) $4 + 2(9 - 12)$ **d)** $6 - (5 + 3)$
  e) $-1(3^2 - 10)$ **f)** $(2^2 - 3) - (3^2 - 2)$

6. Evaluate using a calculator.
  a) $15(9 - 12)$ **b)** $(20 + 8) \div (-7)$
  c) $15^2 - 23^2$ **d)** $-25 - 17(3^2 + 8)$

7. Write an integer expression for each statement. Then, evaluate the expression.
  a) Add -3 to 5 times 12.
  b) Subtract 4 from the product of -9 and 6.
  c) Subtract the square of 5 from the square of 3.

For help with questions 8 and 9, refer to Example 2.

8. Find the mean change in price, in dollars, for each stock.

Stock A	−2	+3	−5	+7	+1
Stock B	+6	−3	−2	+5	−3

9. Flower bulbs need to be planted at certain depths. Find the mean depth for these bulbs.

Bulb	Depth (cm)
Tulip	−15
Daffodil	−20
Crocus	−5
Hyacinth	−19

Apply

10. You owe $100 to your parents. You find a job cutting lawns and are paid $6 each time. You use that money to repay your loan.

a) How much do you still owe after cutting eight lawns?

b) How many more lawns do you need to cut to pay off the rest of your debt?

c) Show another way to solve this problem.

11. Steve drove from Windsor to Toronto at an average speed of 95 km/h. After 2 h, Steve was 172 km away from his destination. How far apart are Windsor and Toronto?

12. Plot the points A(1, 5), B(1, −4), C(−3, −4), and D(−3, 1) on a coordinate grid. Join the points to form a rectangle.

a) What is the length of the rectangle?

b) What is the width of the rectangle?

c) Calculate the perimeter of the rectangle.

d) Calculate the area of the rectangle.

13. These items are on sale during a special tax-free day.

a) Which item changed the most in price?

b) You have $45. Do you have enough to also buy a $12 CD, on sale at 10% off?

Item	Original Price ($)	Percent Discount
Calculator	20	15%
Book	35	40%
Mechanical pencil	2	50%

Chapter Problem

14. In Section 11.3, you learned that the clearnose skate can survive in water temperatures from 6°C to 27°C.

a) If the temperature at the surface of the water is 33°C, and the temperature decreases by 3°C for every 25 m, what is the deepest water the skate can survive in?

b) What is the shallowest water the skate can survive in?

Try This!

15. a) Copy each equation and use the symbols +, −, ÷, ×, and ( ) to make it true.

- 5 ▪ 9 ▪ 7 = 3
- 3 ▪ 5 ▪ 4 = −8
- 20 ▪ 4 ▪ −6 = −4

b) Can you make any of the equations true in more than one way? Explain.

c) What strategies did you try to answer these questions? Which worked best?

Extend

16. Many integers can be expressed as the difference of two squares. For example, $3 = 2^2 − 1^2$ and $−3 = 1^2 − 2^2$.

a) Which integers between −10 and 10 can be expressed as the difference of two squares? Which cannot?

b) Do any integers have more than one solution?

Making Connections

You worked with discounts in Chapter 5.

11.6

Patterns and Trends With Integers

Focus on...
- finding and describing patterns with integers
- trends on graphs

When you hang a mass from an elastic band, it will bounce up and down a few times before becoming still. The amount the elastic band stretches depends on the mass and on the thickness of the elastic.

Discover the Math

Materials
- 3 heavy books
- 2 rulers
- 1 paper clip
- small elastic band
- masses: 50 g, 100 g, 150 g, 200 g, 250 g, 300 g
- centimetre grid paper

Optional:
- BLM 11.6A Integer Patterns Grid

How can you relate integers to patterns?

1. Place a ruler between the top two books in a stack of three books on top of a desk.

2. Hang an elastic band and a paper clip from the ruler.

3. Hook the smallest mass to the paper clip.

4. When the mass stops moving, measure its distance from the top surface of the desk, to the nearest millimetre.

5. Record your results in a table with the headings shown. If the mass reaches below the

Mass (g)	Distance From the Desk Surface (mm)

top surface of the table, record the distance as a negative number.

6. Repeat steps 4 and 5 for the remaining masses.

7. Plot a graph of the results with mass on the horizontal axis and distance on the vertical axis.

8. **Reflect** Describe the pattern or trend of distances that you recorded.

Example 1: Continue a Pattern

Describe each pattern. Then, find the next four numbers in each pattern. Finally, determine which integers, other than 1 and –1, are factors of all the numbers in each pattern.

a) 4, 2, 0, –2, –4, …   **b)** –6, –12, –18, –24, …

Solution

a) The numbers in the pattern decrease by 2 each time.
The next four numbers are –6, –8, –10, and –12.
All the numbers are divisible by 2.
They are also divisible by –2.
So, 2 and –2 are factors of all the numbers in the pattern.

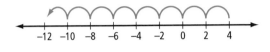

b) The numbers in the pattern decrease by 6 each time.
The next four numbers are –30, –36, –42, and –48.
All the numbers are divisible by 6 and –6. They are also divisible by 3, –3, 2, and –2.
So, 6, –6, 3, –3, 2, and –2 are factors of all the numbers in the pattern.

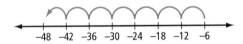

Example 2: Calculate Profit or Loss

When George started a business clearing snow, he borrowed $300 from his parents. He charges $10 per driveway.
a) Calculate George's profit or loss from his business after clearing three driveways.
b) Describe the pattern.
c) George bought a snowblower with the $300. Will he make a profit after clearing 50 driveways?

Solution

a) $-300 + 3 \times 10$
$= -300 + 30$
$= -270$
George has a loss of $270 after clearing three driveways. He still owes his parents $270.

b) For each driveway that George clears, he can pay back $10 to his parents.

c) Profit $= -300 + 10(50)$
$= -300 + 500$
$= 200$
George's profit will be $200 after clearing 50 driveways. He will be able to pay back his parents and have $200 left over.

> **Strategies**
> What other strategy could you use to solve this problem?

Example 3: Temperature Readings

The table shows the temperature readings from 6:00 P.M. to 6:00 A.M.

a) Plot the data on a coordinate grid. Place time on the horizontal axis and temperature on the vertical axis.

b) Describe the trend in temperature.

c) What is the mean decrease in temperature per hour?

d) Predict the temperature at 9 A.M.

Time	Temperature (°C)
6 P.M.	2
7 P.M.	0
8 P.M.	−1
9 P.M.	−1
10 P.M.	−3
11 P.M.	−3
midnight	−4
1 A.M.	−6
2 A.M.	−7
3 A.M.	−9
4 A.M.	−10
5 A.M.	−10
6 A.M.	−10

Solution

a)

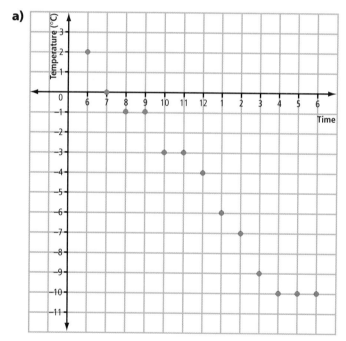

b) The trend is downward from 2°C to −10°C.

c) To calculate the mean decrease over a period of time, add the temperature decreases and divide by the total number of hours.
$$[(-2) + (-1) + 0 + (-2) + 0 + (-1) + (-2) + (-1) + (-2) + (-1) + 0 + 0] \div 12 = -1$$
The mean decrease is 1°C per hour.

> **Making Connections**
>
> You studied trends in Chapter 10.

d)

The trend is going down. Maybe it will be −12 by then.

The sun is coming up. The temperatures will warm. Maybe the trend will reverse. It may be −7 by then.

> **Strategies**
>
> How else could you solve this problem?

- When working with patterns, identify the rules for the pattern.
  - Look for repeated sets of operations.
  - Identify what operation is used.

  For example, Sylvia owes $100. She pays back $5 per week. How long will it take her to pay the debt?

The pattern starts with –$100. Add $5 each week. It will take 20 weeks to pay off the debt?

$5 \times 20 = 100$

- To solve patterns with integers, look for patterns and trends.

The population is dropping. In 2006, the population will likely be about 20 000.

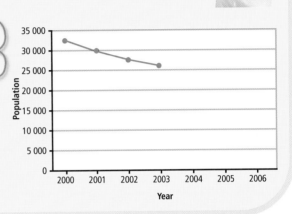

Communicate the Ideas

1. Describe how to find the next integer in each pattern. Explain why your method works.
   a) –2, –5, –8, –11   **b)** –1, –3, –9, –27

2. You owe $200. You plan to pay off $20 a month.
   a) How long will it take to pay off the debt?
   b) Describe the pattern you used to answer this question. Explain why you used this pattern.

3. At 12 noon, the temperature was 8°C. The temperature rose an average of 1°C per hour between 12 noon and 6 P.M.
   a) Predict the temperature at 9 P.M. Explain your prediction.
   b) Jaap predicts that the temperature at 9 P.M. will be 11°C. Explain how he might have made this prediction.
   c) Is Jaap's answer valid? Explain.

1 p.m temperature: 9°C
12 p.m. temperature: 8°C
5°C

Practise

For help with questions 4 to 9, refer to Example 1.

4. Determine the next three numbers in each pattern.

a) –1, –3, –5, –7
b) –3, –6, –12, –24
c) 12, 7, 2, –3
d) 5, –10, 20, –40

5. Describe how to find the next number in each pattern.

a) –4, –7, –10, –13
b) –15, –11, –7, –3
c) –81, –27, –9, –3
d) 7, –49, 343, –2401

6. a) Find the next four numbers in the pattern –3, –6, –9, –12, ….
b) Which integers, other than 1 and –1, are factors of all the numbers in the pattern?

7. a) Find the next four numbers in the pattern –5, –10, –15, –20, ….
b) Which integers, other than 1 and –1, are factors of all the numbers in the pattern?

8. The first four numbers in a pattern are 3, –6, 12, –24.

a) Describe the pattern in two ways.
b) Determine the next three numbers in the pattern.

9. Make up your own pattern like the one in question 8. Give it to a classmate to describe and extend.

Apply

10. What are the first four negative integers that are divisible by 2? Explain how you know.

11. What are the first three negative integers that are divisible by –7? How do you know?

For help with questions 12 and 13, refer to Example 2.

12. Justin started up a business making jewellery for his friends and family. He borrowed $200 from his aunt and used it to buy supplies. Justin charges $5 for each piece of jewellery he makes.

a) Calculate Justin's profit or loss after selling 10 pieces of jewellery.
b) Describe the pattern.
c) Justin makes and sells 30 pieces of jewellery. Will he make a profit?

13. The change in a stock price, in dollars, over 5 days is shown.

Day	Change in Stock Price
1	–3
2	–1
3	1
4	3
5	5

a) Determine the change in stock price on the sixth and seventh days if the pattern continues.
b) Describe the pattern.
c) Determine the change in stock price on the 10th day if the pattern continues.
d) Is the pattern realistic? Explain why or why not.

For help with questions 14 and 15, refer to Example 3.

14. The table shows the temperature and the winning times for cross country ski racing.

Temperature (°C)	Time (min)
−2	27
−6	21
−4	23
−5	23
−10	19
−3	24
−7	20

a) Graph the data on a coordinate grid. Place temperature on the horizontal axis and time on the vertical axis.

b) Describe the trend in the data.

c) What is the mean time?

d) At what temperature would you prefer to ski? Why?

15. The predicted income for a small jewellery business is shown.

Month	Predicted Income ($)
1	−500
2	−200
3	800
4	400
5	700

a) Graph these data.

b) Describe the trend.

c) Predict the income after 8 months.

16. A clothing store sells new coats at
Try This! a regular price of $150. As a clearance sale, each coat is offered at $15 off for every week it is on sale, until it has been sold.

a) Describe the pattern in the sale price.

b) What is the sale price after 6 weeks of the sale?

c) When will this pattern stop working? Explain.

Extend

17. If you start at −600 and count up by 7s, which of the following numbers will be included? Justify your answers.

a) −354

b) −355

c) −208

d) 32

18. The graph shows the height, in metres, of a rider, above and below the centre of a Ferris wheel, for the first minute of the ride.

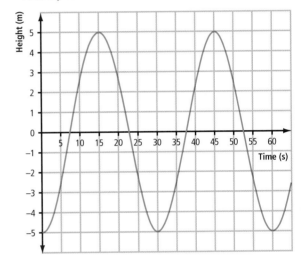

a) What is the height of a rider, relative to the centre, at the beginning of the ride?

b) What is the height of a rider, relative to the centre, after 15 s?

c) What is the approximate height of a rider, relative to the centre, after 25 s?

d) Describe the pattern in the graph.

19. a) The points (2, 7) and (−4, 1) are two vertices of a square. Determine all possible locations of the other two vertices of the square.

b) How would your answers change if the two points were vertices of a rhombus?

Key Words

Match each term with an example.

Term

1. zero principle

2. opposite integers

3. positive integer

4. negative integer

Example

A answer to $(-5) \times (-4)$

B $15 + (-15) = 0$

C -2 and 4

D -20 and 20

E answer to $(-15) \div 3$

11.1 Add Integers, pages 350–355

5. Simplify.

a) $5 + 7$ **b)** $-13 + 13$

c) $-5 + (-12)$ **d)** $8 + (-15)$

e) $-17 + 9$ **f)** $-3 + (-6) + (-9) + 5$

6. Find each sum.

a) $20 + 7$ **b)** $6 + (-6)$

c) $-11 + 5$ **d)** $-2 + (-8)$

e) $12 + 6 + (-4)$

f) $5 + 13 + (-5) + (-10) + 3$

7. The table shows the change in the population of Smallville at each census since 1971.

Year	Change
1971	−20 000
1976	−82 000
1981	+24 000
1986	−12 000
1991	+17 000
1996	+21 000
2001	−33 000

What was the overall change in population?

11.2 Subtract Integers, pages 356–360

8. Evaluate each expression. Do not use a calculator.

a) $10 - 15$ **b)** $-5 - 7$

c) $-14 - (-22)$ **d)** $-53 - 42 - (-25)$

9. Find each difference.

a) $10 - 5$ **b)** $-16 - 14$

c) $-5 - (-5)$ **d)** $11 - (-9)$

10. The table shows each city's time zone relative to GMT, or Greenwich Mean Time.

City	Time Zone
Calgary	GMT − 7
Helsinki	GMT + 2
Tokyo	GMT + 9
Honolulu	GMT − 10

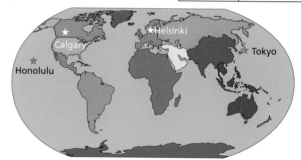

a) How many hours behind Helsinki is Honolulu?

b) How many hours ahead of Calgary is Tokyo?

11.3 Multiply Integers, pages 361–365

11. For each expression, use a pattern to illustrate the rule for multiplying integers.

a) $3 \times (-4)$

b) -2×5

c) $-4 \times (-2)$

12. Multiply. Do not use a calculator.
  a) $7 \times (-2)$
  b) $-3 \times (-6)$
  c) -10×7
  d) $15 \times (-4)$
  e) $-2 \times (-3) \times (-5) \times 10$

13. Explain how you can tell the sign of a product of more than two integers.

14. The average change in the tiger population over the past 100 years is −940 tigers per year.

  a) What was the total change in the tiger population?
  b) What was the change in the tiger population between 1950 and 2000?

11.4 Divide Integers, pages 366–369

15. Divide. Do not use a calculator.
  a) $35 \div (-5)$
  b) $-64 \div (-4)$
  c) $-72 \div 9$
  d) $-56 \div (-8)$

16. Find all the integers, other than 1 and −1, that divide evenly into −10.

17. Write an expression involving integer division for each situation. Evaluate each expression and state its meaning.
  a) While scuba diving, Diane dived 50 m in 10 stages. What was the mean depth of her dive per stage?
  b) A parachutist descended a total of 60 m in 5 s. What was the unit rate of descent?
  c) The temperature dropped 24°C over 8 h. What was the mean hourly temperature drop?

11.5 Order of Operations With Integers, pages 370–373

18. Evaluate.
  a) $2 + 5(7 - 10)$ **b)** $-3(6^2 - 30)$
  c) $4^2 - 5^2$ **d)** $-6 + 12 \div (-2) - 9$

19. The temperature at the top of a 5900-m mountain is −44°C. At the bottom, the temperature is 15°C. What is the mean temperature difference per 100 m?

11.6 Patterns and Trends With Integers, pages 374–379

20. Determine the next four numbers in each pattern. Justify your answers.
  a) −3, −6, −9, −12   **b)** 5, 2, −1, −4
  c) −15, −4, 7, 18
  d) −7, −14, −28, −56

21. Kathy started a business selling crafts at a flea market. Her initial expenses were $700 and she expects weekly sales of $125.
  a) Describe the pattern in her income.
  b) What income can she expect after 2 weeks?
  c) When can Kathy expect to begin to make a profit from her business?

CHAPTER

11

Practice Test

Strand	NSN	MEA	GSS	PA	DMP
Questions	1–10			2, 4, 7	10

Multiple Choice

For questions 1 to 5, select the correct answer.

1. Which statement is false?

A $-2 \times 6 = 6 \times (-2)$

B $-4 + (-5) = -5 + (-4)$

C $7 \times 8 = -7 \times (-8)$

D $7 - 9 = 9 - 7$

2. What are the next three numbers in the pattern 3, −4, −11, …?

A −18, −25, −32

B −14, −21, −24

C −23, −47, −90

D none of the above

3. The product of two integers is

A always negative

B always positive

C negative if the signs of the integers are different

D negative if the signs of the integers are the same

4. Examine the following pattern:

$10 \div 5 = 2$
$5 \div 5 = 1$
$0 \div 5 = 0$
$-5 \div 5 = -1$

The next division statement in the pattern is

A $-10 \div 5 = 2$

B $10 \div (-5) = -2$

C $-10 \div 5 = -2$

D $-10 \div (-2) = 5$

5. In 2001, the population of a small town was 3461. The population increased by 200 in 2002, decreased by 150 in 2003, and decreased by 145 in 2004. Which expression represents the population in 2004?

A $-3461 - 200 - 150 - 145$

B $3461 + 200 - 150 - 145$

C $3461 - 200 - 150 - 145$

D $3461 - 200 - 150 - 145$

Short Answer

6. Evaluate each integer expression.

a) $-3 - 7$ **b)** $12 + (-19)$

c) -8×7 **d)** $54 \div (-6)$

e) $6 + 4 \div 2$ **f)** $4 - 3(5 - 9)$

7. Describe each pattern in words. Then, find the next four numbers in the pattern.

a) −4, −8, −12, −16

b) −15, −9, −3, 3

8. Write an integer expression for each of the following. Evaluate the expression and state its meaning.

a) The highest recorded temperature in North America was 57°C in Death Valley, California. The lowest recorded temperature was −66°C in Northice, Greenland. How much warmer is the first temperature than the second?

b) A magazine publisher lost $240 000 last year. What was the mean loss per month?

c) A submarine starts diving from 10 m below the surface, at a rate of 25 m/min. How deep is the submarine after 6 min?

Extended Response

9. Two students are discussing multiplying and adding integers.

−3 × (−2) = 6
and
−3 + (−2) = 5

No, you're wrong.
−3 + (−2) = −5.

Who is correct? Explain, using pictures, words, and symbols.

10. The graph shows this summer's rainfall and the normal rainfall over the past 100 years.

a) Determine the difference in rainfall, compared to normal, for each month.

b) Summarize the monthly and overall differences using words, an appropriate graph, and measures of central tendency.

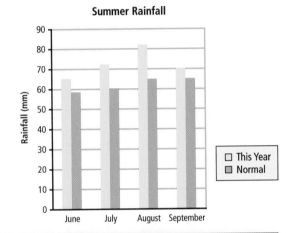

Summer Rainfall

□ This Year
■ Normal

Chapter Problem Wrap-Up

1. When the surface temperature is 27°C, and decreases by 3°C for every 25 m, a sea trout is found at a depth of 150 m. At what temperature should Eleanor set the sea trout tank?

2. Lake trout can live in water from 6°C to 10°C. The average summer temperature at the surface of a small lake in Ontario is 26°C. The temperature drops by 3°C for every 5 m. How deep would the lake have to be for lake trout to survive? What other factors would affect the trout's ability to survive in the lake?

3. Research the temperatures and depths that three other sea creatures prefer. Use mathematics to explain how you would set up an aquarium exhibit to show these creatures. Take into account water temperature, and whether these creatures can live together.

Patterning and Algebra

- Evaluate expressions by substituting whole numbers, fractions, and decimals.

- Write algebraic statements to interpret problems.

- Create problems that give rise to equations.

- Solve equations involving whole numbers and decimals using various techniques.

- Write statements to interpret simple equations.

- Realize that a solution to an equation or inequality makes the statement true.

- Investigate and solve inequalities.

Number Sense and Numeration

- Explain the problem solving process in mathematical language.

Key Words

variable

opposite operation

inequality

whole number

solution set

Patterning and Equations

Going on a school trip can involve a lot of algebra. You might use algebraic statements to determine how much money you will need for the trip and how long the bus ride will be. When you arrive, there are many patterning problems to discover. You might explore a pattern of oars on a rack or the number of lifejackets needed for a group of kayakers.

In this chapter, you will explore various patterns and relationships. You will use your knowledge of algebra to create, model, and solve problems. You will develop new skills for solving equations.

Chapter Problem

Your class is deciding how many buses and kayaks are needed for a class trip. There are 22 seats on a school bus. What formula can you use to model the number of buses needed for n people? You plan to rent two-person kayaks for the trip. What formula can you use to model the number of kayaks needed for p people?

Order of Operations

To evaluate expressions, follow the proper order of operations.

B Brackets
E Exponents
D }
M } Division and Multiplication, from *left* to *right*
A }
S } Addition and Subtraction, from *left* to *right*

$3 + 4 \times 6 \div 3$ **Multiply and divide from left to right.**
$= 3 + 24 \div 3$
$= 3 + 8$
$= 11$

$6^2 \times (3.7 - 2.2)$ **Brackets.**
$= 6^2 \times 1.5$ **Exponent.**
$= 36 \times 1.5$
$= 54$

1. Evaluate.

  a) $15 + 7^2$

  b) $6(16.4 - 10.4) + 3^3$

2. Evaluate.

  a) $6 + 5 \times 4 - 19$

  b) $2(16.7 - 10.2) - 9$

Perimeter

The perimeter is the distance around the outside of a shape.

$P = 6 + 6 + 6 + 6$
$P = 24$

The perimeter of the square is 24 cm.

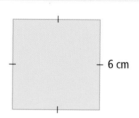
6 cm

3. Find the perimeter of each rectangle.

  a)
  15 cm
  9 cm

  b)
  4.8 cm
  2.2 cm

4. Find the perimeter of each square.

  a)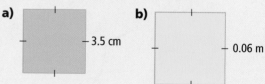
  3.5 cm

  b)
  0.06 m

True Statements

The symbol > means "is greater than." So, $6 > 5$ is a true statement.
The symbol < means "is less than." So, $5 < 6$ is a true statement.
The symbol = means "is equal to." So, $4 = 2 + 2$ is a true statement.

5. Compare the numbers in each pair. Rewrite, using <, >, or = to make a true statement.

a) 3×4 ▇ 3×5 b) 3.2 ▇ 3.2

c) 4 ▇ 3.9 d) $1\frac{1}{2}$ ▇ 1

6. Rewrite each statement using <, >, or = to make it true.

a) $7 - 2$ ▇ $7 - 3$ b) 3×6 ▇ 6×3

c) 2 ▇ -2 d) $\dfrac{12}{4}$ ▇ $\dfrac{12}{3}$

Patterns

Each term in a pattern can be identified by its position.

The perimeter, P, of a pattern of regular hexagons can be modelled with a formula. To find the formula, translate the pattern.

Term	Perimeter	Pattern
1	10	$P = 10 + 4 \times 0$
2	$14 = 10 + 4$	$P = 10 + 4 \times 1$
3	$18 = 10 + 4 + 4$	$P = 10 + 4 \times 2$

This is the same as the term number minus 1.

Let n represent the term number.
The formula for the perimeter is $P = 10 + 4(n - 1)$.

7. A volunteer service delivers three meals per day for clients. Examine the pattern in the table.

Number of Clients	Meals Prepared Daily	Pattern
20	70	$3 \times 20 + 10$
30	100	$3 \times 30 + 10$
40	130	$3 \times 40 + 10$

Write a formula that models the number of meals prepared daily. Define your variables.

8. What other pattern can you identify in question 7?

9. Show the next two terms in each pattern.

a) 13, 19, 25, …

b)

c) 80, 40, 20, …

Model and Solve Equations

At the 2002 winter Olympics, Canada earned three medals for speed skating. Speed skaters can reach speeds of 800 m/min. They travel a distance of d metres around a track in t minutes. This is modelled by the formula $d = 800t$. At this speed, how long will a skater take to complete a 1500-m race? How can you find out?

Discover the Math

Materials
- 2 cups or containers
- supply of counters

How can you model your solution?

1. You have 10 chocolates to share equally with a friend.

   a) Model this situation with cups and counters.

   b) How many counters go in each cup? How did you determine this?

   c) Write equations to model the steps of your solution.

   d) What is your **variable**? What does it represent?

variable
- a letter that represents an unknown number or numbers

2. You have some candies in your pocket. A friend gives you five more candies. When you count all your candies, you have 14.

   a) Model this situation using cups and counters.

   b) What does the cup represent? How can you find the value of the cup?

   c) Write equations to model the steps of your solution.

   d) What does your variable represent?

3. Reflect How can you use mathematical operations to solve an equation?

Example 1: Solve a Problem Using a Balanced Equation

Elana has a bunch of grapes. Her friend Maya pulls off 10 grapes. There are two grapes left on the stem.

a) Model this situation using cups and counters.

b) Find the value of the cup. What does the cup represent?

c) Use a balanced equation to find how many grapes Elana started with. Define your variable.

Solution

a)

> Elana started with 12 grapes. Knowing how to use various methods of problem solving will help me solve problems that are more difficult.

b)

> To find the value of the cup, I need to get the cup alone on one side of the equal sign. If I add 10 counters to the left side, that will undo subtracting 10 counters. So, to keep the equation true, I add 10 counters to the right side of the equal sign too.

To keep the equation true, perform the same operation on each side of the equal sign.

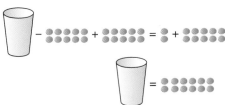

The cup has a value of 12. It represents the number of grapes that were on Elana's original bunch.

c) Let g represent the number of grapes in the bunch.

$$g - 10 = 2$$
$$g - 10 + 10 = 2 + 10$$
$$g = 12$$

Check your equation by substituting $g = 12$ and making sure both sides of the equal sign are balanced.

Left Side = $g - 10$ Right Side = 2
          = $12 - 10$
          = 2

          Left Side = Right Side

Therefore, $g = 12$ is correct.

Elana started with 12 grapes in her bunch.

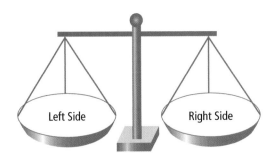

Example 2: Apply the Opposite Operation

Model each equation. Solve by inspection. Then, solve using the
opposite operation . Verify your solution.

a) $2t = 10$

b) $9 = u + 3$

opposite operation
- an operation that undoes a related operation
- $+$ and $-$ are opposite operations
- $\times$ and $\div$ are opposite operations

Solution

a)

$$2t = 10$$
$$\frac{2t}{2} = \frac{10}{2}$$
$$t = 5$$

Left Side = $2t$ Right Side = 10
$$= 2(5)$$
$$= 10$$

Left Side = Right Side

Therefore, $t = 5$ is correct.

> Two *t* masses balance the 10 mass. By inspection, each *t* mass needs to be 5.

> The expression $2t$ is the same as $t \times 2$. To get t by itself, I need to undo $\times 2$. So, I'll divide each side of the equal sign by 2.

b)

> To keep the balance, the unknown mass must be 6.

$$9 = u + 3$$
$$9 - 3 = u + 3 - 3$$
$$6 = u$$

Left Side = 9   Right Side = $u + 3$
$$= 6 + 3$$
$$= 9$$

Left Side = Right Side

Therefore, $u = 6$ is correct.

> I will undo adding 3 by subtracting 3 from the right side of the equal sign. I keep the equation balanced by subtracting 3 from the left side also.

- Equations can be solved in several ways. You can
  - Solve by inspection.

  $16 = x - 5$ The answer is $x = 21$.

  - Model the equation.

  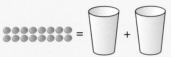 

  - Perform the opposite operation on both sides of the equal sign.

  $$k \times 9.7 = 164.9$$
  $$k \times 9.7 \div 9.7 = 164.9 \div 9.7$$
  $$k = 17$$

- To check your solution, substitute your answer into the equation. Then, compare the left side of the equal sign to the right side.

  Substitute $k = 17$.
  Left Side $= k \times 9.7$ Right Side $= 164.9$
  $= 17 \times 9.7$
  $= 164.9$
  Left Side $=$ Right Side

Communicate the Ideas

1. Explain why multiplication and division are considered opposite operations. How does applying the opposite operation help you solve an equation?

2. Describe a situation that can be modelled with each equation.
   a) $7y = 28$ **b)** $z + 5 = 18$

3. Barbara is solving the equation $k + 19 = 36$.

   a) Barbara realizes that she subtracted the wrong number. What operation did she mean to perform on both sides of the equal sign?

   b) Does she have to start her solution over? Explain.

   $$k + 19 = 36$$
   $$k + 19 - 36 = 36 - 36$$
   $$k - 17 = 0$$

Check Your Understanding

Practise

4. What equation is modelled by the diagram?

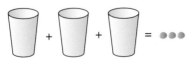

For help with questions 5 to 8, refer to Example 1.

5. What operation needs to be undone to get the cup by itself in each diagram?

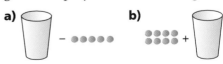

6. Solve the equation modelled by each diagram.

a)

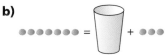

b)

c)

7. Model each equation using cups and counters.

a) $9 = 3w$

b) $m + 4 = 6$

8. Find the value of each unknown mass.

a)

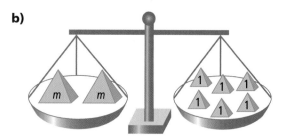

b)

9. Oscar gave $15 toward a school trip. Sandra also gave money toward the trip. Together, they gave $35.

a) Model this situation using cups and counters.

b) What do the cups and counters represent?

c) Write a balanced equation to model this situation.

d) What step would you perform to solve the equation?

10. Bill charges $14 to shovel one driveway. He earned $112 in February.

a) Model this situation using an equation.

b) Solve your equation to find how many driveways Bill shovels in February.

For help with questions 11 to 15, refer to Example 2.

11. For each expression, write the operation that is performed on the variable. Then, write the opposite operation.

a) $15 + s$ **b)** $p - 100$

c) $z \div 54$ **d)** $17 \times k$

12. Solve each equation by inspection. Verify your answer.

a) $5c = 20$ **b)** $16 = 8n$

c) $5 = w + 5$ **d)** $p - 10 = 6$

13. Solve each equation using the opposite operation. Check your answer.

a) $g + 7 = 13$ **b)** $27 = 9m$

c) $6 = j \div 4$ **d)** $q - 4 = 1$

14. Solve each equation. Verify your solution.

a) $j \div 10 = 12$ **b)** $h \div 3 = -6$

c) $7x = 21$ **d)** $18 = f - 2$

15. Solve each equation. Verify your solution.

a) $y + 4.9 = 20$ **b)** $x + 7.9 = 10.3$

c) $-2 = y - 8$ **d)** $5.7 = b + 3.7$

Apply

16. The equation $\angle A + 30° + 80° = 180°$ models the sum of the angles in this triangle. What is the missing angle measure?

17. A speed skater travels 800 m/min. This can be modelled with the formula $d = 800t$.

a) What do the variables represent?

b) How long will it take the skater to travel 5000 m?

Chapter Problem

18. Some students play a game sitting on the dock. The first person names two songs that start with the same word. The second person names four songs that all start with another word. The third person names six songs that all start with another word, and so on.

a) Describe the pattern.

b) Write a formula for the number of songs named by the nth person.

c) What do your variables represent?

d) Nadia is the final player in the game. She names 16 song titles. How many students are playing? Explain how you found your solution.

19. The formula $a + e = 85$ is often used to determine when an employee can retire.

- a represents the employee's age
- e represents the number of years of employment

a) Mrs. Lowry is 51 years old. She has been teaching for 20 years. Can she retire this year? Explain.

b) Mr. Hudson has been teaching for 30 years. How old does he have to be to retire this year?

20. John pays $63 for two shirts.

a) Identify your variable. Write an equation to model John's purchase.

b) What is the full price of one shirt?

 21. Pam creates an equation to show how she spent her money at a movie. She spends $15.

$$15 = p + 2.50 + 9.50$$

a) What could the variable p represent?

b) Show how Pam can simplify her equation.

c) To find the value for p, Pam subtracts 15 from both sides of the equal sign. Will she be able to solve the equation? Explain.

Extend

22. With each rise of 1000 m, the temperature decreases by 6°C. It is 5°C outside your school. It is −37°C outside an airplane flying above the school. How high is the airplane?

23. a) Write an equation to model the diagram.

b) What operations will you undo to get the variable by itself?

c) Solve the equation. Justify your method.

Apply the Opposite Operations

Focus on...
- opposite operations
- solving equations
- the reverse order of operations

Many things are done in a specific order. For example, you turn on the computer. When it boots up, you open the program you want to use. Then, you open a file and start to work. When you are finished, you save your work, and then close the program and shut down the computer. How is the order of turning on a computer and starting to work related to the order of saving a file and shutting down the computer? How is solving an equation like using a computer?

Discover the Math

Materials
- 2 cups or containers
- supply of counters

How can you undo operations to solve equations?

1. Model the equation $2x + 6 = 20$ using cups and counters. Find the value of x.

> Make sure you keep the equation balanced on both sides of the equal sign.

2. What strategies did you use?

3. a) Which operation did you undo first?
b) Which operation did you undo second?

4. Use your strategies to solve the equation $4m - 3 = 5$. Check your solution. Does the right side of the equal sign have the same value as the left side? If not, revise your strategies.

5. Use your strategies to solve the equation $22 = 6n - 2$. Check your solution.

6. Reflect Some equations involve more than one operation. Does the order of undoing the operations on the variable affect the solution? When else do you perform operations in a specific order?

Example 1: Model and Solve an Equation

a) Model the equation $3y + 2 = 8$.
b) Solve the equation by applying the opposite operations.
c) Verify your solution.

Solution

a)

> After removing two masses from each side, I see by inspection that one *y* mass equals 2.

> I can use a balance to model an equation. If I perform an operation on one side, I need to perform the same operation on the other side.

Strategies
What other way can you model your solution?

b)
$$3y + 2 = 8$$
$$3y + 2 - 2 = 8 - 2 \qquad \textbf{Subtract to undo addition.}$$
$$3y = 6$$
$$3y \div 3 = 6 \div 3 \qquad \textbf{Divide to undo multiplication.}$$
$$y = 2$$

> The expression $3y$ means $3 \times y$. The opposite operation is division.

> The order of undoing operations looks like the reverse of the order of operations.

Literacy Connections

You use BEDMAS to help you remember the order of operations. To solve an equation, follow the reverse order of operations.

S Subtraction
A Addition
M Multiplication
D Division,
E Exponents
B Brackets

c) Left Side = $3y + 2$ Right Side = 8
$$= 3(2) + 2$$
$$= 6 + 2$$
$$= 8$$

Left Side = Right Side
Therefore, $y = 2$ is the correct solution.

> Check your solution by substituting your answer into the equation. Then, evaluate each side of the equal sign.

Example 2: Apply the Reverse Order of Operations

Buy Two Sweatshirts
Get Three Energy Bars
for $2.50 each
(Tax Free).

Jake sees this advertisement in a store. Jake pays $51.50 for two sweatshirts and three energy bars. What is the price of one sweatshirt?

Solution

Understand

Energy bars cost $2.50 each. Jake buys three energy bars and two sweatshirts for $51.50. Tax is included. Find the price of one sweatshirt.

Plan

1. Identify the variable.
2. Model Jake's purchase with an equation.
3. Solve the equation.

Do It!

1. Let p represent the price of a sweatshirt.

2. $2p + (3 \times \$2.50) = \$51.50$

Jake buys two sweatshirts. That's $2 \times p$ or $2p$.

Jake also buys three energy bars for $2.50 each. They come to $7.50.

3.
$$2p + 7.50 = 51.50$$
$$2p + 7.50 - 7.50 = 51.50 - 7.50 \quad \text{Subtract to undo addition.}$$
$$2p = 44$$
$$\frac{2p}{2} = \frac{44}{2} \quad \text{Divide to undo multiplication.}$$
$$p = 22$$

The price of one sweatshirt is $22.

Look Back

Check your solution by substituting $p = 22$ into the equation.

Left Side = $2p + 7.50$ Right Side = 51.50
        = 2(22) + 7.50
        = 44 + 7.50
        = 51.50

           Left Side = Right Side

The solution is correct.

- To solve an equation, get the variable by itself on one side of the equal sign.

- When undoing the operations performed on the variable, follow the reverse order of operations.

S	Subtraction
A	Addition
M	Multiplication
D	Division
E	Exponents
B	Brackets

$36 = 5c - 4$
To get c by itself, you need to undo $\times 5$ by dividing and undo -4 by adding.
First perform addition. Then, perform division.

Communicate the Ideas

1. Show the steps to solve the equation $58 = 6h + 4$. Explain each step.

2. Matt and Leanne are solving the equation $75x + 43 = 643$.
Whose strategy is correct? Explain.

First, I divide both sides by 75.

I start by subtracting 43 from both sides.

3. Avi is solving an equation. He models one of his steps.

a) What operation is Avi undoing? What is his reason for performing this step?
b) What will his next step be?
c) Write an equation to model the step shown.

Check Your Understanding

Practise

4. Model each equation.

a) $2c - 8 = 6$ **b)** $24 = 4v + 16$
c) $1 + 5n = 6$ **d)** $9w - 7 = 29$

5. Copy each equation.
- Circle the first operation you undo.
- Underline the second operation you undo.

a) $2n + 4 = 18$ **b)** $3x + 5 = 17$
c) $0.8y - 7 = 9.4$ **d)** $27 = 7q + 6$

For help with questions 6 to 9, refer to Example 1.

6. Solve the equation modelled by each diagram. Check your solution.

a)

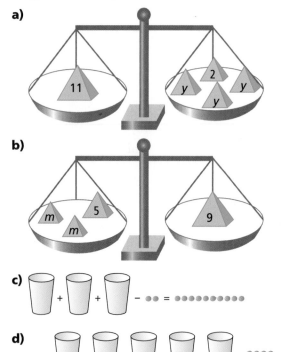

b)

c)

d)

7. Model and solve each equation. Check your solution.

a) $17 = 4k - 3$
b) $29 = 12n + 5$
c) $6x + 7 = 25$
d) $14 = 4n + 2$

8. Solve each equation. Verify your solution.

a) $9 + 5w = 49$
b) $1 + 16.2x = 49.6$
c) $23 = 10y - 7$
d) $0.9 = 0.7f - 1.2$

9. Solve each equation. Verify your solution.

a) $4.5k + 3 = 21$
b) $16y - 8 = 113$
c) $139 = 9x - 14$
d) $1.3v + 19 = 45$

For help with questions 10 and 11, refer to Example 2.

10. HTAM radio holds a Guess-the-Band contest. The radio station gives away three CDs for every correct answer, plus one CD just for being on the air. Leila got 10 CDs.

a) Write an equation to model Leila's CDs.
b) Solve your equation to find how many correct answers she gave.

11. A clothing store is having a "Start the Summer!" sale. Nora pays $37 for two tank tops and a pair of sunglasses.

Buy 2 Tank *Tops* and Pay only *$13* for Sunglasses (Tax-Free).

a) Model Nora's purchase with an equation.
b) Solve the equation to find the price of one tank top.

Apply

12. Steve is saving for a ski vacation that costs $500. If he triples his savings, he will still need $35. This can be modelled as $3s + 35 = 500$, where s represents his savings.

a) Explain how $3s + 35 = 500$ models Steve's savings.
b) How much money has Steve saved so far?
c) What other strategy can you use to find Steve's savings?

13. The total cost of heating a house using solar energy can be modelled with the formula $C = 200n + 9000$, where C represents the cost, in dollars, and n represents the number of years that the solar panel has been in use.

a) After how many years will the cost be $10 600?
b) After how many years will the cost be $13 000?

Chapter Problem

14. A camp charges schools $100 per day to use the camp's equipment plus $25 per day for food and sleep cabins for each student. The cost for one day can be modelled by the formula $C = 25n + 100$.

a) What do the variables C and n represent?
b) If 30 students want to go, how much will it cost per day?
c) The school raised $300 for a one-day trip. How many students can go?

15. The formula $R = 9T - 70$ models the chirping rates of crickets at various temperatures. The variable R represents the mean number of chirps per minute, and T represents the temperature, in degrees Celsius.

a) When the rate is 11 chirps/minute, what is the approximate temperature?
b) What is the chirp rate at 20°C?

16. Bryson sees this printable coupon on an amusement park Web site. Bryson pays $149 for two season passes and parking. What does the first season pass cost? What does the second season pass cost?

Adventure Mountain
Amusement Park

Buy one season pass, and get a second season pass for half price, plus pay only $ 20 for parking. No tax.

Try This! **17.** The perimeter of a rectangular garden is modelled using the formula $2w + 30 = 55$. In the formula, w represents the width of the garden in metres.

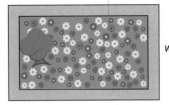

a) Find the width of the garden.
b) What is the meaning of the 55 in the formula?
c) The perimeter in the formula is made smaller. Investigate what happens to the width.
d) Can the perimeter keep getting smaller? For example, can it be 20? Explain.

Extend

18. Isabel tosses a stone off a cliff. The speed of the stone changes as it falls. This is modelled using the formula $v = 10t + 20$. The variable v represents the speed, in metres per second, and t represents the time, in seconds.

a) What is the speed of the stone when it is dropped?
b) At what time is the speed of the stone 60 m/s?
c) How will the formula change if the stone is tossed upward? Explain your answer.

19. The food energy required by a cross-country skier, on the day of a race, can be modelled with the formula $E = 3640 - 30T$. E represents the amount of food energy, in calories, and T represents the air temperature, in degrees Celsius. At what temperature does the skier require 4240 cal of food energy?

Model Problems With Equations

Focus on...
• applying equation skills
• modelling real-world problems

Quilts can have many patterns involving shapes, lines, or colours. What patterns do you see in this quilt?

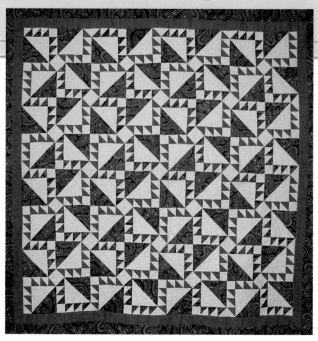

Discover the Math

Materials

• toothpicks

How can you solve a patterning problem?

Natalie is helping her mother decorate a quilt. They sew one piece of ribbon along each side of the equilateral triangles in a pattern.

Strategies
Which strategies are you using?

1. Model the pattern using toothpicks.

2. How many pieces of ribbon are needed for one triangle? two triangles? three triangles? Organize the information.

3. Describe the pattern.

4. Model the pattern using a formula.

5. Verify your formula. Is your formula correct? If not, revise it.

6. Natalie uses 65 pieces of ribbon to make a string of triangles. How many triangles does she sew?

7. Reflect How can a formula help you investigate a patterning problem?

Example 1: Solve a Patterning Problem

Juan measures the heights of stacks of cups to be 8.5 cm, 10 cm, and 11.5 cm.

a) Describe the pattern.
b) Predict the height of the next three stacks of cups.
c) Model the pattern with a formula. Explain what your formula means.
d) You have a stack of 100 cups. Use your formula to find the height.
e) Juan measures a stack to be 52 cm high. How many cups are in the stack?

Solution

a) The first cup is 8.5 cm high. You add 1.5 cm to find the height of each stack.

b) The next three stacks are 13 cm, 14.5 cm, and 16 cm high.

> The height of each stack increases by the height of the rim of one cup or 1.5 cm.

c) Let h represent the height of a stack.
Let c represent the number of cups.

Number of Cups	Height, h (cm)	Pattern
1	8.5 = 7 + 1.5	$h = 7 + 1.5 \times 1$
2	10 = 7 + 1.5 + 1.5	$h = 7 + 1.5 \times 2$
3	11.5 = 7 + 1.5 + 1.5 + 1.5	$h = 7 + 1.5 \times 3$
4	13 = 7 + 1.5 + 1.5 + 1.5 + 1.5	$h = 7 + 1.5 \times 4$

> I see a pattern. This is the same as the number of cups.

> **Strategies**
> Make a table or chart

The formula is

height of base of first cup ⌐ ⌐ height of each rim
$$h = 7 + 1.5 \times c$$
height of stack ⌐ ⌐ number of cups in stack

d) $h = 7 + 1.5 \times c$
$h = 7 + 1.5 \times 100$ **Multiply.**
$h = 7 + 150$
$h = 157$
The height of 100 cups is 157 cm.

> A stack of 100 cups means $c = 100$. I can substitute this into the formula and solve for h.

e) $h = 7 + 1.5 \times c$ **Substitute $h = 52$.**
$52 = 7 + 1.5 \times c$
$52 - 7 = 7 - 7 + 1.5 \times c$ **Subtract to undo addition.**
$45 = 1.5 \times c$
$\dfrac{45}{1.5} = \dfrac{1.5}{1.5} \times c$ **Divide to undo multiplication.**
$30 = c$
There are 30 cups in a stack that is 52 cm high.

> To get c by itself, undo the operations. Use SAMDEB to remember the order.

Example 2: Solve a Problem Using an Equation

Maria has a mould of a square candle dish. Each side length is 10 cm. She wants her new square candle dish to have a perimeter of 60 cm. By how much does Maria have to increase each side length of her mould?

Solution

Let x represent the increase in side length of the mould.

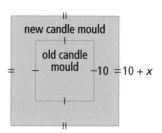

> The perimeter of my new mould will be 60 cm. So, each side is 60 ÷ 4 = 15 cm. My mould has side lengths of 10 cm. So, I need to increase each side of my mould by 5 cm.

Strategies
Make a picture or diagram

> Check the answer using an equation.

$$60 = (10 + x) \times 4$$
$$60 \div 4 = (10 + x) \times 4 \div 4 \qquad \textbf{Divide both sides by 4.}$$
$$15 = (10 + x) \qquad\qquad \textbf{Now you can remove the brackets.}$$
$$15 - 10 = 10 + x - 10 \qquad \textbf{Then, undo the + 10.}$$
$$5 = x$$

> The perimeter of the new mould is the new side length multiplied by four.

The side length of the mould needs to be increased by 5 cm.

Key Ideas

- Problems can be modelled and solved using equations.

- To develop an equation,
  - Draw a diagram or make a table.
  - Identify the variables.
  - Look for a pattern.
  - Translate the information using numbers and operations.

The perimeter of a rectangular frame is 30 cm. This is 14 cm more than the perimeter of the mirror. What is the length of one side of the mirror?

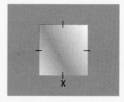

Let x represent the length of one side of the square mirror.
$$30 = 4x + 14$$
$$30 - 14 = 4x + 14 - 14 \qquad \textbf{Subtract to undo addition.}$$
$$16 = 4x$$
$$16 \div 4 = 4x \div 4 \qquad\qquad \textbf{Divide to undo multiplication.}$$
$$4 = x$$
The length of one side of the mirror is 4 cm.

Communicate the Ideas

1. Frankie measures a stack of cups to be 20.5 cm high. The number of cups is modelled using the formula $h = 7 + 1.5c$.

a) Describe the steps to solve the equation.

b) If the formula is rewritten as $1.5c + 7 = h$, will your steps change? Explain.

2. Look at the bookstore flyer. Which statement best defines the variable? Why?

A Let x represent the number of books.

B Let x represent the cost of one book.

C Let x represent the cost of five books.

Only $169 for Five Books
Plus a Magazine
Worth $4

Check Your Understanding

Practise

For help with questions 3 to 5, refer to Example 1.

3. Look at the pattern of marbles.

| Diagram 1 | Diagram 2 | Diagram 3 |

a) Copy and complete the table.

Diagram	Number of Marbles	Pattern
1	$5 = 2 + 3$	$2 + 3 \times 1$
2		
3		
4		

b) Write an equation that models the pattern.

c) How many marbles are in diagram 5?

d) What diagram in the pattern uses 41 marbles?

4. Leo measures the heights of stacks of one, two, and three baskets to be 17 cm, 19 cm, and 21 cm.

a) Describe the pattern.

b) Predict the height of the next three stacks of baskets.

c) Develop a formula for the height of b baskets.

d) How many baskets are in a stack that is 65 cm high?

5. Orly buys movie tickets over the telephone. Tickets cost $9.25 each, plus a $3 service charge for the order.

a) What is the price of ordering one ticket? two tickets? three tickets?

b) Write a formula to model the price of ordering tickets by telephone.

c) Orly pays $58.50. How many movie tickets does she buy?

For help with questions 6 and 7, refer to Example 2.

6. Kareem is designing a mouse pad to use with his computer. He has a design of a square mouse pad with side length 16 cm. He wants to design a mouse pad with a perimeter of 84 cm. By how much does Kareem have to increase each side length?

7. Wei designs floor tiles using a mould of an equilateral triangle. He increases the length of each side of the triangle mould by 8 cm. The perimeter of Wei's new mould is 93 cm. What was the original perimeter of his mould?

Apply

8. Solve each equation using the variables given. What might the variables represent? Justify your answer.

   a) $C = 160 + 160t$. Substitute $C = 171.20$.
   b) $v = d \div t$. Substitute $v = 52.5$ and $t = 4$.
   c) $e = 30h + 25$. Substitute $h = 8\frac{1}{2}$.

9. Filomena decorates the bottom of her jeans. She sews one piece of ribbon along each side of the regular hexagons.

The pattern can be modelled using the formula $r = 1 + 5h$. In the formula, r represents the number of pieces of ribbon and h represents the number of hexagons.

   a) Filomena has 96 pieces of ribbon. How many hexagons can she sew together?
   b) Filomena has 41 pieces of ribbon. How many hexagons can she sew together?

10. Anton developed the formula $m = 1 + 2d$ to model a pattern of marble diagrams.

   a) Describe what the variables could represent.
   b) What might the fifth diagram look like?

11. a) Develop a formula for the perimeter of the kite.

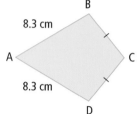

   b) If the perimeter is 31.4 cm, what is the length of side CD?
   c) If the perimeter is 49.8 cm, what is the relationship among the side lengths? Model your answer using an equation.
   d) Design your own kite. Make sure that sides BC and CD are the same length.

Extend

12. Long-stem roses cost $4.25 each. Delivery costs $10. Do not include tax. How many roses can be delivered for $50? Will there be any money left over?

13. Mahendra measures the circumference of each wheel.

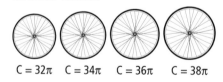

$C = 32\pi$ $C = 34\pi$ $C = 36\pi$ $C = 38\pi$

   a) Copy and complete the table for the wheels.

Wheel	Circumference, C (cm)	Pattern
1	32π	$2\pi(15 + 1)$
2		

   b) The circumference of a wheel is 60π cm. Use an equation to find the wheel number.

Explore Inequalities

Focus on...
- modelling inequalities
- interpreting mathematical statements
- finding solutions to inequalities

Some rides have height restrictions for safety. A sign beside this ride states, "Riders must be at least 135 cm tall." How can you show this mathematically?

Discover the Math

How can you compare numbers using symbols?

inequality

- a mathematical statement using symbols, such as > and <, to compare numbers or expressions

1. Mira is 140 cm tall. Can she go on the ride? Write an **inequality** comparing Mira's height to the height restriction.

2. Lucas is 130 cm tall. Can he go on the ride? Write an inequality comparing Lucas's height to the height restriction.

3. Write an inequality comparing Lucas's and Mira's heights.

4. The symbol ≥ means "is greater than or equal to." How might you use this symbol to model the statement, "Riders must be at least 135 cm tall"?

whole number

- the numbers 0, 1, 2, 3, ...

5. **a)** What **whole number** solutions make your statement from step 4 true?

   b) How would your answer change if you used the symbol >?

6. **Reflect** How can you use a variable in an inequality? Explain what the variable represents.

Example 1: Model Inequalities

Model each sentence. Define your variables. Then, write a mathematical statement using the proper symbol.

a) The mass is less than 8 kg.

b) John gets at least 70 marks on the test.

c) Twelve dollars is more than the cost of the lunch box.

d) Diane takes no more than four cookies.

Solution

a)

> When a scale is not balanced, the lower side has greater mass and the higher side has less mass.

Let *m* represent the unknown mass.
$m < 8$ kg

b)

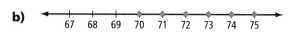

Let *m* represent the number of marks John gets.
$m \geq 70$

> John gets at least 70 marks. That means he gets 70 marks or more. I'll use the ≥ symbol.

c)

Let *C* represent the cost of the lunch box.
$\$12 > C$

> "More than" means greater than. I'll use the > symbol. The 12 goes on the left side because it is a greater amount.

d)

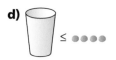

Let *c* represent the number of cookies Diane takes.
$c \leq 4$

> The most cookies Diane could take is four. She could also take fewer than four cookies or she might not take any. I'll use the ≤ symbol.

Example 2: Find the Solution Set for < and > Statements

Model each inequality. Then, write the whole number **solution set**.

a) $x < 3$

b) $72 < h$

> Solution sets can have one number, two numbers, or more.

solution set

- a list of numbers that make a mathematical statement true

Solution

a) *Method 1: Use a Balance*

> The right side of each scale shows the 3 in the inequality. The left side of each scale shows a possible solution for *x*.

$x < 3$
$x = 0, 1, 2$

Method 2: Use a Number Line

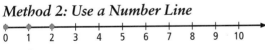

$x < 3$
$x = 0, 1, 2$

> The solution set starts with 2. I include all the whole numbers less than 2.

b)

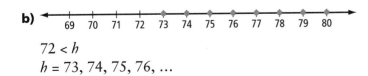

$72 < h$
$h = 73, 74, 75, 76, \ldots$

> The solution set starts at 73 and includes whole numbers greater than 73.

Example 3: Find the Solution Set for ≥ and ≤ Statements

Model each mathematical statement. Then, write the whole number solution set.

a) $3 \geq x$

b) $h \geq 72$

Solution

a) *Method 1: Use Cups and Counters*

$3 \geq x$

$x = 0, 1, 2, 3$

> The cup models the variable *x*. It can have a value of 0, 1, 2, or 3.

> The solution set starts with 3. I include the whole numbers less than 3 as well.

Strategies

What true statement could you write for each model?

Method 2: Use a Balance

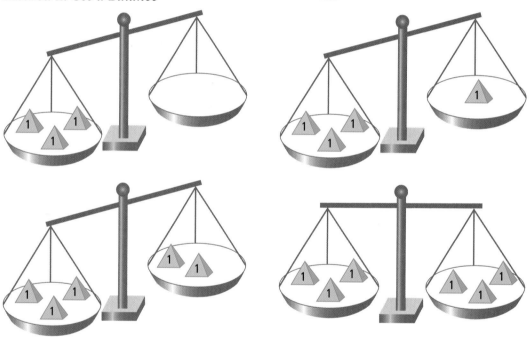

$3 \geq x$

$x = 0, 1, 2, 3$

b)

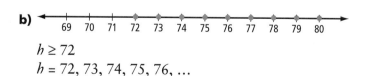

$h \geq 72$

$h = 72, 73, 74, 75, 76, \ldots$

> This is similar to $h > 72$. Putting a line under the symbol shows that *h* can also be equal to 72. The symbol ≥ means is greater than *or* equal to.

Example 4: CD Sales

A local music band is having trouble selling its newest CD.

a) Model the situation with an inequality.

b) Find how many CDs have been sold.

EVEN IF THE SALES DOUBLE, THE BAND WILL STILL SELL FEWER THAN 100,000 CDS.

Solution

a) Let n represent the number of CDs sold.

"Fewer than" means less than. Use the symbol <.

"Double" the sales means n is multiplied by two.

$$2n < 100\ 000$$

b) Since $2n < 100\ 000$, n must be less than $50\ 000$.

$n < 50\ 000$

The band has sold fewer than $50\ 000$ CDs.

I want to find n, the number of CDs sold. I know that $2 \times 50\ 000 = 100\ 000$. By inspection, n is less than $50\ 000$.

Key Ideas

- An inequality uses a symbol to compare numbers or expressions.

Symbol	Meaning	Example
<	less than	$5 < 8$
>	greater than	$8 > 5$
≤	less than or equal to	$5 \leq 8, 11 \leq 11$
≥	greater than or equal to	$8 \geq 5, 2 \geq 2$

- An inequality can involve a variable.

  $9 > m + 5$

  – The variable represents all the numbers that make the inequality true.

$m = 0$	$9 > 0 + 5$	$9 > 5$
$m = 1$	$9 > 1 + 5$	$9 > 6$
$m = 2$	$9 > 2 + 5$	$9 > 7$
$m = 3$	$9 > 3 + 5$	$9 > 8$
~~$m = 4$~~	~~$9 > 4 + 5$~~	~~$9 > 9$~~

  $9 > 9$ is not true. So, $m = 4$ is not in the solution set.

  – The list of numbers is called the solution set.

  $m = 0, 1, 2, 3$

Communicate the Ideas

1. **a)** Write an inequality for the whole number solution set shown on the number line.

   b) Does the number line show the whole number solution set for $5x < 30$? Explain.

2. Copy and complete the sentence for $m \geq 80\%$. Explain your choice of words.

   You must score ▬▬▬ *on an exam to be considered an honours student.*

3. The visual shows a solution set for an inequality. Write the inequality. Can you write the inequality using any other symbol? Explain your answer.

4. Explain the difference between the solution sets for $a > 18$ and $a \geq 18$.

Check Your Understanding

Practise

For help with questions 5 to 7, refer to Example 1.

5. Write an inequality that models each situation. Define your variables.

   a) More than 50 students were surveyed.
   b) The newspaper reported fewer than six UFO sightings.

6. Write a mathematical statement to model each situation. Define your variables.

   a) There are at least 16 slices of pizza.
   b) Renting a video costs no more than $6.
   c) Lisa lives more than 3 km from the school.

7. Describe a situation that can be modelled by each statement. Express the relationship mathematically using the correct symbol.

   a) a is greater than 5.
   b) b is less than or equal to 8.

For help with questions 8 to 10, refer to Example 2.

8. Write each model as an inequality using > or <.

   a)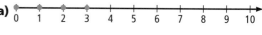

   b)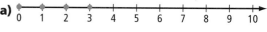

9. Use a number line to show the whole number solution set for each inequality.

   a) $m > 12$ **b)** $9 > p$

10. Model each inequality. Then, write the whole number solution set.

    a) $k < 10$ **b)** $19 > n$

For help with questions 11 to 13, refer to Example 3.

11. Write each model as an inequality using $\geq$ or $\leq$.

    a)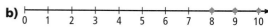

    b)

12. Use a number line to show the whole number solution set for each inequality.

   a) $m \geq 12$

   b) $9 \geq p$

13. Model each inequality. Then, write the whole number solution set.

   a) $k \leq 10$

   b) $19 \geq n$

For help with questions 14 and 15, refer to Example 4.

14. Miranda sells used books. If she triples her sales, she will still sell no more than 18 books.

   a) Model this situation with an inequality.

   b) How many books has Miranda sold?

15. There are fewer than 72 people at the dance. Forty boys are there.

   a) Model this situation with an inequality

   b) How many girls might be at the dance?

Apply

Chapter Problem

16. Students sign up to go on a canoe trip.

   a) Fewer than 30 students want to go. Write an inequality to model this.

   b) Show your solution on a number line.

   c) One teacher is needed for every six students. Write a number sentence to model the number of teachers needed.

   d) If four teachers are available, how many students might be allowed to go? Explain your reasoning.

17. Write the whole number solution set for each inequality.

   a) $n - 8 < 14$

   b) $2t \geq 18$

   c) $15 \leq 3x$

   d) $6 > s + 2$

18. If Teddy's height triples, it will be greater than Sam's height.

   a) Model this situation using an inequality.

   b) Sam is 270 cm tall. How tall might Teddy be?

19. Kim's mass is 28 kg.

   a) Write an inequality to model the mass of Kim's backpack.

   b) Write the whole number solution set to your inequality.

Try This!

20. The cost to organize the 2000 summer Olympics was less than double the cost to organize the 2002 winter Olympics.

   a) Model this situation with an inequality. Define your variables.

   b) In 2000, it cost $715 000 000 to organize the summer Olympics. How much might it have cost to organize the 2002 winter Olympics?

   c) In the 2000 summer Olympics, over 40% of the athletes were women. Write an inequality to model this statement. Show another way to model this statement. What information do you need to solve the inequality?

Extend

21. A healthy person normally has a temperature between 36°C and 38°C, when using an oral thermometer. When using an ear thermometer, the temperature readings can increase by up to 1%. Write two inequalities modelling the normal temperature readings with an ear thermometer. Explain your reasoning.

Key Words

Match each example with the correct term.

1. $\geq$ **A** variable

2. $\div$ and $\times$ **B** inequality

3. For $x < 3$, this would be 0, 1, 2.   **C** greater than

           D less than or equal to

4. 0, 1, 2, 3, 4, ...   **E** whole number solution set

5. y in $7y \leq 9y$

           F greater than or equal to

6. $x > 100$

           G opposite operations

7. $\leq$

           H whole numbers

12.1 Model and Solve Equations, pages 388–393

8. Solve the equation modelled by each diagram.

a)

b)

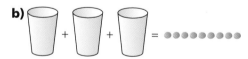

9. Model each equation. Then, solve using the opposite operation.

a) $w + 9 = 15$
b) $26 = 4x$
c) $40 = y \div 5$
d) $1 = z - 4$

10. Solve each equation. Verify your solution.

a) $2m = 62$ **b)** $c \div 3 = 7$
c) $16.5 = 8.25y$ **d)** $d - 10 = 15$
e) $9 = 4 + k$ **f)** $6.3 = x \div 4$

11. Describe a situation that can be modelled with each formula. Define the variable.

a) $12m = 364$ **b)** $d \div 24 = 60$

12. A photocopy company charges 3.4¢ per copy. A recent bill for a large customer came to \$40 851. This can be modelled using the equation $3.4p = 40\ 851$, where p represents the number of photocopies. How many photocopies were made?

12.2 Apply the Opposite Operations, pages 394–399

13. Solve the equation modelled by each diagram. Check your solution.

a)

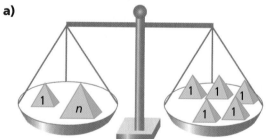

b)

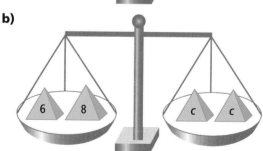

14. For each equation, what operation will you undo first? Why?

a) $2k + 5 = 19$
b) $20.9 = 3y - 1$
c) $16 = 1 + 6n$
d) $12x - 7 = 29$

15. Solve each equation in question 14. Verify your solution.

16. A hawk is hunting its prey. It begins its descent from a height of 63 m. This can be modelled using the formula $63 - h = 5.4t$, where t represents the time, in seconds, and h represents the height, in metres, above the ground. After how many seconds will the hawk reach a height of 5 m? Round your answer to the nearest 0.1 s.

12.3 Model Problems With Equations, pages 400–404

17. Annie charges $35 per month plus $9.50 per hour to cut grass. Annie charges one customer $63.50 for July.

a) Write an equation to model this situation. Define your variables.
b) How many hours did Annie spend cutting grass in July for this customer?

18. The fence around Toni's tree is in the shape of an equilateral triangle. Toni wants to increase the length of each side by 5 cm. The perimeter of her new fence will be 66 cm. What is the original perimeter?

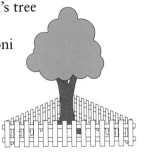

12.4 Explore Inequalities, pages 405–411

19. Model each diagram using an inequality. Then, find the whole number solution set.

a)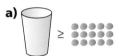

b)

20. Model each situation using an inequality.

a) There are fewer than 20 horses on the farm.
b) He invites up to four people to his cottage.
c) At least 35% of the music played on the radio is by a Canadian.

21. Find the whole number solution set for each inequality.

a) $j + 4 > 35$
b) $17 < w - 3$
c) $2g \leq 12$
d) $5 + 3 \geq m$

22. A family has a monthly budget of $1800 for food, rent, and clothing. They spend $1050 per month on rent and $630 for food. Develop an inequality modelling the money available for clothing each month.

Monthly Budget	$1800
1	food	$630
2	rent	$1050
3	clothing	
4		
5		

Multiple Choice

For questions 1 to 5, select the correct answer.

1. There are 88 keys on a piano. Thirty-six keys are white and the rest are black. This can be modelled with the equation $b + 36 = 88$, where b represents the number of black keys. How many keys are black?

A 58   **B** 124   **C** 52   **D** 62

2. Solve the equation $2.8 + 5b = 17.8$.

   A $b = 20.6$ **B** $b = 4$
   C $b = 3$ **D** $b = 15$

Use this statement about horse racing to answer questions 3 to 5.

"The mass of jockeys and their equipment must be less than 60 kg."

3. The mass of a jockey, j, and the mass of the equipment, e, can be modelled using

   A $j + e > 60$ **B** $j + e \geq 60$
   C $j + e < 60$ **D** $j + e \leq 60$

4. A jockey has a mass of 50 kg. Which statement models the mass of the equipment?

   A $10 \geq e$ **B** $e < 10$
   C $11 > e$ **D** $e < 9$

5. The equipment has a mass of 7 kg. Which number line models the mass of jockey in whole kilograms?

A

46 47 48 49 50 51 52 53 54 55

B

46 47 48 49 50 51 52 53 54 55

C

61 62 63 64 65 66 67 68 69 70

D

61 62 63 64 65 66 67 68 69 70

Short Answer

6. Amanda is solving an equation. She models one of her steps.

a) What operation is Amanda undoing? Explain the reason for this step.

b) What will her next step be? Write an equation that models this step.

7. When solving the equation $0.2n = 10$, George divides both sides by 10, but Indika divides both sides by 0.2. Whose method is correct? Explain.

8. Write the solution set modelled by each number line. Then, write an inequality for each solution set.

a)

0 1 2 3 4 5 6 7 8 9 10 11

b)

13 14 15 16 17 18 19 20 21 22 23

9. Write each inequality in question 8 using a different symbol.

10. Raj uses a square to represent an unknown quantity and buttons to represent numbers. What equation does he model? Solve the equation.

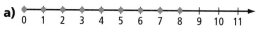

11. Solve each equation.

   a) $20 = x \div 5$ **b)** $26 + q = 27 + 6$
   c) $12 = 11r - 10$ **d)** $2n + 1.3 = 7.8$

Extended Response

12. The population of a city, from 1990 to 2002, can be modelled with the formula $P = 135a + 278\ 950$. In the formula, a represents the year.

a) Make a table of the estimated population from 1990 to 2002. Justify your method.

b) Describe the growth of the population between 1990 and 2002.

c) Would this model be accurate over a longer period of time? Explain.

13. Investigate the pattern of patio stones around a swimming pool.

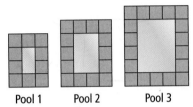

Pool 1   Pool 2   Pool 3

a) Use an equation to find how many patio stones would be around Pool 7.

b) Which pool in the pattern uses 54 patio stones?

c) Patio stones cost $6.50 each. What is the price of purchasing patio stones for Pool 5?

Chapter Problem Wrap-Up

1. Jodi's grade 8 class is going on a four-day school trip to camp.
- It costs $100 to rent the bus plus 25¢/km. This can be modelled using the formula $C = 100 + 0.25d$.
- The camp charges $20 per person per day.

Investigate how much money Jodi's class might need to fundraise for this trip. Use equations and inequalities to model your solutions.

2. After canoeing, students hang their lifejackets to dry. The first peg has two lifejackets hanging on it. Each of the other pegs has three lifejackets.

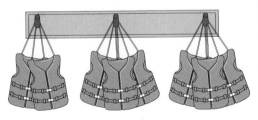

a) Make a chart showing the total number of lifejackets hanging on up to 5 pegs.

b) Describe, in words, the relationship between the number of pegs used and the total number of lifejackets hanging.

c) Write a formula for the total number of lifejackets, L, that are hanging on up to p pegs.

d) How many pegs would be used to hang 35 lifejackets?

e) A camper puts a total of five lifejackets on the first peg. The other pegs still have three lifejackets each. How will this change your formula?

Integer Card Game

An integer card game uses black cards as negative integers and red cards as positive integers. Black aces are worth –1 and red aces are worth 1.

Play the game with 1 to 3 classmates.

I will play the two 6s.

- Deal out 6 cards to each player. Place the remaining cards face down.
- On your turn, play any combination of cards from your hand with a sum of zero.
- If you cannot make zero, pick up one card from the deck.
- The person to your left plays next.
- The winner is the first person to run out of cards.

I will play the 6 of hearts, 4 of clubs, and 2 of spades. If I get a red ace on my next draw, I can go out!

The Stock Market

The table shows the gains and losses, in cents, of three stocks on two days last week.

	Monday	Tuesday
Stock A	–5	+1
Stock B	–7	–6
Stock C	–2	+3

1. How much more did Stock C gain than Stock A on Tuesday?

2. How much greater was Tuesday's gain than Monday's loss for Stock C?

3. How much more did Stock B lose than Stock C on Monday?

Solar Energy

Solar panels are an efficient way of generating electricity. Research how a solar power system works. Do any homes in your community use solar power? Investigate other forms of generating electricity. Report on the costs and benefits of using different forms of energy. How can you use equations to report on what you learned?

 Go to www.mcgrawhill.ca/links/math8 and follow the links to get started.

Design a Garden

City Council is selecting a landscaping company to design a public garden. The designs will be given an environmental score using the scoring system below.

Scoring System

concrete (–1)

P plants (1)

Sample Garden

Score for Sample Garden

$7 \times (-1) = -7$
$2 \times 1 = 2$
$-7 + 2 = -5$

Greenscapes Company has submitted the first three designs in a pattern.

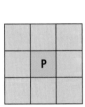

Design 1

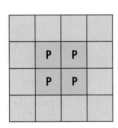

Design 2

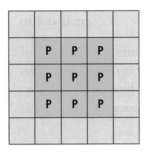

Design 3

1. Continue the pattern for three more designs. Then, calculate the environmental score of each design. Describe the first design that has a positive environmental score. Explain how you found your answer.

2. How would your answer to question 1 change if each concrete block were given a score of –2? (The plant score stays the same.)

3. The map shows the location of the public garden. Each grid square represents 1 m². Design a garden with a maximum of 20 squares around the outside. Try to design the garden with the highest possible environmental score.
   - Garden edges need concrete blocks unless they are along a tree line or a river, or adjacent to a building.

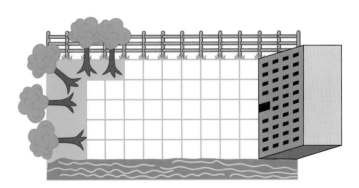

4. What other designs provide good environmental scores? Which design do you prefer?

Chapters 9–12 Review

Chapter 9 Data Management: Collection and Display

A sample group of teens are asked how important healthy eating is. The results for males and females are recorded separately. Use this information for questions 1 and 2.

Response	Number of Male Teens	Number of Feale Teens
Very important	14	18
Important	22	30
Not important	4	2

1. The population for this study is 800 male teens and 1000 female teens. Use the sample data to predict how many of each gender think healthy eating is important.

2. a) Draw a comparative bar graph to show both data sets.
   b) What conclusions can you draw from this graph?

3. Keira records the current temperature, in degrees Celsius, for a number of cities across Canada.

   3   11   9   10   13   9   10   10
   13   13   19   20   20   18   18   10

   a) Organize the temperatures into intervals of 5.
   b) Draw a histogram to show the data.

4. a) Describe a problem you could solve using a database in a library.
   b) Describe some advantages of using a spreadsheet to create graphs and perform calculations for data.

Chapter 10 Data Management: Analysis and Interpretation

5. Kelly is interested in being an industrial mechanic. She finds data listing starting salaries for this career. How much might she expect to earn?

Salaries ($)	
Stem (thousands)	Leaf (hundreds)
30	2 3
31	1 4 4
32	8 9

6. Dominic is training for a 100-m race. His practice times, in seconds, are shown.

   10.7   10.5   12.3   10.4   10.6   10.3

   a) Find the mean, median, and mode.
   b) One of the practice times is unusual. Recalculate the mean without this value. How much has the mean changed?

7. Claire thinks that the school's library is too small. She asks four of her friends, who all agree. She presents her findings to the student council. Identify the bias in Claire's sample.

8. Aly conducts a random survey to find which option grade 8 students prefer for a school trip. He claims that the majority of students prefer SPORTSWORLD.

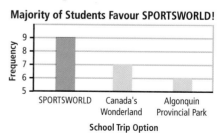

Majority of Students Favour SPORTSWORLD!

How has Aly distorted data to make a convincing argument?

Chapter 11 Integers

9. a) Use integer chips or a number line to model $5 + (-7)$.

b) Use integer chips or a number line to model $(-2) - (-6)$.

c) Draw a triangle for the multiplication statement $5 \times (-3) = -15$. Then, write the related division statements.

10. Evaluate each expression.

a) $-2 + (-7)$ **b)** $-12 + 4$

c) $17 - 25$ **d)** $15 - (-4)$

e) -6×8 **f)** $-5 \times (-7)$

g) $42 \div (-7)$ **h)** $-32 \div (-8)$

11. Evaluate. Check your answers with a calculator.

a) $-2(5 - 9)$ **b)** $-6 + 3(4^2 - 6)$

c) $2^2 - 9^2$ **d)** $(10 - 15) \div (-5)$

12. A grade 8 science class recorded the water levels of Laurel Creek. The table shows the weekly water level readings, in centimetres, above or below the mean level.

Week	1	2	3	4	5	6
Level	-7	-9	-4	+3	-1	+6

a) The mean water level is 123 cm. Compare the 6-week mean to this value.

b) In which season might these recordings have been taken? Explain why.

13. The first four numbers in a pattern are 12, 8, 4, 0.

a) Describe the pattern.

b) Determine the next three numbers in the pattern.

Chapter 12 Patterning and Equations

14. Model each equation. Then, solve using the opposite operation.

a) $m + 4 = 20$ **b)** $7 = y - 1$

c) $16 = 5x$ **d)** $33 = n \div 3$

15. Alfred charges $28 per month plus $9.25 per hour for cutting grass. He charges a customer $74.25 for June.

a) Model this situation with an equation.

b) How many hours did Alfred spend cutting grass in June?

16. Ruby designs patio stones using a mould of an equilateral triangle. She increases the length of each side of the triangle mould by 4 cm. The perimeter of Ruby's new mould is 90 cm. What was the original perimeter of her mould?

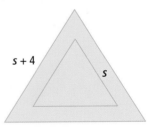

17. Model each diagram using an inequality. Then, find the whole number solution set.

a)

b)

c)

Geometry and Spatial Sense

- Identify and investigate the relationships of angles for triangles and for intersecting, perpendicular, and parallel lines.

- Construct and solve problems involving lines, angles, and triangles.

- Construct line segments and angles.

Number Sense and Numeration

- Justify calculation methods, and use estimation to assess reasonableness.

- Explain the process and conclusions in problem solving and investigations.

Patterning and Algebra

- Create and solve first degree equations with one variable.

Key Words

internal angles
interior angles
intersecting lines
perpendicular lines
opposite angles
supplementary
  angles
complementary
  angles
parallel lines
transversal
alternate angles
corresponding
  angles

Geometry of Angle Properties

Flags have been used as symbols throughout much of human history. Archaeologists have found the remains of Roman flags from over 2000 years ago. Even older flags were used in ancient Egypt and ancient China.

Flags are now used more than ever. Countries, provinces, and some cities have flags. So do some organizations, such as the United Nations. Some events, such as the Olympic Games, also have flags. Many flags include geometric figures, such as angles and triangles.

In this chapter, you will investigate the relationships of angles in triangles and identify the angle properties of intersecting, parallel, and perpendicular lines.

Chapter Problem

Look at the flag of Newfoundland and Labrador.

What types of angles do you see?

What types of triangles do you see?

As you work through this chapter, you will learn about the designs of some flags, including the flag of Newfoundland and Labrador. Then, you will design flags of your own.

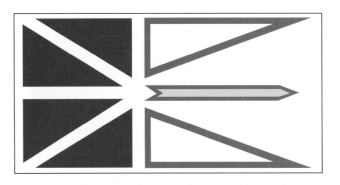

Classify Angles

You can classify angles using their measures.

| An **acute angle** measures less than 90°. | A **right angle** measures 90°. | An **obtuse angle** measures between 90° and 180°. | A **straight angle** measures 180°. |

1. Classify each angle.

a)

b)

2. Classify each angle.

a)

b)

3. Classify each angle.

a) 180°   **b)** 90°   **c)** 89°   **d)** 125°

Name and Measure Angles

The angles shown are angle ABC and angle XYZ. You can also write ∠ABC or ∠B and ∠XYZ or ∠Y. The middle letter names the vertex.

A protractor is used to measure angles.

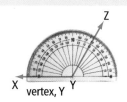

∠ABC is acute. Read the 60° measure, not the 120° measure.

∠XYZ is obtuse. Read the 120° measure, not the 60° measure.

4. Name each right angle in rectangle PQRS.

5. Name each acute angle and each obtuse angle in the diagram.

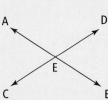

6. Measure each acute angle and each obtuse angle in the diagram.

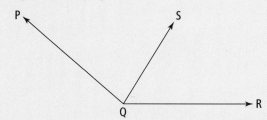

Draw Angles With a Protractor

You can use a protractor to draw an angle. ∠ABC measures 115°.

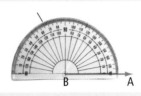 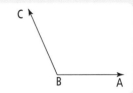

7. Draw each angle.

a) 90°   b) 43°   c) 139

8. Draw each angle.

a) ∠XYZ = 80°   b) ∠STU = 101°

Classify Triangles

You can classify triangles using their side lengths or their angle measures.

scalene triangle
• no sides equal
• no angles equal

isosceles triangle
• two sides equal
• two angles equal

equilateral triangle
• three sides equal
• three angles equal

acute triangle
• three acute angles

right triangle
• one right angle

obtuse triangle
• one obtuse angle

9. Classify each triangle using its side lengths.

a)
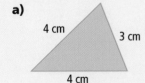
4 cm, 3 cm, 4 cm

b)

3 cm, 3 cm, 3 cm

c)
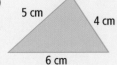
5 cm, 4 cm, 6 cm

10. Classify each triangle in two ways using its angle measures.

a)

30°, 110°, 40°

b)

45°, 45°

c)

60°, 60°, 60°

Internal Angles of a Triangle

Focus on...
- the sum of the angle measures in a triangle
- angle measurement problems for triangles

Triangles are often used in architecture. For example, the famous large glass pyramid at the Louvre art gallery in Paris has four triangular faces. How would you classify the angles in each triangle?

Discover the Math

Materials
- ruler
- protractor
- scissors

Alternative:
- Use Technology on page 429

How are the internal angles of a triangle related?

1. a) Draw a large triangle like the one shown.
   b) Use a protractor to measure the three **internal angles**. Record the three measures and find their sum.
   c) Repeat part b) for two other triangles of different shapes.

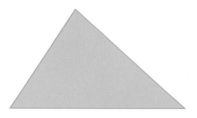

internal angle
- an angle inside a triangle or other polygon
- also called an interior angle

2. a) Cut out each triangle you drew in step 1. Label the angles as *a*, *b*, and *c*.

   b) Tear one triangle into three pieces. Make sure each piece contains an angle of the triangle.

   c) Place the three angles of the triangle so that their vertices are at the same point, as shown. What does this arrangement tell you? Explain.

   d) Repeat parts b) and c) for the other two triangles.

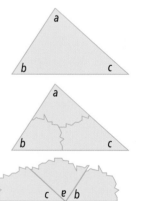

3. Reflect Compare your results with those of your classmates. Write a general statement about how the internal angles of a triangle are related.

Example 1: Find an Angle Measure

Two angles in a triangle measure 33° and 48°. Find the third angle.

Solution

Draw a diagram.
The angle measures in a triangle add to
180°.

$x + 33° + 48° = 180°$

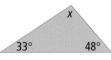
Estimate: 30 + 50 = 80

$x + 81° = 180°$
$x + 81° - 81° = 180° - 81°$

Estimate: 180 - 80 = 100

$x = 99°$

Check: $33° + 48° + 99° = 180°$

The third angle is 99°.

> I can calculate an internal angle in a triangle if I know the other two internal angles.

Example 2: Find Two Equal Angle Measures

The glass pyramid at the Louvre art gallery has four triangular faces. The angle at the top of each face measures about 64°. The other two angles are equal. Find each of the equal angles.

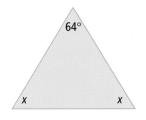

> Two equal angles means this is an isosceles triangle.

> I only need to know one angle measure if the other two angles are equal.

Solution

The angle measures in a triangle add to 180°.

$x + x + 64° = 180°$
$2x + 64° = 180°$
$2x + 64° - 64° = 180° - 64°$

Estimate: 180 - 60 = 120

$2x = 116°$
$\dfrac{2x}{2} = \dfrac{116°}{2}$
$x = 58°$

Check: $64° + 58° + 58° = 180°$

Each of the equal angles measures 58°.

- The measures of the internal angles in a triangle add to 180°.

- You can use the sum of the internal angles to find unknown angle measures in triangles.

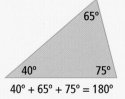

$40° + 65° + 75° = 180°$

Communicate the Ideas

1. Try to draw a triangle so that the sum of the internal angles is not 180°. Discuss your findings with your classmates.

2. Describe how to find the measure of the third angle in this triangle.

3. Explain why the sum of the angles in a triangle is 180°.

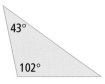

Check Your Understanding

Practise

For help with questions 4 and 5, refer to Example 1.

4. What is the unknown angle measure in each triangle?

a)

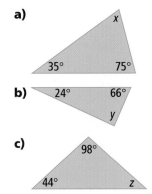

b)

c)

5. The measures of two angles in a triangle are given. What is the measure of the third angle?

a) 49° and 62°
b) 57° and 112°
c) 39° and 39°

6. Write a question like one of the parts of question 4 or question 5. Have a classmate answer your question.

For help with questions 7 and 8, refer to Example 2.

7. What are the unknown angle measures in each isosceles triangle?

a)

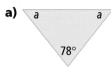

b)

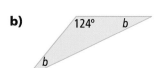

c)

8. The measure of one angle in an isosceles triangle is given. The other two angles are equal. What is the measure of each equal angle?

a) 36°

b) 88°

c) 155°

9. Write a question like one of the parts of question 7 or question 8. Have a classmate answer your question.

10. a) Draw a large scalene triangle. Estimate the measure of each angle.

b) Add your three estimates. Compare the result with the expected sum.

c) Repeat parts a) and b) for other triangles to improve your estimation skills.

Apply

11. Find the unknown angle measure in the triangle.

12. Two angles in a right triangle are equal. Find the measure of each equal angle.

13. A triangle has three equal angles. What are their measures?

14. A building casts a shadow on a sunny day.

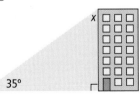

a) Use the diagram to find the measure of the unknown angle x.

b) What happens to the angles in the triangle as the sun climbs higher in the sky?

15. Can two angles in a triangle each measure 95°? Explain.

16. How many acute angles can a triangle have? Explain.

17. Part of the roof of a house looks like a triangle. The angle at the top is 118°, as shown in the diagram. The other two angles are equal. Find each of these angles.

18. The angles in a triangle have measures of x, $2x$, and $3x$ degrees. Find the values of the angle measures.

19. A totem pole is supported by two wires. Each wire makes a 68° angle with the ground. Find the unknown angle in each triangle.

20. Two triangles have different sizes. Each triangle has a 60° angle and an 80° angle. What can you conclude about the two triangles? Explain.

21. Home plate on a baseball diamond is in the shape of an irregular pentagon, as shown in the diagram.

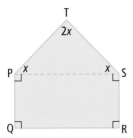

What are the five internal angles on home plate?

22. The diagram shows a triangle drawn on triangular dot paper. Find the angle measures in the triangle. Explain your reasoning.

23. a) Create a problem that involves the angle measures in a triangle.

b) Check that you can solve the problem.

c) Have a classmate solve your problem.

d) Compare your solutions.

e) Describe ways you might change the problem to make it more difficult.

Extend

24. a) Use triangles to predict the sum of the internal angles in a quadrilateral. Describe your method.

b) Find a way to check your prediction. Describe your method.

c) Check your prediction and describe your findings.

25. If one side of a triangle is extended, the new angle created is called an exterior angle of the triangle.

a) How is the exterior angle related to the internal angle that is next to it?

b) How is the exterior angle related to the other two angles in the triangle? Explain.

Making Connections

Paper Folding

Paolo said that he could show the sum of the angles in a triangle by paper folding. The diagrams show the three folds he made.

  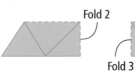

1. Describe what Paolo did.

2. How did he show the sum of the angles in the triangle?

3. Use Paolo's method for a few triangles of different shapes. Describe your findings.

Explore the Internal Angles of a Triangle Using *The Geometer's Sketchpad®*

Focus on...

• the sum of the angle measures in a triangle

This is another way to do the investigation that appears on page 424.

1. Open *The Geometer's Sketchpad®* and begin a new sketch.

2. Construct and label a triangle ABC as follows. Hold the shift key down and use the **Point Tool** to construct three points that are not in a line. From the **Construct** menu, select **Segments**. Deselect the segments by clicking in any white space. Select a point. From the **Display** menu, choose **Show Labels** to label the point A. Repeat for points B and C.

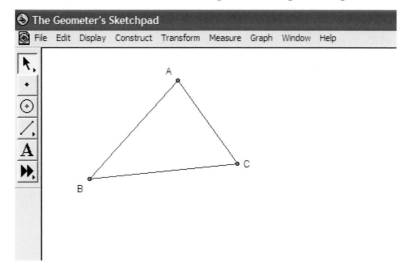

Technology Tip

• You can also select the **Text Tool** and click on each point to label it.

Technology Tip

• To measure an angle, select a point on one arm, then the vertex, and then a point on the other arm. Always select the vertex second.

Materials

• computer
• *The Geometer's Sketchpad®* Software

Optional:

• TECH 13.1A Explore Angles in a Triangle (GSP 4)
• TECH 13.1B Explore Angles in a Triangle (GSP 3)

3. a) To measure ∠ABC, select points A, B, and C in that order. From the **Measure** menu, choose **Angle**.

b) Measure the other two angles in the triangle.

4. a) From the **Measure** menu, choose **Calculate**. Click on the measure of the first angle. Then, click on the + sign on the calculator. Click on the measure of the second angle. Then, click on the + sign on the calculator. Click on the measure of the third angle. Then, click on **OK** on the calculator. What is the sum of the angle measures?

b) Drag point A, point B, or point C to change the angle measure. Does the sum of the angle measures change?

5. Reflect Describe how the angles in a triangle are related.

Angle Properties of Intersecting and Perpendicular Lines

Focus on...

- angle properties of intersecting and perpendicular lines
- problems involving intersecting lines

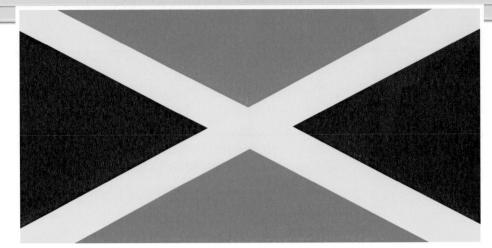

The diagram shows a Jamaican flag. The yellow diagonals cross, or intersect. Can you name the types of angles the diagonals make?

Materials

- ruler
- protractor

Alternative:

- Use Technology on page 435

intersecting lines

- lines that cross each other

perpendicular lines

- lines that intersect at right angles

Discover the Math

How are the angles formed by intersecting lines related?

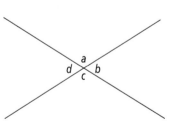

1. Draw two **intersecting lines** that form acute and obtuse angles.

   a) Measure the acute and obtuse angles.

   b) Repeat part a) for two other pairs of intersecting lines.

   c) Describe any patterns you see in the angle measures.

2. Draw two **perpendicular lines**. Describe patterns in the angle measures when the lines are perpendicular.

3. **Reflect** Compare your results with those of your classmates. Describe how the angles formed by intersecting lines are related.

Example 1: Opposite and Supplementary Angles

The diagonals of a Jamaican flag intersect to form four angles. One of the acute angles measures about 53°. Find the measures of the other three angles.

Solution

Draw a diagram.

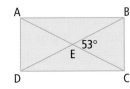

∠BEC and ∠AED are **opposite angles**.
They are equal.
∠AED = 53°

∠AEB and ∠BEC form a straight angle.
They are **supplementary angles**.

$$∠AEB + ∠BEC = 180°$$
$$∠AEB + 53° = 180°$$
$$∠AEB + 53° − 53° = 180° − 53°$$
$$∠AEB = 127°$$

Check: 53° + 127° = 180°

Estimate: 180 − 50 = 130

∠AEB and ∠DEC are opposite angles. They are equal.
∠DEC = 127°

The other three angles have measures of 53°, 127°, and 127°.

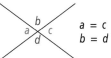
Literacy Connections

Remembering Opposite Angles
Opposite angles are X-angles.

supplementary angles

• two angles that add to 180°

120° 60°

• the two angles together make a straight angle

120° 60°

Did You Know?

After Confederation in 1867, Canada did not have its own flag for almost 100 years. Canada's flag was an unofficial version of the Canadian Red Ensign until 1965. Many Canadians had strong opinions about a national flag. The choice of the maple leaf design took months of heated debate in the House of Commons in Ottawa.

Canadian Red Ensign

Canadian Flag

Example 2: Complementary Angles

Find the measure of ∠ZYM in the diagram.

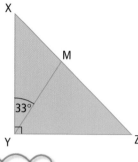

Solution

∠XYZ is a right angle, so it measures 90°.
∠ZYM and ∠XYM are **complementary angles**.

$$\angle ZYM + \angle XYM = 90°$$
$$\angle ZYM + 33° = 90°$$
$$\angle ZYM + 33° - 33° = 90° - 33°$$
$$\angle ZYM = 57°$$

Check: 33° + 57° = 90°

Estimate: 90 − 30 = 60

The measure of ∠ZYM is 57°.

complementary angles

• two angles that add to 90°

• the two angles together make a right angle

Key Ideas

- Two intersecting lines form two pairs of opposite angles. Opposite angles are equal.

- Two angles whose measures add to 180° are supplementary angles.

  50° + 130° = 180°

- Two angles whose measures add to 90° are complementary angles.

  50° + 40° = 90°

Communicate the Ideas

1. Wei drew two intersecting lines on a piece of paper. She used paper folding to find patterns in the measures of the angles. Describe what she did. What patterns did she find?

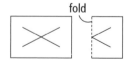 fold
 fold

2. How would you find an angle that is supplementary to the one in the diagram?

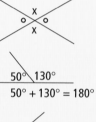
55°

3. An angle measures 73°. How would you find the measure of a complementary angle?

Remembering Complementary and Supplementary

• C is before S in the alphabet, and 90 is before 180 numerically.

• Supplementary and straight angle both start with S; and a straight angle measures 180°.

Practise

For help with questions 4 and 5, refer to Example 1.

4. What is the measure of each unknown angle?

a)

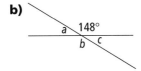

b)

c)

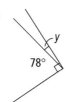

5. Two intersecting lines form the angle with the given measure. What are the measures of the other acute and obtuse angles formed by the intersecting lines?

a) 32°　　**b)** 91°　　**c)** 179°

For help with questions 6 and 7, refer to Example 2.

6. What is the measure of the unknown angle?

a)

b)

c)

7. ABCD is a rectangle. What is the measure of ∠BDA?

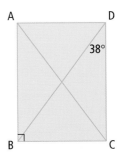

8. Find the measure of the angle that is complementary to the given angle.

a) 30°

b) 87°

c) 5°

9. Find the measure of the angle that is supplementary to the given angle.

a) 45°

b) 90°

c) 161°

Apply

10. The diagram shows the two angles formed by a railway line and a siding. If the larger angle is 152°, what is the smaller angle?

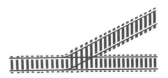

11. Find the unknown angle measures in the diagram. Explain your reasoning.

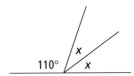

12. The diagram shows the flag of Newfoundland and Labrador. Use words and diagrams to identify pairs of supplementary angles and pairs of complementary angles in the design.

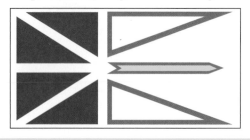

13. Find the unknown angle measures in the diagram. Explain your reasoning.

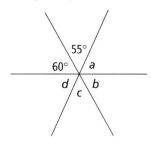

14. Two angles are complementary. The difference in their measures is 20°. What is the measure of each angle?

15. Identify the complementary angles in △ABC. Explain your reasoning.

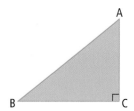

16. ∠A and ∠B are supplementary. ∠A and ∠C are supplementary. How are ∠B and ∠C related?

 17. The diagram shows some directions of the compass.

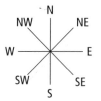

a) How many acute angles are there? What are their measures?

b) How many right angles are there?

c) How many obtuse angles are there? What are their measures?

d) How many pairs of complementary angles are there? Explain your reasoning.

Extend

18. a) Choose any acute angle. Find its complementary angle.

b) Double the complementary angle. Then, add the acute angle.

c) Repeat parts a) and b) until you see a pattern in the sum.

d) Describe the pattern.

e) Explain the pattern.

Explore Intersecting and Perpendicular Lines Using *The Geometer's Sketchpad®*

Focus on...

- angle properties of intersecting and perpendicular lines

This is another way to do the investigation that appears on page 430.

1. Open *The Geometer's Sketchpad®* and begin a new sketch.

2. a) Construct two points so that one is a few centimetres to the right of the other. Construct a line segment to join them.

b) Construct a point above the segment and a point below the segment. Construct a segment that joins the two new points.

c) Use the **Point Tool** to construct the point of intersection of the two segments.

d) Display the labels that name the five points.

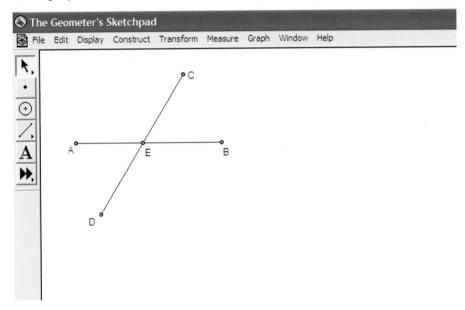

Technology Tip

- Another way to construct the point of intersection is to select both line segments. From the **Construct** menu, choose **Intersection**.

Materials

- computer
- *The Geometer's Sketchpad®* Software

Optional:

- TECH 13.2A Explore Intersecting and Perpendicular Lines (GSP 4)
- TECH 13.2B Explore Intersecting and Perpendicular Lines (GSP 3)

3. a) Measure the four acute and obtuse angles formed by the two segments.

b) Describe any patterns you see in the angle measures.

4. a) Add the measures of pairs of angles.

b) Describe any patterns you see in the sums of angle measures.

5. Drag an endpoint of one of the segments. Do the patterns you described change? Explain.

6. Reflect Describe how the angles formed by intersecting lines are related.

13.3

Angle Properties of Parallel Lines

Focus on...
- angle properties of parallel lines and transversals
- problems involving parallel lines

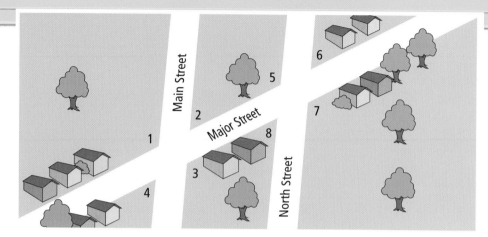

On the map, Main Street and North Street are parallel. Major Street cuts across them. The streets form 8 angles, as shown. Which angles look equal to you? Do your classmates agree?

Materials
- ruler
- protractor

Alternative:
- Use Technology on page 441

Discover the Math

parallel lines
- lines in the same plane that do not intersect
- marked by matching arrowheads
- two parallel lines are always the same distance apart

How are the angles formed by parallel lines and a transversal related?

1. a) Draw two **parallel lines** along opposite sides of a ruler, as shown.
Then, draw a **transversal** to create acute and obtuse angles, as shown.
Measure the acute and obtuse angles.

b) Repeat part a) for different sets of parallel lines and different transversals.

c) Describe patterns you see in the angle measures.

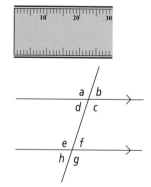

transversal
- a line that crosses two or more lines

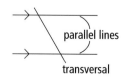

2. Draw two parallel lines. Draw a transversal that is perpendicular to them. Describe the patterns you see in the angle measures.

3. Reflect Compare your results with those of your classmates. Describe how angles formed by parallel lines and a transversal are related.

Example: Parallel Lines and a Transversal

Find ∠EHB, ∠FHG, and ∠EHG.

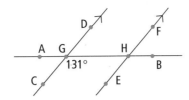

Solution

∠CGH and ∠EHB are a pair of **corresponding angles**.
They are equal.
∠EHB = 131°

∠CGH and ∠FHG are a pair of **alternate angles**.
They are equal.
∠FHG = 131°

∠CGH and ∠EHG are a pair of **interior angles**.
They are supplementary.

$$∠CGH + ∠EHG = 180°$$
$$131° + ∠EHG = 180°$$
$$131° + ∠EHG − 131° = 180° − 131°$$
$$∠EHG = 49°$$

Estimate: 180 − 130 = 50

Check: 49° + 131° = 180°

∠EHB = 131°, ∠FHG = 131°, and ∠EHG = 49°.

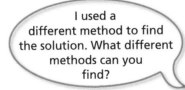

I used a different method to find the solution. What different methods can you find?

corresponding angles

• a pair of equal angles on the same side of a transversal crossing a pair of parallel lines

$a = w$
$b = x$
$c = y$
$d = z$

• four pairs are:
a and w, b and x,
c and y, d and z

alternate angles

• a pair of equal angles formed between a pair of parallel lines and on opposite sides of a transversal

$c = w$
$d = x$

• c and w are one pair; d and w are another pair

interior angles

• a pair of supplementary angles formed between a pair of parallel lines and on the same side of a transversal

$d + w = 180°$
$c + x = 180°$

• d and w are one pair; c and x are another pair.
• also known as co-interior angles

Key Ideas

- Two parallel lines and a transversal create
  - two pairs of alternate angles
  - four pairs of corresponding angles
  - two pairs of interior angles

alternate angles   corresponding angles   interior angles

- The alternate angles in each pair are equal.

- The corresponding angles in each pair are equal.

- The interior angles in each pair are supplementary. They add to 180°.

Communicate the Ideas

1. The diagram shows the angles created by two parallel lines and a transversal.

   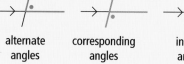

   Identify all pairs of
   a) interior angles
   b) alternate angles
   c) corresponding angles

2. In the diagram, the transversal is perpendicular to the parallel lines. How many angles have the same measure as angle *a*? Explain.

   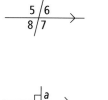

3. Angles *x* and *y* are a pair of interior angles created by two parallel lines and a transversal. If you know the measure of angle *x*, how can you calculate the measure of angle *y*?

Literacy Connections

Remembering Angles

Letter names may help you remember these types of angles.

Alternate angles are Z-angles.

Corresponding angles are F-angles.

Interior or co-interior angles are C-angles.

Practise

For help with questions 4 to 9, refer to the Example.

4. Find the measure of angle x.

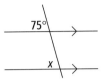

5. Find the measure of angle y.

6. Find the measure of angle z.

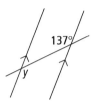

7. Find $\angle HEG$. Explain your reasoning.

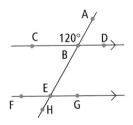

8. Find $\angle TUW$. Explain your reasoning.

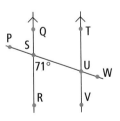

9. Find $\angle LPQ$, $\angle QPR$, and $\angle SPR$. Explain your reasoning.

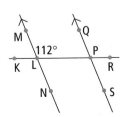

Apply

10. The number symbol, #, is used on computer keyboards and telephones.

a) Use diagrams to show all the angles that equal x. Justify your reasoning.

b) Use diagrams to show all the angles that are supplementary to x. Justify your reasoning.

c) The diagram you use to play tick-tack-toe looks like a number symbol. However, the intersecting lines are perpendicular.

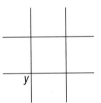

Use diagrams to show all the angles that equal y.

11. The measures of angles a and b add to $108°$. Find the measures of angles c and d.

12. What is the sum of angles w, x, y, and z? Explain how you know.

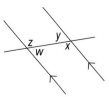

13. a) Create a problem that involves at least one pair of parallel lines and at least one transversal.

b) Check that you can solve the problem.
c) Have a classmate solve your problem.
d) Compare your solutions.
e) Describe ways you might change the problem to make it more difficult.

Chapter Problem

14. The diagram shows the flag of Lesotho. Use words and diagrams to identify the following. State any assumptions you make.

a) as many pairs of interior angles as possible
b) as many pairs of corresponding angles as possible

15. The diagram shows one section of a railing beside a staircase. Three parallel rails are supported on two vertical posts. The measure of one angle is shown. Draw a diagram to show the measures of all the other acute and obtuse angles.

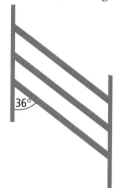

16. a) How are the angles in a parallelogram related? Explain.

b) What is the sum of the angles in a parallelogram? How do you know?

17. How could you show that angles x and z are supplementary without measuring them?

18. There are three parallel horizontal boards in a farm gate. The diagonal board makes the gate stronger.

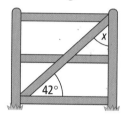

a) Find angle x. Justify your method. State any assumptions you make.
b) Show other ways to find angle x. Justify your methods. State any assumptions you make.

Extend

19. Two parallel lines and a transversal create eight acute and obtuse angles. Describe how you could use each of the following to find relationships between the angles.

a) tracing paper and translations
b) tracing paper and rotations
c) paper folding

20. The diagram shows a sidewalk and one corner of a parking lot. The edges of the sidewalk are parallel to the edges of the parking lot.

How are the two acute angles related? Explain and justify your reasoning.

Explore Parallel Lines Using *The Geometer's Sketchpad®*

Focus on…

• angle properties of parallel lines

This is another way to do the investigation that appears on page 436.

1. Open *The Geometer's Sketchpad®* and begin a new sketch.

2. a) Construct two points so that one is a few centimetres to the right of the other. Construct a line through them.

b) Construct a point above the line. Select the line and the point. From the **Construct** menu, choose **Parallel Line**.

c) Use the **Point Tool** to construct another point on the new line.

d) Construct one point above the parallel lines and one point below the parallel lines, as shown.

e) Construct a line through the two points you constructed in part d).

f) Construct the point of intersection of the transversal with each of the parallel lines.

g) Display the labels that name all the points you constructed.

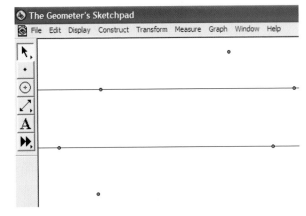

Technology Tip

• Another way to construct a point on the parallel line is to select the line. From the **Construct** menu, choose **Point on Parallel Line**.

Materials

• computer
• *The Geometer's Sketchpad®* Software

Optional:
• TECH 13.3A Explore Parallel Lines (GSP 4)
• TECH 13.3B Explore Parallel Lines (GSP 3)

3. a) Measure the eight acute and obtuse angles formed by the parallel lines and the transversal.

b) Describe any patterns you see in the angle measures.

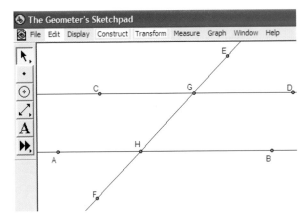

4. Drag a point on the transversal to change all the angle measures. Do the patterns you described change? Explain.

5. Reflect Describe how the angles formed by parallel lines and a transversal are related.

Apply Angle Measures

The design of this bridge includes many angles, triangles, and parallel segments. Identify pairs of equal angles. How did you identify them?

Discover the Math

How can you apply angle measures to solve problems?

Example 1: Triangles and Intersecting Lines

Find the measure of ∠EBD in the diagram.

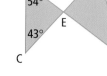

Solution

Understand

The problem involves two triangles.
You need to find an unknown angle measure in one of them.

Plan

To find the unknown angle, you need to know the other two angles in △DEB.
The measure of ∠BDE is given.
You need to find ∠DEB before you can find ∠EBD.
Two angle measures are given for △ACE. Find the third angle in that triangle.

Do It!

In △ACE,

$$\angle AEC + \angle ACE + \angle CAE = 180°$$
$$\angle AEC + 43° + 54° = 180°$$
$$\angle AEC + 97° = 180°$$
$$\angle AEC + 97° - 97° = 180° - 97°$$
$$\angle AEC = 83°$$

> If I know two angles in a triangle, I can find the third angle. The angles in a triangle add to 180°.

> Estimate: 40 + 55 = 95

> Estimate: 180 − 100 = 80

Strategies
Choose a formula

∠AEC and ∠DEB are opposite angles.
∠DEB = 83°

Opposite angles are equal.

In ΔDEB,
∠EBD + ∠BDE + ∠DEB = 180°
∠EBD + 60° + 83° = 180°
∠EBD + 143° = 180°
∠EBD + 143° − 143° = 180° − 143°
∠EBD = 37°
The measure of ∠EBD is 37°.

Estimate: 60 + 80 = 140

Estimate: 180 − 140 = 40

Look Back   Check that the angles in each triangle add to 180°.
83° + 43° + 54° = 180°
37° + 60° + 83° = 180°

Example 2: Triangles and Parallel Lines

The diagram shows a side view of a table. The legs are perpendicular to each other. The tabletop is parallel to the ground. Find the measures of angles x and y.

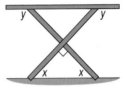

Solution

The angles in a triangle add to 180°.
In the lower triangle,
$$x + x + 90° = 180°$$
$$2x + 90° = 180°$$
$$2x + 90° − 90° = 180° − 90°$$
$$2x = 90°$$
$$\frac{2x}{2} = \frac{90°}{2}$$
$$x = 45°$$
Check: 45° + 45° + 90° = 180°

The top of the table is parallel to the ground, so the table legs are transversals.

Each table leg creates a pair of interior angles with the tabletop and the ground. Interior angles are supplementary.

Interior angles form a C-pattern.

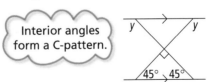

$$y + 45° = 180°$$
$$y + 45° − 45° = 180° − 45°$$
$$y = 135°$$
Check: 135° + 45° = 180°

Estimate: 180 − 40 = 140

The measure of x is 45°. The measure of y is 135°.

- You can apply angle measures to solve problems.

- To solve problems, you can apply the angle properties of
  - triangles
  - intersecting and perpendicular lines
  - parallel lines and transversals

Communicate the Ideas

1. Describe two different methods you could use to find the measure of angle y.

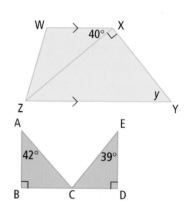

2. Describe how you could find the measure of ∠ACE.

3. Can you find the measure of angle x in this diagram? Explain.

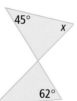

Check Your Understanding

Practise

For help with question 4, refer to Example 1.

4. Find the measure of angle x.

For help with questions 5 and 6, refer to Example 2.

5. Find the measure of ∠KPL.

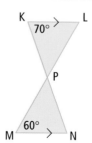

6. Find the measure of angle z.

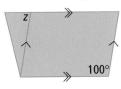

7. Find the measure of angle r.

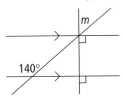

8. Find the measure of angle m.

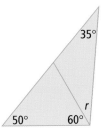

9. Find the measure of $\angle$BCD.

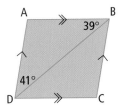

Apply

10. a) How can you use the parallel lines to show that the sum of the angles in the triangle is 180°?

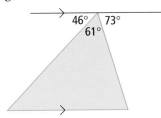

b) Use the diagram to show that the sum of the angles in any triangle is 180°.

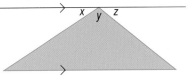

11. On some road bridges, parallel cables connect the main supports and the road.

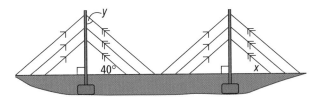

Use the diagram of the bridge to find angles x and y.

13. The diagram shows the runways at an airport.

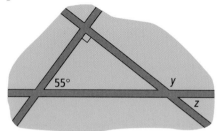

Find angles y and z.

14. The diagram of Marco's kite shows the plastic frame and the coloured cover.

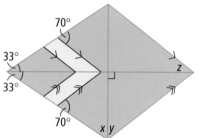

Find angles x, y, and z.

15. The diagram shows part of a road map. Oak Street and Elm Street are parallel.

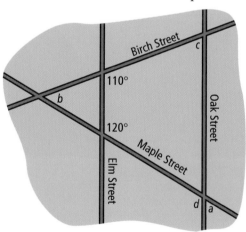

Find angles a, b, c, and d.

16. In the diagram, DE is parallel to BC. How are ΔABC and ΔADE related? Explain.

 17. a) Create a problem that involves the angle measures in at least two triangles.

b) Check that you can solve the problem.

c) Have a classmate solve your problem.

d) Compare your solutions.

e) Describe ways you might change the problem to make it more difficult.

Extend

18. How do angles x and y compare?

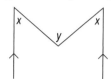

19. Find the measure of angle z.

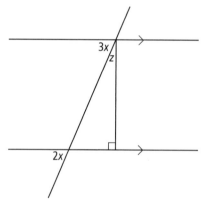

13.5 Construct Line Segments and Angles

Focus on...
- constructing line segments
- constructing angles

When builders construct a house, they must construct angles accurately. What would happen if the builders could not construct right angles accurately?

Discover the Math

Materials
- ruler
- compasses
- protractor

Optional:
- transparent mirror

How can you construct line segments and angles?

1. Use paper folding or a transparent mirror to construct each angle. Describe your method. Check the measure of the angle with a protractor.

   a) 90°   **b)** 45°   **c)** 135°

2. **a)** Use the steps shown to construct a 60° angle with a ruler and compasses. Use a protractor to check that the angle measures 60°.

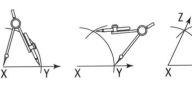

   b) Join Y and Z to make △XYZ. Use the triangle to explain why ∠YXZ measures 60°.

3. Start with a 60° angle. Use paper folding or a transparent mirror to construct each of the following angles. Describe the method you used. Check the measure of each angle with a protractor.

   a) 30°   **b)** 120°   **c)** 90°   **d)** 150°

4. **Reflect** Explain why your constructions with paper folding or a transparent mirror worked. Compare explanations with your classmates.

Example: Use Compasses to Construct a Triangle

Construct a triangle with side lengths of 6 cm, 5 cm, and 4 cm.

Solution

Step 1: Use a ruler to draw a 6-cm line segment. _____

Step 2: Set your compasses to 5 cm.

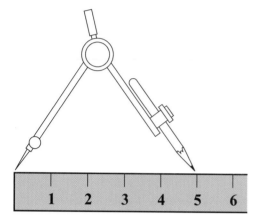

Step 3: Put the compass point on one end of the segment. Draw part of a circle.

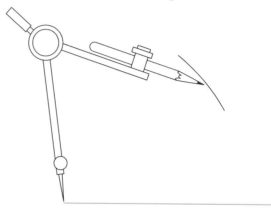

Step 4: Set your compasses to 4 cm. Put the compass point on the other end of the segment. Draw a part of a circle so that it intersects the first one you drew.

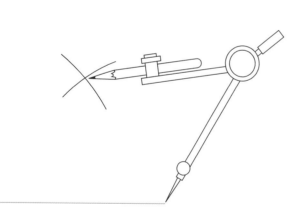

Step 5: Draw two line segments to complete the triangle.

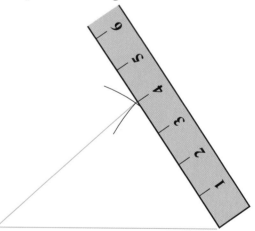

The result is a triangle with side lengths 6 cm, 5 cm, and 4 cm.

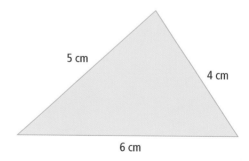

5 cm

4 cm

6 cm

- You can construct angles by different methods, such as using paper folding, a transparent mirror, or a protractor.

- You can construct line segments by different methods, such as using compasses and a ruler.

Communicate the Ideas

1. Describe how you could divide an angle into two equal parts without using a protractor.

2. Describe how you could construct a 90° angle with arms that are 5 cm long.

3. Try to construct this triangle using only a ruler and a pencil. Explain why compasses were used in the Example.

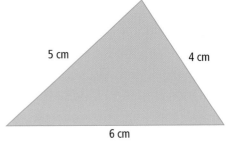

4. Describe how you could divide a line segment into two equal parts without using a ruler.

Check Your Understanding

Practise

5. Construct a 75° angle using a ruler and a protractor.

6. How could you construct a 75° angle without using a protractor?

7. Draw a line segment that is 6 cm long. Starting with this segment, use paper folding to construct segments with the following lengths. Describe what you did.

a) 3 cm
b) 12 cm
c) 9 cm

8. a) Use a protractor and a ruler to construct a 50° angle.

b) Start with the angle from part a). Use paper folding or a transparent mirror to construct an equal angle. Use a protractor to check the measure of this angle.

For help with questions 9 and 10, refer to the Example.

9. Construct a triangle with side lengths of 7 cm, 6 cm, and 5 cm.

10. Construct a triangle with side lengths of 4 cm, 7 cm, and 8 cm.

Apply

11. Without using a protractor, construct the triangle shown in the diagram. Describe your method.

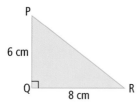

12. Measure the distance between the points. Construct a square with this side length.

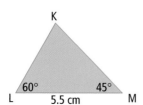

13. Construct the triangle shown. Describe your method.

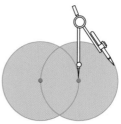

14. Construct the triangle shown.

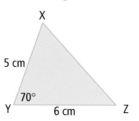

15. Construct a rectangle with side lengths of 5 cm and 4 cm. Describe your method.

16. The diagrams show a way to use compasses to construct an equilateral triangle.

Draw a circle.

Put the point of the compasses on the circle. Draw a second circle with the same radius.

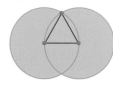

Draw a triangle.

a) Explain why this method works.
b) Use compasses to draw an equilateral triangle with a side length of 5 cm.
c) Modify the method by making the second circle smaller than the first circle. What type of triangle did you construct? Explain.

17. Use a ruler and a protractor to construct the parallelogram.

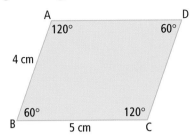

18. A math drawing set usually includes two plastic triangles.

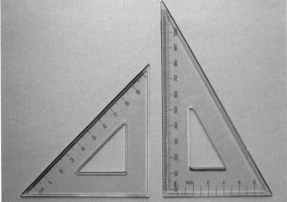

a) What are the angle measures in each plastic triangle?

b) Use the plastic triangles to draw angles with the measures from part a). Describe the method you used.

c) What acute angles could you construct using the two plastic triangles? Describe the methods you would use. Then, check that the methods work.

d) What obtuse angles could you construct using the two plastic triangles? Describe the methods you would use. Then, check that the methods work.

Extend

19. a) Without using a protractor, construct a triangle with angle measures of 30°, 60°, and 90°. Describe your method. Then, use a protractor to check the angle measures.

b) Construct a bigger triangle with the same angles as in part a). How are the two triangles related? Explain.

20. a) Can you construct triangles with sides of the given lengths? If not, explain why not.
4 cm, 6 cm, 8 cm
7 cm, 4 cm, 3 cm
9 cm, 3 cm, 5 cm

b) Use your answers to part a) to write a rule for the side lengths in a triangle.

Literacy Connections

Use a Mind Map
A mind map can help you organize what you know about a topic. This mind map shows different methods for constructing angles.

You can add ovals below each method to extend this mind map to the next level. What instructions would you place in the ovals at the next level?

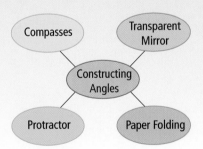

Key Words

Copy and complete each statement by unscrambling the highlighted letters.

1. Lines that intersect at right angles are called R E P E P C N L R I U D A lines.

2. Two angles that add to 180° are T M U P A E E P N Y L R S angles.

3. Two angles that add to 90° are O L M M C T E R N Y E P A angles.

4. Lines in the same plane that do not intersect are called R A A L L L P E lines.

5. A line that crosses two or more lines is called a L N S T A S E R R A V.

6. R L A E N E A T T angles are a pair of equal angles formed between a pair of parallel lines and on opposite sides of a transversal.

7. T I R E R I N O angles are a pair of supplementary angles formed between a pair of parallel lines and on the same side of a transversal.

13.1 Internal Angles of a Triangle, pages 424–428

8. In a right triangle, one angle measures 28°. Find the measures of the other two angles.

9. One angle in a triangle measures 30°. The other two angles are equal. Find the measure of each equal angle.

10. What is the greatest number of obtuse angles a triangle can have? Explain.

11. The angles in a triangle have measures of x, $2x$, and $2x$ degrees. Find the values of the angle measures.

13.2 Angle Properties of Intersecting and Perpendicular Lines, pages 430–434

12. College Street and City Avenue intersect to form two acute angles and two obtuse angles. One of the obtuse angles measures 103°. Find the measures of the other three angles.

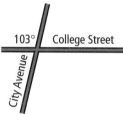

13. Find the unknown angle measures in the diagram. Explain your reasoning.

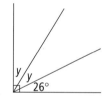

14. Two angles are supplementary. The difference in their measures is 30°. What is the measure of each angle?

15. $\angle X$ and $\angle Y$ are complementary. $\angle Y$ and $\angle Z$ are complementary. How do $\angle X$ and $\angle Z$ compare?

16. Can two angles in a triangle be supplementary? Explain.

13.3 Angle Properties of Parallel Lines, pages 436–440

17. Draw a diagram of two parallel lines and a transversal. Show the locations of a pair of corresponding angles, a pair of interior angles, and a pair of alternate angles.

18. What is the sum of the angles in the trapezoid? Explain how you know.

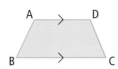

19. How are angles x and y related? Explain how you know.

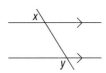

13.4 Apply Angle Measures, pages 442–446

20. Find the measures of angles x and y.

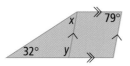

21. In the diagram, ∠BAC and ∠BCA are equal. Find the measure of ∠CAD.

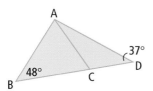

22. Find the measure of angle z.

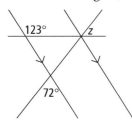

23. The diagram shows part of a bridge. Find the measures of angles a, b, and c. Explain your reasoning.

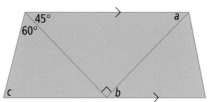

13.5 Construct Line Segments and Angles, pages 447–451

24. Describe how you could use a plastic triangle from a math set to draw two perpendicular lines.

25. Construct a trapezoid with two right angles and one parallel side twice as long as the other.

26. The diagram shows some directions of the compass. Describe a method for constructing this diagram.

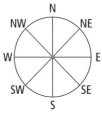

27. a) Construct ∆PQR with PQ = 3 cm, QR = 4 cm, and PR = 5 cm.
b) Measure each angle in the triangle, to the nearest degree.

CHAPTER

13

Practice Test

Strand	NSN	MEA	GSS	PA	DMP
Questions	1, 6, 7, 8, 10, 11, 14		1–15	6, 7, 8, 10, 11, 14	

Multiple Choice

For questions 1 to 4, choose the best answer.

1. Two angles have measures of 23° and 57°. The angles are

A supplementary

B complementary

C supplementary and complementary

D neither supplementary nor complementary

2. The sum of the angle measures in a triangle is

A 360°

B 180°

C 90°

D different for different triangles

3. Two lines are parallel. A transversal is not perpendicular to them. There are

A four pairs of alternate angles

B eight pairs of opposite angles

C four equal acute angles and four equal obtuse angles

D eight right angles

4. For two parallel lines and a transversal, the angles in a pair of corresponding angles are

A equal

B acute

C obtuse

D supplementary

Short Answer

5. Can a right triangle have two right angles? Explain.

6. Two angles are equal and supplementary. What are their measures?

7. Two intersecting lines form a 67° angle. What are the measures of the other acute and obtuse angles they form?

8. A triangle has internal angles that measure 12° and 109°. What is the measure of the third angle?

9. The diagram shows two parallel airport runways and a third runway that cuts across them. The measure of one acute angle formed is x. How many other angles in the diagram have the same measure? Explain.

10. Find the measure of angle b.

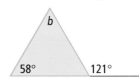

11. Find the measures of angles *p, q, and r*.

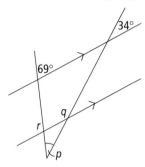

12. Construct △ABC.

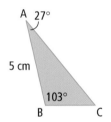

13. Construct △DEF with DE = 3 cm, DF = 4 cm, and EF = 6 cm.

Extended Response

14. Find ∠CHG, ∠DGF, and ∠DCH. Explain your reasoning.

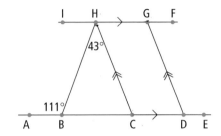

15. Without using a protractor, construct a triangle with angle measures of 45°, 45°, and 90°. Describe your method. Then, use a protractor to check the angle measures.

Chapter Problem Wrap-Up

You have explored angles on the following flags:
- Jamaica in Example 1 on page 431
- Newfoundland and Labrador in question 12 on page 434
- Lesotho in question 14 on page 440
- Antigua and Barbuda in question 12 on page 445

1. Design two different rectangular flags. Each one must have
- at least two transversals
- at least two pairs of opposite angles
- at least two pairs of complementary angles

2. For each flag, describe what you did to meet each requirement in question 1.

3. Use words and diagrams to describe the relationships between angles on your flags.

Answers

GET READY FOR GRADE 8

1 Fractions, Metric Units, Estimation, pages 2–3

1. a) < **b)** < **c)** > **d)** =
3. a) less than; $A = 8$ cm^2 **b)** less than; $A = 1.5$ cm^2
5. A
7. B
9. a) 32 cm^2 **b)** They are all equal. **c)** 224 cm^2
11.

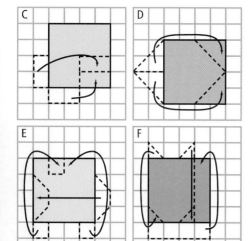

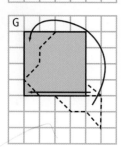

13. Area is the amount of space a shape covers. It is measured in square units. Perimeter is the distance around a shape.

2 Convert Fractions, Decimals, and Percents; Perfect Squares and Square Roots, pages 4–5

1. a) 50% **b)** 25% **c)** 20% **d)** 60%
3. a) 25% **b)** 45% **c)** 90% **d)** 33.3%

5. Answers may vary. All must be less than 0.5. For example, 0.2, 0.35, 0.1111.
7. a) 6 cm **b)** 2 cm **c)** 11 cm
9. a) $\frac{1}{4}$ **b)** 0.25, 25%

11. a) $\frac{3}{4}$, 75% **b)** $\frac{1}{4}$, 25%

13. Answers may vary.
15. Answers may vary. One suggestion is to spin until the letters in M-A-T-H have come up in any order.

3 Patterns With Natural Numbers, Fractions, and Integers, pages 6–7

1. a) 19, 24, 29 **b)** −11, −14, −17 **c)** 8, 13, 21
d) −2, −4, −6 **e)** 8, 7, 10 **f)** −3, 1, 5
3. a) 8; it is not a perfect square. **b)** 6; it is not a prime number. **c)** $\frac{6}{15}$; it is not equivalent to $\frac{1}{3}$.
5. a) 10 **b)** 49
7. a)

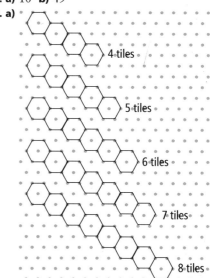

4 tiles
5 tiles
6 tiles
7 tiles
8 tiles

b)

Number of Tiles	Number of Clips
1	6
2	10
3	14
4	18
5	22
6	26
7	30
8	34

9. a) $23.39 **b)** Answers may vary.
11. Answers may vary.

CHAPTER 1

Get Ready, pages 10–11

1. a) 26 mm **b)** 4 mm
3. a) 38 cm **b)** 1 cm
5. 6:4, $\frac{6}{4}$, 6 ÷ 4
7. a) 9 **b)** 100 **c)** 6.25
9. a) 36 mm² **b)** 1 cm²

1.1 Discover the Pi Relationship, pages 14–15

3. a) d = 9.5 cm, C = 29.8 cm **b)** d = 3.1 m, C = 9.7 m
5. a) d = 2.2 cm, C = 6.9 cm **b)** d = 2.8 cm, C = 8.8 cm
c) d = 3.6 cm, C = 11.3 cm
7. r = 1.1 cm, r = 1.4 m, r = 1.8 cm
9. Answer to all three is 1:2 or 0.5.
11. Measurements are not exact.
13. a) 6:2 **b)** 3 times longer
15. 12.1 m; circumference is about 3 times diameter, so divide 38 m by 3.
17. Answers may vary.

1.2 Circumference Relationships, pages 19–21

5. 63 cm
7. 1.6 m
9. 75 mm
11. 101 cm
13. The radius, r, is 6 cm, not 12 cm. $C = 2 \times \pi \times 6$, C = 37.7. The circumference is about 38 cm.
15. Mateo: 471 cm; Yvonne: 467 cm. Mateo's racer travels farthest.
17. back row 175 people, front row 60 people, difference 115 people; find the circumference of each half circle and divide by 0.5 m.

1.3 Discover the Area of a Circle, pages 24–25

5. 2.0 m²
7. 7854 km²
9. a) 12.6 cm² **b)** 33.2 cm²
11. 616 m²
13. 491 m²
15. a) 908 cm² **b)** 104 cm² **c)** Answers may vary. One solution is $\pi \times 17^2 - \pi \times 16^2$.

1.4 Draw Circles Using a Set of Compasses, pages 28–29

3. a) **b)** **c)**

5. a) 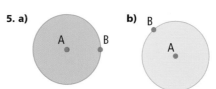 **b)**

7. b) 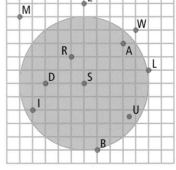 **c)** The letters that fall inside the circle spell RADIUS.

9. a) 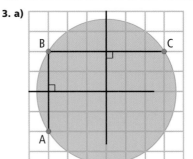 **b)** 19 cm **c)** 28 cm²

11. Answers will vary.

1.5 Construct Circles From Given Data, page 32

3. a) 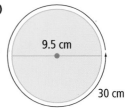 **b)** Answers will vary.

5. Answers may vary. There is always one way to draw a circle through 3 points as long as they are not on the same line.

1.6 Choose and Apply Circle Formulas, pages 39–41

3. a) 2.5 cm **b)** 6.5 mm
5. a) 4.4 m **b)** 5.6 cm
7. a) 9.5 cm **b)**

9. 75 cm

11. $66

13. 5655 cm^2

15. a) 250 m **b)** $6275

17. a) $C = 16$ m, $d = 5$ m, $r = 2.5$ m **b)** 20 m^2

19. a) Not fair. Maria has the advantage; she runs 250 m while Chico runs 160 m. **b)–c)** Answers may vary.

21. $C = 56$ cm, $r = 8.9$ cm; Change 42 m to 4200 cm first. Then, divide 4200 cm by 75 to find the distance once around the hamster wheel. This is the circumference. Substitute $C = 56$ into $C = 2 \times \pi \times r$ and solve for r.

Review, pages 42–43

1. area, A

3. diameter, radius

5. a) π **b)** All should be close to π (3.14).

7. 16 m

9. 50 m^2

11. a)   **b)**

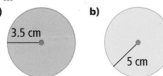

13. a)

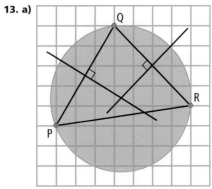

b) Answers may vary.

15. 201 m^2

17. a) 16 cm **b)** Answers may vary.

Practice Test, pages 44–45

1. B

3. A

5. 1018 cm^2

7. a) 6.3 m **b)** 8 laps **c)** 3.1 m^2

9. a) circle gets larger **b)** circle gets smaller

11. a)   **b)**

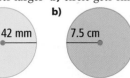

13. a) 38.7 m **b)** 77 m **c)** Answers may vary. For part a), substitute 119 for A in $A = \pi r^2$ and solve for r. For part **b)**, realize that the piece of glass is a rectangle curved around. Its length is the circumference and its height is 2 m. Use the formula $A = l \times w$.

CHAPTER 2

Get Ready, pages 48–49

1. a) scalene, acute **b)** scalene, right

3. a) 25 **b)** 49 **c)** 4 **d)** 64

5. a) $P = 28$ m, $A = 49$ m^2 **b)** $P = 44$ cm, $A = 121$ cm^2

7. a) 8 **b)** 9 **c)** 12 **d)** 13

2.1 Discover the Pythagorean Relationship, pages 53–55

5. a) 32 m^2 **b)** 56 cm^2

7. a) 7 cm^2 **b)** 28 cm^2

9. a) 26 cm^2 **b)** 14 m^2 **c)** 28 cm^2 **d)** 39 m^2

11. a) 17 cm^2 **b)** isosceles triangle

13. This is not a right triangle. The square on the longest side has area 81 cm^2. The areas of the squares on the two shorter sides are 25 cm^2 and 49 cm^2. Then, $25 + 49 = 74$, not 81.

17. Answers will vary.

2.2 Find Approximate Values of Square Roots, pages 60–61

3. a) 11 **b)** 10 **c)** 1 **d)** 9

5. a) 8 **b)** 80 **c)** 0.8

7. a) True **b)** True **c)** False, $3 < \sqrt{10} < 4$ **d)** True

9. Answers may vary.

11. a) Always true **b)** Sometimes true; true for numbers less than 1. For example, $\sqrt{0.25} = 0.5$ and $0.5 > 0.25$. **c)** Sometimes true **d)** False **e)** False

13) $\sqrt{25} < \sqrt{28} < \sqrt{30} < 5.8 < 6$

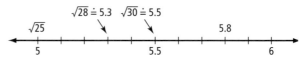

17. a) no **b)** no, $8^2 = 4^2 \times 2^2$ **c)** no, $10^2 = 5^2 \times 2^2$ **d)** $(a \times b)^2 = a^2 \times b^2$

2.3 Apply the Pythagorean Relationship, pages 65–67

5. a) 0.5 km **b)** 25.5 m

7. a) 5.2 m **b)** 12.3 m

9. a) 10.8 m **b)** 5.8 cm

11. 11.2 cm

13. 48 m

15. a) 100 cm **b)** 141 cm

17. 4

19. 6.8 cm

21. 14.8 km

2.4 Use the Pythagorean Relationship, pages 70–71

5. a) 2 m **b)** 2.1 m

7. 1.4 m

9. a) 136 m **b)** 1156 m^2

13. 3.4 m

Review, pages 72–73

1. a) PR **b)** PQ **c)** Answers may vary. $PQ^2 + RQ^2 = PR^2$
d) RQ
3. $a^2 + b^2 = c^2$, where c is the hypotenuse and a and b are the legs.
5. a) yes **b)** no
7. a) 2.24 **b)** 6.40 **c)** 8.66
9. $x^2 + y^2 = z^2$

11. a) 60 cm by 80 cm **b)** 100 cm **c)** 40 cm
13. 3.4 m

Practice Test, pages 74–75

1. C
3. C
5. 15 cm
7. 65 m
9. The sum of 9 and 36 is 45, so place the two square sheets as legs of a right triangle. Then, the third side of this triangle has length $\sqrt{45}$. Measure its length with a ruler.

CHAPTER 3

Get Ready, pages 80–81

1. a) 6, 12, 18, 24 **b)** 3, 6, 9, 12 **c)** 5, 10, 15, 20
d) 10, 20, 30, 40
3. a)

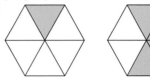

b)

c)

5. a)

b)

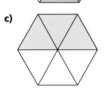

7. a) $\dfrac{3}{4}$ **b)** $\dfrac{7}{10}$ **c)** $\dfrac{5}{9}$
9. a) 7 **b)** 22 **c)** 13 **d)** 20

3.1 Add and Subtract Fractions, pages 85–87

5. Answers may vary. **a)** $\dfrac{7}{10} - \dfrac{1}{2}$ **b)** $\dfrac{5}{8} - \dfrac{2}{8}$

7. a) 15 **b)** 36

9. a) $\dfrac{5}{12}$ **b)** $\dfrac{13}{24}$ **c)** $\dfrac{7}{30}$ **d)** $\dfrac{19}{36}$

11. a) $\dfrac{5}{12}$ **b)** $\dfrac{3}{8}$ **c)** $\dfrac{19}{30}$ **d)** $\dfrac{1}{20}$

13. a) $\dfrac{1}{8}$ **b)** $\dfrac{7}{20}$ **c)** $\dfrac{1}{5}$ **d)** $\dfrac{13}{24}$

15. $\dfrac{1}{2} + \dfrac{2}{5}$

17. The solutions are equally good, with the exception that Matan's is in lowest terms and Kathy's is not.

19. a) $\dfrac{5}{12}$ **b)** $\dfrac{7}{24}$ **c)** $\dfrac{1}{6}$ **d)** $\dfrac{11}{24}$

21. a) $\dfrac{3}{8} + \dfrac{1}{2}$ **b)** 7 **c)** $\dfrac{3}{8}$

23. a) Estimates may vary. $2\dfrac{3}{4}$ h **b)** 5 min **c)** February

has 4 weeks, so multiply $2\dfrac{3}{4}$ h by 4.

3.2 Investigate Multiplying Fractions, pages 90–91

3. a) $\frac{1}{4} \times 4$ **b)** $\frac{1}{5} \times 10$ **c)** $\frac{1}{2} \times \frac{1}{5}$ **d)** $\frac{1}{3} \times \frac{3}{8}$

5. a) $\frac{2}{5}$ **b)** $\frac{2}{7}$ **c)** $\frac{5}{8}$ **d)** $\frac{1}{2}$

7. a) \$12 **b)** \$10

9. a) $\frac{1}{3}$ **b)** $\frac{1}{10}$

11. a) 16 **b)** $\frac{1}{6}$

13. a) $\frac{3}{14}$ **b)** $\frac{11}{14}$ **c)** 6 **d)** Answers may vary. Assume all the people who raised over \$50 actually raised \$51. Assume all of the people who raised less than \$50 actually raised \$1. Then, the minimum amount raised is $(51 \times 6) + (1 \times 22) = \$328$.

15. a) $\frac{4}{15}$ **b)** $\frac{1}{8}$

3.3 Investigate Dividing Fractions, pages 94–95

5. a) 4 can be divided into 12 sections of $\frac{1}{3}$, so

$4 \div \frac{1}{3} = 12$.

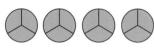

b) 5 can be divided into 10 sections of $\frac{1}{2}$, so

$5 \div \frac{1}{2} = 10$.

c) 9 can be divided into 6 sections of $\frac{3}{2}$, so $9 \div \frac{3}{2} = 6$.

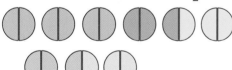

7. a) $\frac{3}{2}$ **b)** 2 **c)** $\frac{4}{5}$

9. a) $\frac{1}{3}$ **b)** $\frac{2}{3}$ **c)** $\frac{1}{4}$ **d)** $\frac{5}{3}$

11. a) Answers may vary. **b)** 6 **c)** Answers may vary.
d) 12 min or $\frac{2}{10}$ h.

13. Answers may vary.
15. It is because both numbers are between 0 and 1.

3.4 Order of Operations With Fractions, pages 98–99

3. a) $\frac{1}{2} - \frac{1}{4} \div \frac{1}{2}$ **b)** $\frac{3}{4} \times 2 \div \frac{1}{2}$ **c)** $\frac{9}{10} - \frac{1}{2} + \frac{1}{3}$

d) $\left(\frac{3}{8} + \frac{1}{4} \right) \div \frac{2}{3}$

5. a) $\frac{1}{6}$ **b)** $\frac{9}{20}$

7. a) 2 **b)** $\frac{7}{6}$

9. $\frac{2}{7}$

11. a) $12 \times \left(\frac{1}{3} + \frac{1}{2} \right) = 10$ **b)** No brackets needed.

c) $\frac{3}{4} \div \left(\frac{5}{6} - \frac{3}{4} \right) \times \frac{2}{3} = 6$ **d)** No brackets needed.

13. Jerry is not correct. The first expression is equal to $\frac{2}{3}$, while the second expression is equal to $\frac{3}{8}$.

15. a) $\frac{11}{6}, \frac{7}{3}, \frac{4}{3}, \frac{17}{6}$ are some of the possible answers.

b) $\frac{29}{18}, \frac{101}{54}, \frac{89}{18}$ are some of the possible answers.

3.5 Operations With Mixed Numbers, pages 104–105

5. a) $3\frac{2}{3}$ **b)** $3\frac{3}{5}$ **c)** $6\frac{7}{10}$ **d)** $9\frac{1}{4}$

7. a) $2\frac{1}{4}$ **b)** $4\frac{1}{4}$ **c)** $2\frac{3}{10}$ **d)** $3\frac{3}{4}$

9. a) $3\frac{3}{7}$ **b)** $\frac{4}{5}$ **c)** $3\frac{1}{9}$ **d)** $3\frac{11}{15}$

11. $1\frac{1}{3}$ h

13. $\frac{27}{32}$

15. a) $\frac{81}{80}$ **b)** $\frac{1}{2}$

17. a) $A = b \times h \div 2$, so, $A = 6 \times \left(\frac{5}{3} \times 6 \right) \div 2$.

b) 30 cm² **c)** 4

Review, pages 106–107

1. PRIME
3. FACTOR TREE
5. RECIPROCALS

7. a) $\frac{7}{6}$ **b)** $\frac{17}{20}$ **c)** $\frac{19}{24}$ **d)** $\frac{5}{6}$

9. a) $\frac{13}{20}$ **b)** $\frac{7}{20}$

11. a) 12 **b)** 6 **c)** 12

13. a) $\frac{5}{6}$ **b)** $\frac{3}{4}$ **c)** $\frac{15}{16}$ **d)** $\frac{2}{5}$

15. a) yes **b)** 7

17. a) $\frac{5}{6} \times \left(\frac{1}{2} + \frac{3}{5}\right) - \frac{11}{12} = 0$

b) $\left(\frac{1}{4} + \frac{2}{5} - \frac{3}{10}\right) \times 2 = \frac{7}{10}$

19. a) $7\frac{1}{3}$ **b)** $3\frac{9}{20}$ **c)** $20\frac{5}{8}$ **d)** $4\frac{5}{12}$

Practice Test, pages 108–109

1. D

3. C

5. C

7. a) The LCD can be found by multiplying the denominators and then dividing by the common prime factors. The common denominator is $6 \times 8 \div 2 = 24$.
b) The product of prime numbers is always composite because it can be divided evenly by the two prime numbers.

9. $\frac{1}{6} \times \left(\frac{3}{4} + \frac{2}{3}\right) \div \frac{1}{3} = \frac{17}{24}$

11. a) 3 h **b)** $\frac{1}{2}$ h

13. a) 3 pages **b)** They should make the advertisements $\frac{2}{3}$ their present size. They should be $\frac{1}{12}$, $\frac{1}{6}$, and $\frac{1}{3}$

pages respectively.

CHAPTER 4

Get Ready, pages 112–113

1. a) equivalent

$\frac{4}{16} =$

$\frac{1}{4} =$

b) not equivalent
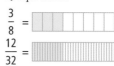
$\frac{6}{10} =$

$\frac{4}{5} =$

c) not equivalent

$\frac{3}{4} =$

$\frac{9}{11} =$

d) equivalent

$\frac{3}{8} =$

$\frac{12}{32} =$

3. a) $\frac{2}{5} = \frac{4}{10}, \frac{2}{5} > \frac{3}{10}$ **b)** $\frac{1}{4} = \frac{5}{20}, \frac{17}{20} > \frac{1}{4}$
c) $\frac{9}{10} = \frac{27}{30}, \frac{14}{15} = \frac{28}{30}, \frac{14}{15} > \frac{9}{10}$

5. a)
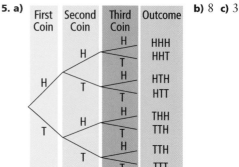

b) 8 **c)** 3

7. a)

First Coin	Second Coin	Outcome
B	Y	BB
	R	BY
		BR
Y	B	YB
	Y	YY
	R	YR
R	B	RB
	Y	RY
	R	RR

b) 1 **c)** 2

4.1 Explore Basic Probability, pages 118–119

3. a) total = 2, favourable = 1 **b)** total = 6, favourable = 1
c) total = 4, favourable = 1
5. a) total = 5, favourable = 2 **b)** total = 10, favourable = 2
7. a) 4 **b)** 1 **c)** $\frac{1}{4}$

d) You would expect $\frac{1}{4} \times 100 = 25$ times.

9. a) 0, 0% **b)** $\frac{2}{4}$, 50% **c)** 1, 100%

11. a) $\dfrac{2}{11}$ **b)** $\dfrac{7}{11}$ **c)** $\dfrac{4}{11}$ **d)** The probability is different for each letter because there is not the same number of each letter.

13. Answers may vary. **a)** rolling a 7 on a number cube **b)** tossing a coin and getting tails **c)** rolling a number from 1 to 6 on a number cube

17. a) Answers may vary. There are two outcomes when tossing a coin. One outcome can represent true. The other can represent false.

b) Answers may vary. Simon could toss the coin twice and use the four outcomes to represent the four choices: HH = A, HT = B, TH = C, TT = D.

4.2 Organize Outcomes and Compare Probabilities, pages 123–125

3. a) heads, tails **b)** yellow, blue, green, orange
c) 1, 2, 3, 4, 5, 6

5.

First Spinner	Second Spinner	Outcome
1	1	1,1
	2	1,2
2	1	2,1
	2	2,2

7.

		Spinner		
		1	2	3
Coin	H	H, 1	H, 2	H, 3
	T	T, 1	T, 2	T, 3

9. a)

		Spinner					
		Blue	Blue	Blue	Orange	Yellow	Red
Coin	Heads	H, B	H, B	H, B	H, O	H, Y	H, R
	Tails	T, B	T, B	T, B	T, O	T, Y	T, R

b) $\dfrac{1}{12}$ **c)** $\dfrac{3}{12}$

11. Experimental probabilities differ when the experiment is only carried out a few times. The more experiments that are performed, the closer it becomes to the predicted probability.

13. a)

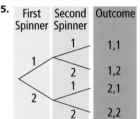

Spinner 1	Spinner 2	Outcome
1	1	1,1
	2	1,2
	3	1,3
2	1	2,1
	2	2,2
	3	2,3
3	1	3,1
	2	3,2
	3	3,3
4	1	4,1
	2	4,2
	3	4,3

b) The products are 1, 2, 3, 2, 4, 6, 3, 6, 9, 4, 8, 12.
c) $\dfrac{1}{12}$ **d)** $\dfrac{2}{12}$ **e)** $\dfrac{8}{12}$

4.3 More on Predicted Probabilities, pages 128–130

5. a) $\dfrac{5}{24}$ **b)** $\dfrac{7}{24}$ **c)** $\dfrac{12}{24}$ **d)** 0 **e)** $\dfrac{12}{24}$

7. a) $\dfrac{1}{12}$ **b)** $\dfrac{1}{12}$ **c)** $\dfrac{1}{12}$

9. a)

Frist Spin	Second Spin	Outcome
A	A	AA
	B	AB
	C	AC
B	A	BA
	B	BB
	C	BC
C	A	CA
	B	CB
	C	CC

b) $\dfrac{1}{9}$ **c)** $\dfrac{2}{9}$

11. a) $\dfrac{1}{15}$ **b)** $\dfrac{2}{15}$ **c)** $\dfrac{3}{15}$ **d)** $\dfrac{4}{15}$

13. a) $\dfrac{1}{6}$ on each cube

b)

		Cube 1					
		1	2	3	4	5	6
Cube 2	1	1, 1	2, 1	3, 1	4, 1	5, 1	6, 1
	2	1, 2	2, 2	3, 2	4, 2	5, 2	6, 2
	3	1, 3	2, 3	3, 3	4, 3	5, 3	6, 3
	4	1, 4	2, 4	3, 4	4, 4	5, 4	6, 4
	5	1, 5	2, 5	3, 5	4, 5	5, 5	6, 5
	6	1, 6	2, 6	3, 6	4, 6	5, 6	6, 6

There are 36 possible outcomes and only 1 favourable outcome for double 6s.

Probability(double 6s) = $\dfrac{1}{36}$

15. a) $\dfrac{1}{3}$ **b)** $\dfrac{1}{9}$ **c)** Answers may vary. The operator would probably use the second option because it makes it harder to win.

17. a) Probability(doubles) = $\dfrac{\text{favourable outcomes}}{\text{all outcomes}}$

$\dfrac{6}{36} = \dfrac{1}{6}$, Probability(no doubles) = $1 - \dfrac{1}{6}$ or $\dfrac{5}{6}$

b) $\dfrac{1}{36}$ **c)** Yes, one method is to multiply $\dfrac{1}{6} \times \dfrac{1}{6} = \dfrac{1}{36}$.

d) Probability(3 doubles in a row) = $\dfrac{1}{6} \times \dfrac{1}{6} \times \dfrac{1}{6}$ or $\dfrac{1}{216}$

4.4 Extension: Simulations, pages 132–133

5. a) 16 **b)** 4 or 6 could have been last because their tallies are each 1.

7. a) Spin the wheel until each of the 3 letters has been landed on at least once. **b)** Spin the wheel until each of the 3 colours has been landed on at least once. **c)** Spin the wheel until each of the 3 colours has been landed on at least once.

9. Answers may vary. **b)** Use a seven-section spinner with four sections for CD1 and one section for each of the other three CDs.

11. Answers may vary **a)** You could use a spinner with seven sections. Five letters get one section each, and one letter gets two sections. **b)** Answers may vary. **c)** The more likely the outcome, the higher is the probability.

4.5 Apply Probability to Real Life, pages 136–137

3. a) $\frac{1}{2}$ **b)** 50%

5. a) 0 **b)** 1

7. 50%

9. a) 0.4 **b)** 0.6

11. a) $\frac{6}{36}$ or $\frac{1}{6}$ **b)** $\frac{6}{36}$ or $\frac{1}{6}$ **c)** Find the sum of the favourable outcomes for 10, 11, and 12.

Probability(10 or higher) $= \frac{3 + 2 + 1}{36}$ or $\frac{1}{6}$

13. a) $\frac{8}{20}$ or $\frac{2}{5}$ **b)** $\frac{12}{20}$ or $\frac{3}{5}$ **c)** $\frac{96}{400}$ or $\frac{6}{25}$

Review, pages 138–139

1. experimental probability

3. outcomes, favourable outcomes

5. a) $\frac{1}{10}$ **b)** $\frac{2}{10}$

7. Answers may vary. **a)** rolling a 7 **b)** rolling an even number **c)** rolling a number from 1 to 6

9. a)

+		Cube 2					
		1	2	3	4	5	6
Cube 1	1	1 + 1 = 2	3	4	5	6	7
	2	2 + 1 = 3	4	5	6	7	8
	3	3 + 1 = 4	5	6	7	8	9
	4	4 + 1 = 5	6	7	8	9	10
	5	5 + 1 = 6	7	8	9	10	11
	6	6 + 1 = 7	8	9	10	11	12

b) Probability(rolling a 9) $= \frac{4}{36}$,

Probability(rolling an 11) $= \frac{2}{36}$; Laura has a better chance of not having to do her chores.

11. a) Probability(3 and pink) $= \frac{1}{15}$,

Probability(prime number and yellow) $= \frac{3}{15}$,

Probability(even number and blue) $= \frac{2}{15}$

b) Yes, the predicted probability of spinning a 3 and pink is always the same. There is one favourable outcome for this out of a total of 15 outcomes.

13. a) $\frac{3}{10}$ **b)** 70%

Practice Test, pages 140–141

1. D

3. A

5. B

7. a) $\frac{1}{6}$ **b)** $\frac{2}{6}$ **c)** $\frac{4}{6}$ **d)** $\frac{3}{6}$

9. a)

		Spinner 1						
		1	2	3	4	5	6	7
Spinner 2	B	1, B	2, B	3, B	4, B	5, B	6, B	7, B
	Y	1, Y	2, Y	3, Y	4, Y	5, Y	6, Y	7, Y

b) $\frac{2}{7}$

11. a)

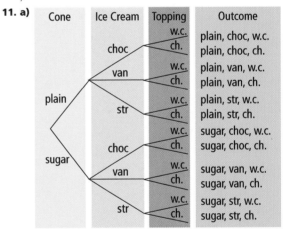

Key: choc = chocolate, van = vanilla, str = strawberry, w.c. = whipped cream, ch. = cherries

b) $\frac{1}{12}$ **c)** Answers may vary. She could use a spinner with three sections, one for each flavour of ice cream.

Chapters 1–4 Review, pages 144–145

1. a) 345.6 m **b)** 9503.3 m²

3. Answers may vary.

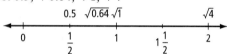

5. a)

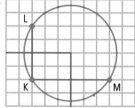

b) Fold to find the bisector of KL; fold again to find the bisector of KM. The point where these two bisectors meet is the centre.

7. 43.6 m

9. 0.5, $\sqrt{0.64}$, $\sqrt{1}$, $\sqrt{4}$

$$
\begin{array}{c}
\quad 0.5 \; \sqrt{0.64}\,\sqrt{1} \qquad\qquad \sqrt{4} \\
\end{array}
$$

0    $\frac{1}{2}$ 1 $1\frac{1}{2}$ 2

11. 9 times

13. $2\frac{1}{4}$ h

15. $\frac{2}{5}$

17. a) $\frac{7}{8}$ **b)** $\frac{3}{4}$

19. a) $\frac{1}{6}$ **b)** $\frac{1}{2}$ **c)** 0

21. Answers may vary. **a)** Use a number cube. Order the CDs from 1 to 6, roll the number cube, and choose the CD that matches the number rolled. **b)** Use the ace, 2, … 9, 10 of one suit of a deck of cards. Order the videos from 1 to 10. Shuffle the ten cards and place face down. Pick one card and choose the video that matches the number drawn. **c)** Use 5 white counters, 3 blue counters, and 2 black counters. Place the coloured counters in a bag and take one out without looking.

23. a) $\frac{14}{25}$ **b)** 26% **c)** Brad, $\frac{9}{50}$

CHAPTER 5

Get Ready, pages 148–149

1. a) 4:6 **b)** 4:3 **c)** 3:13

3. a) 2:3 **b)** 4:3 **c)** 3:13

5. Answers may vary. For example: **a)** $\frac{8}{10}$ **b)** $\frac{6}{14}$ **c)** $\frac{4}{100}$ **d)** $\frac{6}{16}$

7. a) 2.6 **b)** $1.\overline{3}$ **c)** 1.25

9. a) 0.065 **b)** 0.0775 **c)** 0.0525

11. a) 6.6 **b)** 25.5

5.1 Apply Ratio and Proportion, pages 153–155

3. a) red:green **b)** yellow:green **c)** yellow:all **d)** green:all

5. a) 1:2 **b)** 3:1 **c)** 2:5 **d)** 12:5

7. a) 9 **b)** 4 **c)** 1 **d)** 2

9. a) oil:vinegar = 3:4 **b)** 360 mL **c)** 300 mL of oil, 400 mL of vinegar

11. a) 4:3; this means that the team wins 4 games for every 3 that it loses. **b)** 45 **c)** 92 games

13. Answers may vary.

15. 16:25

17. a) 9:10; 1: 10; 9:1 **b)** 19:20; 1:20; 19:1

5.2 Explore Rates, pages 160–161

5. a) $64.75 **b)** $342.25

7. a) 4 km/day **b)** 2.4°C/h **c)** 6 tomatoes per week

9. a) Answers may vary. **b)** The smaller bottle is the better buy. It costs $0.40 per 100 mL compared to $0.43 per 100 mL for the larger bottle.

11. a) 12 points per game **b)** 288 points

13. a) Karla: She earns $12/h. Enzo earns $11/h. **b)** $88

15. a) $1.25/100 g **b)** $9.38 **c)** $25

17. a) $10.39 **b)** Answers may vary.

19. a) $20 **b)** $16.16 **c)** $3.84

21. Raoul: first 500 m: rate 6 m/s, time 83.3 s; second 500 m: rate 12 m/s, time 41.67 s. So, the time for Raoul to complete the race is 125 s. Shaun: 100 m in 20 s, so, 1000 m in 200 s. Raoul will win the race by 75 s.

5.3 Apply Percent to Sales Taxes and Discounts, pages 164–165

3. a) $1.40 **b)** $1.05 **c)** $0.14

5.

	Item	Price	PST	GST
a)	CD	$18.99	$1.52	$1.33
b)	In-line skates	$325.00	$26.00	$22.75
c)	Scarf	$10.95	$0.88	$0.77

7. Estimates will vary. **a)** $36.74 **b)** $25.60 **c)** $209.97

9. Estimates will vary.

	Item	Price	Sale Price	Final Price
a)	T-shirt	$9.79	$4.90	$5.64
b)	Crayons	$4.59	$4.13	$4.75
c)	Computer	$1199.00	$839.30	$965.20

11. No, Matt is not correct.
Sale price = $30 × 0.85 = $25.50.
Then, final price = $25.50 × 1.15 = $29.33.
13. a) between $2.40 and $3.60 **b)** Answers may vary.
You could make a formula Tip = PST + GST.

5.4 Apply Percent to Commission, pages 168–169

3. a) $25 **b)** $45
5. a) $37.50 **b)** $105
7. $880
9. a) $234.60 **b)** Methods may vary.
13. $1130
15. a) Sandeep $100, Andre $105 **b)** Sandeep $140, Andre $135 **c)** $600

5.5 Calculate Simple Interest, pages 172–173

5. a) $120 **b)** $620
7. a) $4.06 **b)** $329.06
9. a) $4.75 **b)** $204.75
11. Interest from Account 1 $6.13, from Account 2 $4.00; so, the money in Account 1 earns more interest.

Review, pages 174–175

1. rate
3. unit price
5. sales taxes
7. a) 3:5 **b)** 1:2
9. a) 6:5 **b)** 90 wins and 75 losses. This is assuming that the team's performance stays the same.
11. a) $0.49/100 mL **b)** $7.35
13. small jar $0.83/100 g, large jar $0.80/100 g; so, the larger jar is the better buy.
15. a) $4.79 **b)** $14.96 **c)** $5.60
17. a) $226.85 **b)** $260.88
19. a) $4500 **b)** $200 000
21. $394.63

Practice Test, pages 176–177

1. C
3. D
5. B
7. a) oranges $0.29 per orange, onions $0.76/kg, cereal $1.26/100 g or 1.26¢/g, jam $0.89/100 mL or 0.89¢/mL
b) oranges $1.45, cereal $11.34, jam $3.12, total $15.91
9. $19 500
11. a) $10.42 **b)** $510.42 **c)** $41.67 **d)** No. After 20 months the amount in the account will be $552.08. The price of the guitar with sales taxes is $592.24.

CHAPTER 6

Get Ready, pages 180–181

1. a) 243, 729, 2187 **b)** $\frac{1}{10}$, $\frac{1}{12}$, $\frac{1}{14}$ **c)** 40, 30, 20

3. a) Add 4 to get the next term. The pattern starts with 7, 11. **b)** Increase side length of each triangle by 1 to get the next figure:

c) Divide by 2 to get each next term: 32, 4.
d) Start with 5 mm. Add 5 mm to get each next height: 15 mm, 20 mm.

5. b)

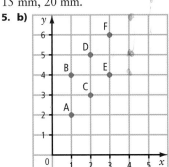

c) (4, 5), (4, 7)

7. a) 5 cm **b)** 20 cm

6.1 Identify Patterns, pages 184–185

5. no CDs: 1 way, one CD: 4 ways, 2 CDs: 6 ways, 3 CDs: 4 ways, 4 CDs: 1 way
7. Two branches that are half the length of the original branch are drawn at a 120° angle to the original branch.

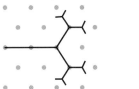

9. a) Start with 14. Add 3 to get the next term.
b) Start with $\frac{3}{2}$. Add 2 to the numerator to get the next term.
11. a) multiplication: 625, 3125 **b)** division: 3, 1
c) addition: 58, 72
13. a) It is the fourth term in the third diagonal.
b) Yes, this pattern happens in other diagonals. For example, in the fourth diagonal, the sum of the first four numbers is the fifth number; in the fifth diagonal, the sum of the first five numbers is the sixth number, and so on.

15. a)

Number	Sum Up To Number	Result
1	1	1
2	1 + 2	3
3	1 + 2 + 3	6
4	1 + 2 + 3 + 4	10
5	1 + 2 + 3 + 4 + 5	15
6	1 + 2 + 3 + 4 + 5 + 6	21

b) They are located on the third diagonal. **c)** The sum of numbers from 1 to n is equal to the nth number in the third diagonal of Pascal's triangle.

6.2 Define Patterns Using Algebra, pages 189–191

5. a) The perimeter is 2 greater than the number of triangles. **b)** $P = 2 + n$, where n is the number of triangles. **c)** 16

7. a) Each row has 5 more seats than the previous row.

b)

Row	Number of Seats
1	15
2	20
3	25
4	30
5	35

c) $S = 10 + 5n$, where n is the row number and S is the number of seats. **d)** 90

9. The fifth and sixth terms are as follows. **a)** $\frac{1}{7}$, $\frac{1}{8}$

b) 6, 2 **c)** 17, 20 **d)** 63, 54

11.

Term, n	Number of Marbles, m	Pattern
1	3	$1 + (2 \times 1)$
2	5	$1 + (2 \times 2)$
3	7	$1 + (2 \times 3)$
4	9	$1 + (2 \times 4)$
5	11	$1 + (2 \times 5)$
6	13	$1 + (2 \times 6)$
n	m	$1 + 2n$

13. a) 1834, 1910, 1986

b)

Sighting After 1758	Year	Pattern
1	1834	$1758 + (76 \times 1)$
2	1910	$1758 + (76 \times 2)$
3	1986	$1758 + (76 \times 3)$
4	2062	$1758 + (76 \times 4)$

c) $Y = 1758 + 76n$ **d)** 2518

15. a) José will need 16 posts. **b)** To build any square pen the number of posts needed is 4 times the number of posts per side, then subtract 4.

6.3 Explore Relationships on a Grid, pages 195–197

5. a)

Number of Circles, n	Number of Lines, l
1	4
2	8
3	12
4	16

b)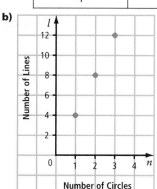

c) The number of lines is 4 times the number of circles.

7. a)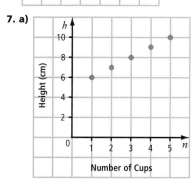

b) The height is 5 cm more than the number of cups. **c)** $h = 5 + n$, where n is the number of cups and h is the height, in centimetres. **d)** 45 cm

9. a)

Number of Hot Dogs Sold	Adriana's Earnings ($)
0	50
10	52
20	54
30	56
40	58

b)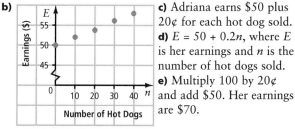

c) Adriana earns $50 plus 20¢ for each hot dog sold. **d)** $E = 50 + 0.2n$, where E is her earnings and n is the number of hot dogs sold. **e)** Multiply 100 by 20¢ and add $50. Her earnings are $70.

11. Answers will vary. The points are symmetric about (4, 21). The x-variable could represent time, and the y-variable could represent the height of an object that is thrown into the air and falls back down to the ground.

13. a)–b) Ruth jogs 1.5 km farther at each practice.

Shawn jogs 3.5 km during the first practice. Then, he jogs 1 km farther each next practice.
c) Answers will vary. During the fifth practice, Ruth and Shawn will jog the same distance, 7.5 km.

6.4 Apply Patterning Strategies, pages 202–203

5. a) One table seats 5 students. Adding each extra table adds 3 more students.

b)

Number of Tables, n	Number of Students, S
1	5
2	8
3	11

c) $S = 2 + 3n$, where n is the number of tables. **d)** 23
e) Answers may vary. The table of values may be extended.

7. a)

Number of Rounds	Number of Competitors
1	3
2	6
3	12
4	24
5	48

b) 48
9. a) increases by 6 cm **b)** Perimeter is 2 added to 6 times the number of L-shapes. **c)** 74 cm
11. a) 5, 10, 15 **b)** The dimensions of the second triangle are twice as large as the first, and the dimensions of the third triangle are three times those of the first triangle. Other patterns are possible. **c)** Answers may vary.
13. a) Each circle touches an adjoining circle in two places.
b) 198 **c)** Answers will vary.

Review, pages 204–205

1. D
3. B
5. 4
7. Answers will vary.

9. a) Each row has 2 more rosebushes than the previous row. **b)**

Row	Number of Rosebushes
1	3
2	5
3	7
4	9
5	11

c) $R = 1 + 2n$, where n is the row number and R is the number of bushes. **d)** 21

11. a)

Each time x increases by 1, y increases by 4. This can be modelled by the equation $y = 5 + 4x$.

13. a)–b)

x	y
1	2
2	4
3	6
4	8
5	10
6	12

c) The y-coordinate is twice the x-coordinate.
d) $y = 2x$

15. a) 32 **b)** 2^n

Practice Test, pages 206–207

1. D
3. C
5. B
7. The pattern can be modelled using an equation such as $N = 1 + 3r$, where N is the number of people in a particular row and r is the row number. The pattern can also be modelled using a diagram.
9. a) The first hexagon has a perimeter of 6. Each extra hexagon added increases the perimeter by 4.

Number of Hexagons	Perimeter
1	6
2	10
3	14
4	18

b) $P = 2 + 4n$ **c)** 70
11. The tree will have 127 ancestors, including Gavin.
13. a) $C = 100 + 75m$, where m is the number of months and C is the cost. **b)** 19

CHAPTER 7

Get Ready, pages 212–213

1. a) 79 m^2 **b)** 452 cm^2
3. a) $500 + 80 + 3$ **b)** $50\,000 + 600 + 1$
c) $500\,000 + 60\,000 + 7000 + 200 + 30 + 3$
d) $4\,000\,000 + 30\,000 + 5000 + 100 + 20$
5. a) 11 **b)** 15 **c)** 11 **d)** 9
7. a) $2 \times 3 \times 3 \times 3$ **b)** $2 \times 2 \times 2 \times 2 \times 2 \times 2 \times 2$
c) $2 \times 2 \times 5 \times 5 \times 5$
9. 45 cm^3

7.1 Pattern With Powers and Exponents, pages 217–219

5. a) 2^3 **b)** 8^5 **c)** 7^6
7. a) 2^5 **b)** 4^4 **c)** 11^3 **d)** 10^5
9. a) 128 **b)** 81 **c)** 216
11. a) 2.56 **b)** 0.0001 **c)** 0.125
13. a) 16 m^2 **b)** 12.96 cm^2
15. Answers may vary. **a)** 7^2 can be shown by the area of a square with side length 7. **b)** 7^3 can be shown by the volume of a cube with side length 7.
17. a) 125 **b)** 7 **c)** 4
19. a) yes **b)** no
21. a) 16^2, 4^4, 2^8 **b)** 27^2, 9^3, 3^6 **c)** 1000^2, 100^3, 10^6
23. a) 1, 3, 5, 7, 9 **b)** Answers may vary. **c)** 1 999 999
27.a) 10 000, 1000, 100, 10
b)

Power	Standard Form
3^4	81
3^3	27
3^2	9
3^1	3

c) $10^0 = 1$, $3^0 = 1$ **d)** 1 **f)** 1 **g)** Any power with exponent 0 has value 1.

7.2 Order of Operations With Exponents, pages 223–225

5. a) 32 **b)** 13 **c)** 32 **d)** 1.6
7. a) 5 **b)** $\frac{1}{6}$ or $0.1\overline{6}$
9. a) 6 **b)** 1.5 **c)** 6 **d)** 20
11. a) $(2.5)^2 - (1.2 \times 1.3)$ **b)** 4.69 m^2
13. a) $(2 + 4)^2 - 3 \times 5 = 21$ **b)** $2 + (4^2 - 3) \times 5 = 67$
c) $(2 + 4^2 - 3) \times 5 = 75$
15. Answers may vary.
17. 27 m^2
19. a) 0, 0, 0, 0 **b)** $6^3 - (5 \times 6 \times 7 + 6) = 0$,
$7^3 - (6 \times 7 \times 8 + 7) = 0$ **c)** Answers may vary. If the number is n, then the pattern is
$n^3 - [(n-1) \times n \times (n+1) + n] = 0$ **d)** Answers may vary.
21. a) 4, 9, 16, 25 **b)** 36, 49 **c)** $20^2 + 22^2 - 443 = 441$

7.3 Discover Scientific Notation, pages 229–231

5. a) $3 \times 10^2 + 4 \times 10^1 + 5$ **b)** $5 \times 10^3 + 4 \times 10^2 + 1$
c) $6 \times 10^4 + 5 \times 10^3 + 2 \times 10^1$
d) $1 \times 10^6 + 5 \times 10^3 + 2 \times 10^2$
7. a) 5×10^2 **b)** 2.8×10^4 **c)** 9.54×10^4 **d)** 8.432×10^6
e) $4.567\,21 \times 10^5$ **f)** 6.501×10^4
9. a) 40 000 **b)** 6200 **c)** 300 000 **d)** 20 500 000
11. 456 000 is greater.
13. a) $1 \times 10^4 + 2 \times 10^2 + 3 \times 10^1 < 1.23 \times 10^4 < 12\,310$
b) $350\,000 < 3 \times 10^5 + 5 \times 10^4 + 5 \times 10 < 3.51 \times 10^5$
15. a) 25×10^2 should be 2.5×10^3 **c)** 0.55×10^4 should be 5.5×10^3
17. a) 1.21×10^4 **b)** 1.32×10^5 **c)** 1.5×10^8
d) 1.64×10^{12}
19. 7×10^{22}
21. a) 180 million $= 1.8 \times 10^8$, 135 million $= 1.35 \times 10^8$, 45 million $= 4.5 \times 10^7$ **b)** Answers may vary.
25. 9.4608×10^{12}

7.4 Solve Fermi Problems, page 235

3. A volleyball has a diameter of 0.25 m. A cube with a side length of 0.25 m has a volume of approximately 0.0156 m^3. For a gym with dimensions 50 m by 20 m by 20 m, about 1.28×10^6 balls will fit.
5. Assume you can write 100 8s per minute and you can fit 1000 8s on one sheet of paper.
a) 10 min **b)** 1000 **c)** 16 667 h **d)** 10 000 pages
7. Assume 1 cm of grass has 50 blades, and a soccer field is 100 m by 50 m. The area of the field is 5×10^7 cm^2. A soccer field will have approximately 2.5×10^9 blades of grass.
9. If a dog wags its tail once per second on average, and lives for 10 human years, then it will wag its tail approximately 3.1536×10^8 times during its life.
11. Assume it takes an average of 10 s to say each number (since very large numbers take a long time to say). Then, in one year, approximately 3.1536×10^6 numbers can be counted and it will take about 317 years to count to one billion.
13. Assume that the average T-shirt costs $10 and each person owns 10 T-shirts. The population of Canada is about 33 000 000. The total cost of the T-shirts is $\$3.3 \times 10^9$.
15. Earth has a diameter of about 12 756 km, which is 1.2756×10^9 cm. A golf ball has a diameter of about 4 cm and the dimple in a golf ball is about 0.1 cm deep. We would expect the ratio of diameter to dimple to be the same.

$$\frac{\text{depth of hole}}{1.2756 \times 10^9} = \frac{0.1}{4}$$

$$\text{depth of hole} = \frac{0.1 \times 1.2756 \times 10^9}{4}$$

$$= 31\,890\,000$$

Each dimple would be about 319 km deep.

Review, pages 236–237

1. power
3. expanded form
5. Fermi problems
7. a) 256 **b)** 59 049 **c)** 35.937
9. a) 4^4 **b)** 2^8
11. a) 32 **b)** 24 **c)** 5
13. $(3 + 5)^2 = 8^2 = 64$; $3 + 5^2 = 3 + 25 = 28$
15. a) $3 \times 10^3 + 5 \times 10^2 + 6 \times 10^1 + 2$
b) $2 \times 10^5 + 4 \times 10^3 + 3 \times 10^2 + 1 \times 10^1$
17. $5 \times 10^5 + 4 \times 10^4 + 2 \times 10^2 < 542\ 000 < 5.421 \times 10^5$
19. 3.1×10^{13}
21. Assume the elephant lives 70 years and its heart beats 60 beats per minute. Its heart will beat 2.2×10^9 in its lifetime.
23. The distance from Earth to the moon is about 385 000 km or 3.85×10^{10} cm. Assume the length of a pencil is 15 cm. Approximately $3.85 \times 10^{10} \div 15$, or 2.57×10^9, pencils are needed.

Practice Test, pages 238–239

1. D
3. A
5. a) 32 **b)** 64 **c)** 1.21
7. a) 12 **b)** 1 **c)** 8
9. 6^3
11. a) $4 \times 3 + \pi \times 2^2$ **b)** 25 m^2
13. a) 4, 9, 16, 25 **b)** $7 \times 5 + 1 = 36$
c) $101^2 = 102 \times 100 + 1 = 10\ 201$

CHAPTER 8

Get Ready, pages 242–243

1. a) 165 m^2 **b)** 54 m^2
3. a) cube **b)** triangular prism **c)** rectangular prism
d) pentagonal prism
5. a) 312 cm^2 **b)** 238 cm^2
7. a) 10 cm by 10 cm by 10 cm **b)** 600 cm^2

8.1 Recognize and Sketch Three-Dimensional Figures, pages 246–247

5. a)

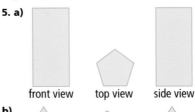

front view   top view   side view

b)

front view   top view   side view

7. a) sphere, cylinder **b)** cube, square-based prism
9.

11. Answers may vary.
13. a) yes **b)** yes **c)** no
15. As well as the arrangement shown in the text, the following four different arrangements can be made. Views may vary depending on which view as chosen as the front.

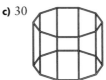

8.2 Build Models of Three-Dimensional Figures, pages 251–252

3. Answers may vary.
5. triangular prism
7. a) 18   **b)** 24

c) 30

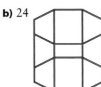

9. a) 6 edges and 4 vertices **b)** 8 edges and 5 vertices
c) 10 edges and 6 vertices
11. a) cube **b)** rectangular prism **c)** triangular prism
d) hexagonal pyramid
13.

17. Yes, demonstrations will vary.

8.3 Surface Area of a Triangular Prism, pages 256–258

3. a) 21 cm^2 **b)** 84 cm^2 **c)** 126 cm^2
5. 364 cm^2
7. 13 000 cm^2 or 1.3 m^2
9. a) Answers may vary. **b)** A: 312 cm^2, B: 480 cm^2;
B has a greater surface area
11. 1018 cm^2
13. 7 m^2
17. Answers may vary. Refer to the *Did You Know?*
below the question; make sure there are 12 units of
horizontal length for each vertical unit.

8.4 Volume of a Triangular Prism, page 261–263

3. a) 34.1 cm^3 **b)** 21.5 m^3
5. a) 2.5 m^3 **b)** 146.4 m^3
7. 8 cm
9. a) 2021 cm^3 **b)** 5.7 cm; this is the same as the height
of the rack.
11. Yes, the cottage has a volume of 484 m^3.
13. a) The triangular end is the base of a triangular prism.
80 cm^2 **b)** 1600 cm^3 **c)** Answers may vary. Assume that
all the space in the triangular prism shape is filled. This is
probably not the case. Depending on the contents of the
bag there may be empty space at the top.
17. a) A: 0.12 m^3, B: 0.96 m^3, C: 3.24 m^3, D: 7.68 m^3
b) Answers may vary. B = 8A, C = 27A, D = 64A.
c) When each dimension is multiplied by *n*, the volume
increases by n^3.

8.5 Surface Area or Volume of Triangular Prisms, pages 266–267

3. a) 288 cm^2 **b)** 270 cm^3
5. a) 14 740 cm^2 **b)** 145 200 cm^3 **c)** Answers may vary.
The amount will be more than part b) because earth can
be piled up in the scoop.
7. a) False. S.A. = area of *two* triangular faces + area of
rectangular faces. **b)** true **c)** true
11. a) 50 cm^2 **b)** Answers may vary: any triangular prism
with height 8 cm and base area 50 cm^2.

Review, pages 268–269

1. triangular prism
3. faces
5. a) pentagonal pyramid **b)** cylinder (lying on its side)
7. B

9. 8 faces, 12 vertices, and 18 edges

11. Vase A: 170 cm^2, Vase B: 80 m^2, Vase C: 311 cm^2
13. 31.9 cm^3
15. a) 9600 cm^2 **b)** 72 000 cm^3

Practice Test, pages 270–271

1. D
3. D
5. B
7. 488 cm^2
9. Yes; 0.96 L of batter is needed to fill the pan to a depth
of 4 cm.
11. A has a volume of 56 cm^3, which is 6.25¢/cm^3; B has
a volume of 227.5 cm^3, which is 2.11¢/cm^3; C has a
volume of 600 cm^3, which is 1.0¢/cm^3. So, C is the best
buy.

Chapters 5–8 Review, pages 274–275

1. a) 2:3 **b)** 20 **c)** 30
3. smaller size costs 1.475¢/mL, larger size costs
1.38¢/mL. So, the larger size is the better buy, assuming
they are the same quality.
5. 8 different ways; no topping: 1 way, one topping:
3 ways, two toppings: 3 ways, three toppings: 1 way
7. 5.5, 7.5, 9.5, 11.5; substitute *n* = 1, 2, 3, and 4 into
the expression 3.5 + 2*n*.
9. 32
11. 16 (4, 9, 13, 18, 22, 27, 31, 36, 40, 45, 54, 72, 81,
88, 90, 97)
13. 6.1×10^6; express all four as a number multiplied by
10^6, then compare the first numbers.
15. a) square prism, cylinder **b)** triangular pyramid,
triangular prism
17. 4 cans
19. a) 100.6 cm^2 **b)** 45 cm^3

CHAPTER 9

Get Ready, pages 278–279

1. Science fiction 12, Teen romance 6, History 3, Biography 3

3. a) Science fiction **b)** There are twice as many teen romances as history books.

c) $\frac{1}{4}$

5. The bar graph best displays the data. The circle graph makes it difficult to compare categories with each other.

7. a) 3.5 **b)** 1.5

9. a) 14 **b)** 70

9.1 Collect, Organize, and Use Data, pages 284–285

5. a)

How Often	Number of Teens	Fraction	Decimal	Sector Angle
Daily	55	$\frac{55}{100}$	0.55	198°
1 to 6 days a week	40	$\frac{40}{100}$	0.40	144°
Less often	5	$\frac{5}{100}$	0.05	18°
TOTAL	100	1	1	360°

b) How Often Teens Use a Computer

7. How Often Teens Use the Internet

9. a) Simulation: 99, Quest: 39, Trivia: 36, Role play: 51, Strategy: 51, Other: 24 **b)** Answers may vary. The two main strategies are ratios and percents. In this situation, percent is more efficient since the circle graph gives these values.

9.2 Comparative Bar Graphs, pages 290–291

3. a) shop **b)** art **c)** music

5. a) shop, engineering **b)** computer science, art

7. a) Grade 7 students: Physical Education 24, Art 18, Science 12, Other 6; Grade 8 students: Physical Education 21, Art 10, Science 15, Other 4

b)

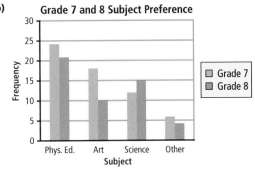

c) It appears that Physical Education is more popular with grade 7 students.

9. a) There are 3 groups: Records, Cassette tapes, and CDs. **b)** In 1988 CDs had not yet been invented. **c)** CDs have become more popular. Records have decreased in popularity. Cassette tapes have stayed at about the same level.

9.3 Histograms, page 296

3. a) 2 **b)** 24 to 26, 2 **c)** 16 to 18, 6

5.

Score	Tally	Frequency
50–59	III	3
60–69	IIII	5
70–79	IIII I	6
80–89	III	3
90–99	II	2

7. a)

Score	Tally	Frequency
50–54	I	1
55–59	II	2
60–64	II	2
65–69	III	3
70–74	III	3
75–79	III	3
80–84	II	2
85–89	I	1
90–94	II	2

b)

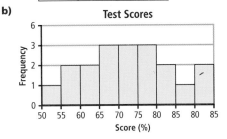

9. Answers may vary. A histogram is used to show a large set of data by organizing it into intervals. A histogram could be used to display the test scores of a class. A bar graph is used to compare categories. A bar graph could be used to show how many of each type of movie a person owns.

11. a)

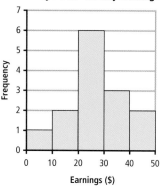

Babysitters' Weekly Earnings

b) They look identical. The number of leaves gives a visual representation of the frequency.

9.4 Use Databases to Solve Problems, pages 302–303

5. Each record has 3 fields: Name, Address, and Phone.
7. outgoing calls, incoming calls, and missed calls
9.–11. Answers may vary.
13. Answers may vary.

9.5 Use a Spreadsheet to Present Data and Solve Problems, pages 308–309

5.

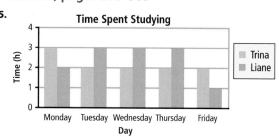

Time Spent Studying

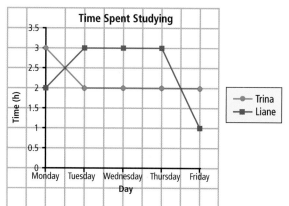

Time Spent Studying

The line graph will clearly identify each person's study trends. This is because line graphs are good for showing how data change over time.
7. Yes, it is possible for each team to win. There are only 6 points separating first and third place.
9. Answers may vary. Some advantages are speed, accuracy, and ability to experiment with different types of graphs.

Review, pages 310–311

1. sample
3. median
5. population
7. mean
9. census
11. a) 36 **b)** 40
13. a)

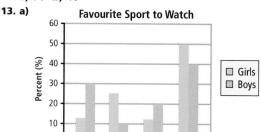

Favourite Sport to Watch

b) hockey **c)** figure skating and hockey
15. Answers may vary. **a)**

Scores	Tally	Frequency
15–19	I	1
20–24	I	1
25–29	IIII	4
30–34	HHI	5
35–39	IIII	4
40–44	IIII	4
45–49	I	1

b) The values range from 19 to 46, so a good choice is intervals of 5 starting at 15.
c)

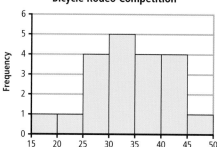

Bicycle Rodeo Competition

17. a) Sadia **b)** Kizzy; her mean weekly income is $207.50.

19. a) Spreadsheets are organized by rows and columns. Databases are organized by records and fields.
b) Answers may vary. A database could be used for names, addresses, telephone numbers, and e-mail addresses of everybody in the school.
c) Answers may vary. A spreadsheet could be used to analyse the results of a class test.

Practice Test, pages 312–313

1. B
3. C
5. D
7. Answers may vary. **a)** Perform a research study of the correlation between age and wealth using data from the latest government census database.
b) Calculate the weekly paycheque of a newspaper delivery boy based on the number of hours worked and newspapers delivered.
9. a)

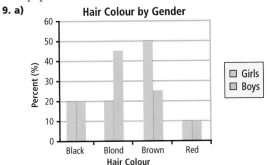

Hair Colour by Gender

b) brown **c)** black and red

CHAPTER 10

Get Ready, pages 316–317

1. a) 45 min **b)** 25 min **c)** Answers may vary. The least time spent studying is 15 min, the plot shows study times for 10 students, and half of the students study for 30 min or more.
3. a) mean 15.6, median 16, mode 16 **b)** mean 65, median 60, mode 60
5. a) B **b)** C **c)** A
7. a) cheese **b)** 5 **c)** Count the number of symbols in a category. Then, multiply by 2.

10.1 Analyse Data and Make Inferences, pages 322–323

3. The number of fans has increased over the years 1995 to 2002.
5. 2001
7. a) 19°C **b)** 32°C
9. a) Claudette's performance is improving because the number of errors is decreasing.
b) Answers may vary. Yes. If the current trend continues, she will have 0 errors by her 10th practice.
c) Answers may vary. Possible factors might be injuries and being nervous.
11. a) The number of people that obtain music from the Internet increased over the years 1988 to 2002.
b) Answers may vary. The graph doesn't show whether the music is obtained legally or not. If the line graph shows illegal music sharing, then the artists' claim is justified.

10.2 Understand and Apply Measures of Central Tendency, pages 326–327

3. a) mean 75.8, median 80, no mode **b)** median
5. a) mean 65, median 64 **b)** mean 70, median 64
c) The mean changed because another score was added. So, the sum of the scores and number of scores changed. When the data are arranged in order, the median changes from the second score to the third score, but these values are the same.
7. a situation that involves a small set of data that contains an unusual value

10.3 Bias in Samples, pages 331–333

3. No. A sample of two players is too small.
5. Yes. The sample size is too small, and one of the values is very different from the others.
7. Yes. Names are picked without looking.
9. Yes. Only school athletes are randomly asked. They will probably all enjoy taking Physical Education classes.
11. No. A random sample from the population is asked.
13. a) No. Kelly only asked his friends. **b)** The sample is not random, does not represent the school population, and is too small. **c)** Answers may vary. Kelly could randomly survey people as they enter the cafeteria.

15. Answers may vary. **a)** A sample of 2 will not represent the school population. **b)** Increasing the sample size to 4 is better, but still too small. **d)** The closer the sample size is to the population, the more closely the results will match the population.

10.4 Make and Evaluate Arguments Based on Data, pages 338–339

3. a) The Big Cheese. The burger is much bigger than the other one. **b)** It makes it look like a lot more people prefer The Big Cheese than Bonzo Burger.

5. a)

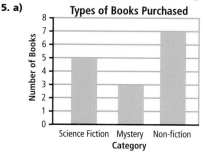

Types of Books Purchased

b) No. 7 out of 15 is not a majority.
7. a) Cheng is the better salesperson because Cheng's mean sales are $7400, while Benson's mean sales are $6600. **b)** Benson is the better salesperson because Benson's mean sales for February to May are $7500, while Cheng's mean sales are $7400.
9. a) A pot of gold represents earning lots of money.
b) No. It does not appear to be misleading.
c) Answers may vary.
11. Answers may vary.

Review, pages 340–341

1. population
3. random sample
5. majority
7. measures of central tendency
9. Science fiction: Sales have stayed the same from June to October. Mystery: Sales increased from June to August and then decreased until October. Non-fiction: Sales decreased from June to October.
11. The mode is the most important. Ashley needs to know the most popular size of jeans so she can order more.
13. Yes. Only basketball fans were surveyed, and they will likely choose basketball.
15. Answers may vary. **a)** highest overall sales or most consistent **b)** steadily improving or becoming more popular

Practice Test, pages 342–343

1. D
3. A
5. a) the choice of title, use of colour, and a vertical scale that does not start at 0 **b)** Change the title, keep all bars the same colour, and start the scale at 0.
7. Answers may vary.

CHAPTER 11

Get Ready, pages 348–349

1. a) −6 < +8 **b)** +1 > −3
3. a) (−4, −4); 4 blocks west and 4 blocks south
b) (−4, 4); 4 blocks west and 4 blocks north
c) (0, −2); 2 blocks south
5. a) $171 **b)** 147 cm
7. a) 40 **b)** 4 **c)** 1

11.1 Add Integers, pages 353–355

5. a) 3 + 5 = 8 **b)** −7 + (−2) = −9
7. a)

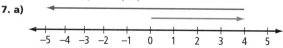

b) ●●●
●●●●

c)

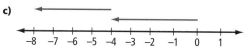

d) ●●
●●●

9. a) 4 + (−4) = 0 **b)** −5 + 5 = 0. The results are both zero. They show the zero principle.
11. a) 14 **b)** −6 **c)** −9 **d)** −9 **e)** 3 **f)** −8
13. a) 15 **b)** −5 **c)** −40 **d)** −93 **e)** −10 **f)** −26
15. Jeannie: −11, Cameron: −9. Jeannie's score was better than Cameron's.
17. a) −273°C **b)** −2°C **c)** −173°C **d)** 0°C
19. Answers will vary. Withdrawals: $20, $30, Deposit: $15.

11.2 Subtract Integers, pages 359–360

5. a) 7 **b)** 9 **c)** −10 **d)** 5
7. a) −6 **b)** 15 **c)** −12 **d)** −13 **e)** 12 **f)** −7
9. a) −2 **b)** 1 **c)** 8 **d)** −9
11. a) −5 **b)** −5 **c)** 11 **d)** 5 **e)** 5 **f)** −11
13. a) −14 **b)** −9 **c)** −9 **d)** −10 **e)** −10 **f)** −17
15. 10 203 m
19. a) $40 **b)** Answers may vary. The negative sign might have been missed.

11.3 Multiply Integers, pages 365–365

5. a) 72 **b)** −18 **c)** −15 **d)** −33
7. a) 15 **b)** 32 **c)** 54 **d)** 84
9. a) 6 × (−5) = −30; the scuba diver dove a total of 30 m.
b) 3 × (−20) = −60, Susan withdrew $60 so her mother deposited $60.
11. a) 378 **b)** −47 304 **c)** −6 **d)** 1440 **e)** 64
f) 1 500 625
13. If there is an odd number of negative numbers, you will get a negative answer. If there is an even number of negative numbers, you will get a positive answer.
15. a) 0 × (−5) = 0, 1 × (−5) = −5, 2 × (−5) = −10, 3 × (−5) = −15

b) $1 - (-7) = -7$, $0 \times (-7) = 0$, $-1 \times (-7) = 7$, $-2 \times (-7) = 14$, $-3 \times (-7) = 21$, $-4 \times (-7) = 28$

17. Answers may vary. You made 12 withdrawals of $4 each. How much did your bank balance change?

19. The number line shows $(-4) + (-4) + (-4)$, which is expressed using multiplication as $3 \times (-4)$.

23. a)

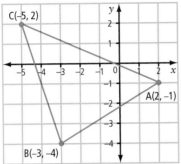

b)

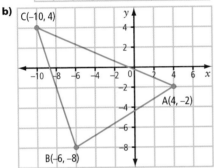

This triangle is the same shape as the triangle in part a), but it has larger dimensions.

c)

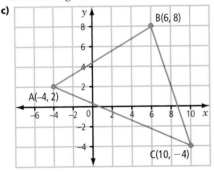

This triangle is the same shape and size as the triangle in part b), but it is rotated 180° around the point (0, 0).

d)

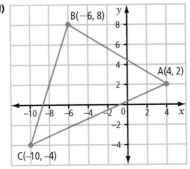

This triangle is the same shape and size as the triangle in parts b) and c), but it has been reflected and rotated.

11.4 Divide Integers, pages 368–369

5. a) 4 **b)** 9 **c)** –8 **d)** 10

7. a) –8 **b)** 5 **c)** 3 **d)** –6

9. 5 m

11. a) 1, –1, 3, –3, 5, –5 **b)** 1, –1, 2, –2, 3, –3, 4, –4, 6, –6, 8, –8, 12, –12, 24, –24

13. Answers will vary.

15. a) 6 m/min **b)** 60 m **c)** 96 m **d)** 135 m

19. a) $5^2 = 25$, $(-5)^2 = 25$, $6^2 = 36$, $(-6)^2 = 36$. $5^2 = (-5)^2$. Since there are two negative signs in $(-5)^2 = (-5) \times (-5)$, the result is positive, so it is the same as 5^2. The same is true for $(-6)^2$. **b)** No, since a negative times a negative always makes a positive number.

11.5 Order of Operations With Integers, pages 372–373

5. a) –8 **b)** 6 **c)** –2 **d)** –2 **e)** 1 **f)** –6

7. a) $5 \times 12 + (-3) = 57$ **b)** $-9 \times 6 - 4 = -58$ **c)** $3^2 - 5^2 = -16$

9. –14.75 cm

11. 362 km

13. a) the book **b)** No, you need $49.80.

11.6 Patterns and Trends With Integers, pages 378–379

5. a) Subtract 3 to find the next number. **b)** Add 4 to find the next number. **c)** Divide by 3 to find the next number. **d)** Multiply by –7 to find the next number.

7. a) –25, –30, –35, –40 **b)** 5, –5

9. Answers will vary.

11. –7, –14, –21; –7 divides evenly into each integer.

13. a) 7, 9 **b)** Add 2 to get the next number. **c)** 15 **d)** The pattern is probably not realistic because it means that the stock's price would increase forever.

15. a)

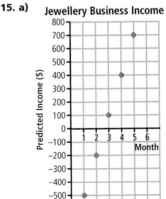

b) Income increases by $300 each successive month. **c)** $1600

17. –355, –208

19. a) option 1: (2, 1), (–4, 7); option 2: (2, –5), (8, 1); option 3: (–10, 7), (–4, 13) **b)** There would be an infinite number of solutions.

Review, pages 380–381

1. B
3. A
5. a) 12 **b)** 0 **c)** –17 **d)** –7 **e)** –8 **f)** –13
7. –85 000
9. a) 5 **b)** –30 **c)** 0 **d)** 20
11. a) $3 - 1 = 3, 3 - 0 = 0, 3 \times (-1) = -3, 3 \times (-2) = -6,$
$3 \times (-3) = -9, 3 \times (-4) = -12$ **b)** $1 \times 5 = 5, 0 \times 5 = 0,$
$-1 \times 5 = -5, -2 \times 5 = -10$ **c)** $-4 \times 1 = -4, -4 \times 0 = 0,$
$-4 \times (-1) = 4, -4 \times (-2) = 8$
13. The product is positive if there is an even number of negative numbers. The product is negative if there is an odd number of negative numbers.
15. a) –7 **b)** 16 **c)** –8 **d)** 7
17. a) $-50 \div 10 = -5$; Diane's mean depth per dive was 5 m. **b)** $-60 \div 5 = -12$; the unit rate of descent was 12 m/s. **c)** $-24 \div 8 = -3$, the mean hourly temperature drop was 3°C.
19. –1°C per 100 m in height
21. a) Her income will increase by $125 each week.
b) –$450 **c)** sometime during her sixth week

Practice Test, pages 382–383

1. D
3. C
5. B
7. a) Subtract 4 to get the next number: –20, –24, –28, –32. **b)** Add 6 to get the next number: 9, 15, 21, 27.
9. Brian is correct. You can explain this using a number line or integer chips.

CHAPTER 12

Get Ready, pages 386–387

1. a) 64 **b)** 63
3. a) 48 cm **b)** 14 cm
5. a) < **b)** = **c)** > **d)** >
7. $m = 3n + 10$, where n is the number of clients and m is the number of meals.
9. a) 31 **b)** 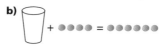 **c)** 10, 5

12.1 Model and Solve Equations, pages 391–393

5. a) subtract 5 **b)** add 8
7. a)

b)

9. a)

b) The cup represents the amount of money that Sandra gave. **c)** $15 + s = 35$ **d)** Subtract 15 from both sides.
11. a) + 15, – 15 **b)** – 100, + 100 **c)** ÷ 54, × 54
d) × 17, ÷ 17
13. a) $g = 6$ **b)** $m = 3$ **c)** $j = 24$ **d)** $q = 5$
15. a) $y = 15.1$ **b)** $x = 2.4$ **c)** $y = 6$ **d)** $b = 2$
17. a) d represents distance travelled, in metres; t represents time, in minutes. **b)** 6.25
19. a) No, she cannot retire because $a + e = 71$ and $71 < 85$. **b)** 55
23. a) $2m = m + 8$ **b)** Two times the variable m is equal to m plus 8. Subtract m from both sides. **c)** $m = 8$

12.2 Apply the Opposite Operations, pages 397–399

5. a) $\underline{2}n \boxed{+ 4} = 18$ **b)** $\underline{3}x \boxed{+ 5} = 17$
c) $\underline{0.8}y \boxed{- 7} = 9.4$ **d)** $27 = \underline{7}q \boxed{+ 6}$
7. a)

$k = 5$
b)

$n = 2$
c)

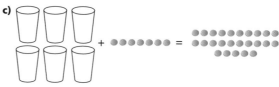

$x = 3$

d)

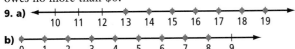

$n = 4$

9. a) $k = 4$ **b)** $y = 7.5625$ **c)** $x = 17$ **d)** $v = 20$

11. a) $2t + 13 = 37$ **b)** \$12

13. a) 8 years **b)** 20 years

15. a) 9°C **b)** 110 chirps/min

19. $-20°$ C

12.3 Model Problems With Equations, pages 403–404

3.

Diagram	Number of Marbles	Pattern
1	5 = 2 + 3	2 + 3
2	8	2 + 3 + 3
3	11	2 + 3 + 3 + 3
4	14	2 + 3 + 3 + 3 + 3

b) $m = 2 + 3n$ **c)** 17 **d)** 13

5. a) \$21.50; \$30.75 **b)** $P = 3 + 9.25t$ **c)** 6

7. 69 cm

9. a) 19 **b)** 8

13. a)

Wheel	Circumference	Pattern
1	32π	$2\pi \times (15 + 1)$
2	34π	$2\pi \times (15 + 2)$
3	36π	$2\pi \times (15 + 3)$
4	38π	$2\pi \times (15 + 4)$

b) 15

12.4 Explore Inequalities, pages 410–411

5. a) $n > 50$, where n is the number of people surveyed.
b) $s < 6$, where s is the number of UFO sightings.
7. Answers may vary. **a)** Alice is older than 5. **b)** Brad owes no more than \$8.

9. a)

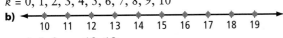

b)

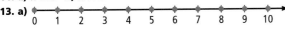

11. a) $x \leq 3$ **b)** $x \geq 8$

13. a)

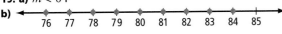

$k = 0, 1, 2, 3, 4, 5, 6, 7, 8, 9, 10$

b)

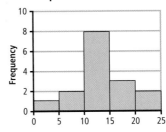

$n = 0, 1, 2, ..., 18, 19$

15. a) $40 + g < 72$ **b)** Fewer than 32 girls are at the dance.

17. a) $n = 0, 1, 2, ..., 21$ **b)** $t = 9, 10, 11, ...$
c) $x = 5, 6, 7, ...$ **d)** $s = 0, 1, 2, 3$

19. a) $m < 84$

b)

21. $t < 1.01n$ and $t > n$. The first equation says that the temperature using an ear thermometer can be no more than 1% higher than that using a regular thermometer. The second equation says that the temperature using an ear thermometer is always higher than the temperature using a regular thermometer.

Review, pages 412–413

1. F

3. E

5. A

7. D

9. a) $w = 6$ **b)** $x = 6.5$ **c)** $y = 200$ **d)** $z = 5$

11. Answers will vary. **a)** Twelve men earned \$364.
b) When a number of dollars was shared among 24 people, they each received \$60.

13. a) $n = 4$ **b)** $c = 7$

15. a) $k = 7$ **b)** $y = 7.3$ **c)** $n = 3$ **d)** $x = 3$

17. a) $P = 35 + 9.50h$ **b)** 3 h

19. a) $n \geq 15; n = 15, 16, 17, ...$
b) $2n \leq 10; n = 0, 1, 2, ...$

21. a) 32, 33, 34, ... **b)** 21, 22, 23, ...
c) 0, 1, 2, 3, 4, 5, 6 **d)** 0, 1, 2, 3, 4, 5, 6, 7, 8

Practice Test, pages 414–415

1. C

3. C

5. A

7. Indika's method is correct. It will undo the multiplication of n by 0.2.

9. a) $x \leq 8$ **b)** $x \geq 17$

11. a) $x = 100$ **b)** $q = 7$ **c)** $r = 2$ **d)** 3.25

13. a) $s = 6 + 4n$, where n is the pool number and s is the number of stones. Pool 7 uses 34 stones. **b)** pool 12
c) \$169

Chapters 9–12 Review, pages 418–419

1. males: 440, females: 600

3. a) Intervals may vary.

Temperature (°C)	Tally	Frequency
0–4	I	1
5–9	II	2
10–14	⫴ III	8
15–19	III	3
20–24	II	2

b)

Temperatures Across Canada

5. mean 31 443, median 31 400, mode 31 400. She should expect a starting salary of about \$31 400.

7. Claire's sample is not random, too small, and does not represent the school population. She only interviewed her friends. Her friends are much more likely to agree with her than the average person.

9. a)

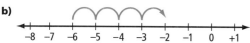
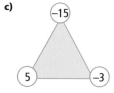

b)

c)

$-15 \div 5 = -3$ and $-15 \div (-3) = 5$

11. a) 8 **b)** 24 **c)** -77 **d)** 1
13. a) Each term is 4 less than the previous term.
b) $-4, -8, -12$
15. a) $74.25 = 28 + 9.25t$, where t represents the number of hours worked. **b)** 5
17. a) $x \geq 8$ **b)** $2x \leq 12, x \leq 6$ **c)** $x - 3 < 7, x < 10$

CHAPTER 13

Get Ready, pages 422–423

1. a) right **b)** obtuse
3. a) straight **b)** right **c)** acute **d)** obtuse
5. acute: ∠DEB, ∠AEC; obtuse: ∠AED, ∠CEB
7. a) 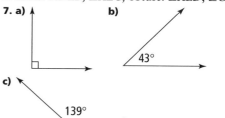 **b)**

c)

9. a) isosceles **b)** equilateral **c)** scalene

13.1 Internal Angles of a Triangle, pages 426–428

5. a) 69° **b)** 11° **c)** 102°
7. a) 51° **b)** 28° **c)** 49.5°
9. Answers will vary.
11. 21°
13. 60°
15. No, because the angle sum would be more than 180°.
17. 31°
19. 22°
21. ∠P and ∠S are 135°, ∠Q, ∠R, and ∠T are 90°.
25. a) $c + d = 180°$
b) $d = a + b$

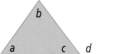

13.2 Angle Properties of Intersecting and Perpendicular Lines, pages 433–434

5. a) 37°, 143°, 143° **b)** 91°, 89°, 89° **c)** 179°, 1°, 1°
7. 52°
9. a) 135° **b)** 90° **c)** 19°
11. 35°
13. $a = 65°, b = 60°, c = 55°, d = 65°$
15. ∠A and ∠B are complementary.

13.3 Angle Properties of Parallel Lines, pages 439–440

5. 137°
7. 120°
9. ∠LPQ = 68°, ∠QPR = 112°, ∠SPR = 68°
11. $c = 54°, d = 126°$
13. Answers will vary.

15.

17. Answers may vary. Step 1: y and z are supplementary. Step 2: $y = x$ because they are corresponding angles. Step 3: Therefore, x and z are supplementary.

19. Answers may vary.

13.4 Apply Angle Measures, pages 444–446

5. $50°$

7. $35°$

9. $100°$

11. $x = 40°$, $y = 50°$

13. $z = 35°$, $y = 145°$

15. $a = 60°$, $b = 50°$, $c = 70°$, $d = 120°$

19. $18°$

13.5 Construct Line Segments and Angles, pages 449–451

5.

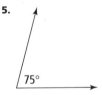

7. Answers may vary.

9.

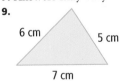

11.–15. Answers may vary.

17. Answers may vary.

19. a) Answers may vary. **b)** They are similar triangles. They are the same shape but different sizes.

Review, pages 452–453

1. PERPENDICULAR

3. COMPLEMENTARY

5. TRANSVERSAL

7. INTERIOR

9. $75°$

11. $36°$, $72°$, $72°$

13. $y = 32°$

15. $\angle X = \angle Z$

17.

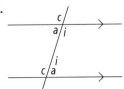

19. They are supplementary.

21. $29°$

23. $a = 45°$, $b = 45°$, $c = 75°$

25. Answers may vary.

27. b) $\angle RQP = 90°$, $\angle QRP = 37°$, $\angle RPQ = 53°$

Practice Test, pages 454–455

1. D

3. C

5. No; if a triangle had two right angles, then the third angle would be $0°$.

7. $113°$, $67°$, $113°$

9. 3

11. $p = 35°$, $q = 146°$, $r = 111°$

13. Answers may vary.

15. Answers may vary.

Glossary

A

acute angle An angle whose measure is less than 90°.

acute triangle A triangle in which each of the three interior angles is less than 90°.

alternate angles A pair of equal angles formed between two parallel lines and on opposite sides of a transversal.

$$c = w$$
$$d = x$$

approximate Given to a certain number of decimal places.

area The space covered by a two-dimensional shape.

B

bar graph A graph that uses horizontal or vertical bars to represent data visually.

base (exponential form) The factor you multiply.

In 5^2, the base is 5.

BEDMAS A way of remembering the order of operations

B	Brackets
E	Exponents
D	} Division and Multiplication,
M	} from *left* to *right*
A	} Addition and Subtraction,
S	} from *left* to *right*

bias An emphasis on characteristics that are not typical of an entire population. Certain responses can be encouraged by the wording of a question.

C

census A survey of an entire population.

circle graph A graph in which a circle representing a whole is divided into sections to compare each category to the whole data set. Also called a pie chart.

circumference The distance around a circle. Short form is C.

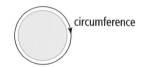

circumference

co-interior angles A pair of supplementary angles formed between two parallel lines and on the same side of a transversal. Also called interior angles.

$$d + w = 180°$$
$$c + x = 180°$$

commission A payment earned for sales made. Usually expressed as a percent of sales.

common denominator A number that is a multiple of the denominators of two or more fractions.

10 is a common denominator for $\frac{1}{2}$ and $\frac{1}{5}$.

comparative bar graph A bar graph in which two or more groups of data are shown side by side.

complementary angles Two angles that add to 90°.

composite number A number that has factors other than 1 and itself.

8 has four factors: 1, 2, 4, and 8.

cone A three-dimensional object with a circular base and a curved surface.

congruent figures Figures that have the same size and shape.

△ABC and △DEF are congruent.

coordinate grid The two-dimensional or (x, y) plane. Also known as the coordinate or Cartesian plane.

corresponding angles A pair of equal angles on the same side of a transversal crossing two parallel lines.

$a = w$
$b = x$
$c = y$
$d = z$

cube A polyhedron with six congruent square faces.

cube (cubic number) The product of three equal factors. Represents the volume of a cube.

$2 \times 2 \times 2 = 2^3$

cylinder A three-dimensional object with two parallel circular bases.

D

database An organized collection of information. Often stored electronically.

denominator The number of equal parts in the whole or the group.

$\frac{3}{4}$ has denominator 4.

diameter The distance from one side of a circle to the other, passing through the centre. Short form is d.

discount An amount subtracted from a regular price to give a sale price.

E

edge Where two faces of a three-dimensional figure meet.

edge

equilateral triangle A triangle with three equal sides and three equal angles.

equivalent fractions Two or more fractions that represent the same part of a whole or a group.

$\frac{1}{3}$ and $\frac{2}{6}$ are equivalent fractions.

estimate A reasonable guess found using mental mathematics strategies.

expanded form A way of writing a number that shows the value of each digit.

The number 4793 in expanded form is $4000 + 700 + 90 + 3$.

experimental probability The chance that something will happen based on results from an experiment.

exponent The number of factors you multiply.

$3^4 \leftarrow$ exponent

exponential form A shorter way of writing repeated multiplication.

$3 \times 3 \times 3 \times 3 = 3^4$

expression Numbers and variables, combined by operations.

$3x + 2y$ is an expression.

F

face A flat or curved surface of an object.

factor tree A diagram used to factor a number into its prime factors.

factors The numbers that are multiplied to produce a specific product.

2 and 3 are factors of 6, since $2 \times 3 = 6$.

favourable outcome An outcome that counts for the probability being calculated.

fractal A pattern of shapes, lines, or colours that gets smaller as it repeats.

frequency table A table used to show the number of occurrences in an experiment or survey.

G

Goods and Services Tax (GST) Money collected by the federal government on sales and services.

Greatest Common Factor (GCF) The greatest number that is a factor of two numbers. Used to write a fraction in lowest terms.

H

height The perpendicular distance from the base of a polygon to the opposite side or vertex. Short form is h.

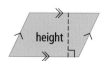

heptagon A polygon with seven sides.

hexagon A polygon with six sides.

hexagonal prism A prism whose bases are congruent hexagons.

histogram A connected bar graph that shows data organized into intervals.

hypotenuse The longest side of a right triangle. Opposite the right angle.

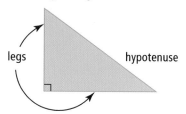

legs   hypotenuse

I

improper fraction A fraction in which the numerator is greater than the denominator, such as $\frac{8}{5}$.

inequality A mathematical statement using the symbols > and < to compare numbers or expressions.

$5 > 2$ and $2 < 5$ are inequalities.

inspection A method of solving equations using mental math.

integer A number in the sequence ..., –3, –2, –1, 0, +1, +2, +3, ...

interior angles A pair of supplementary angles formed between two parallel lines and on the same side of a transversal. Also called co-interior angles.

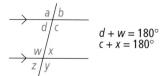

$d + w = 180°$
$c + x = 180°$

internal angle An angle inside a polygon.

intersecting lines Lines that cross each other.

irregular polygon A polygon that does not have all sides equal and all angles equal.

isosceles triangle A triangle with exactly two equal sides and two equal angles.

L

legs (of a right triangle) The shorter two sides of a right triangle. Legs meet at 90°.

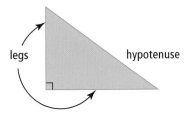

legs   hypotenuse

lowest common denominator (LCD) The lowest common multiple of the denominators of two or more fractions.

The LCD of $\frac{1}{2}$ and $\frac{2}{3}$ is 6.

lowest common multiple (LCM) The lowest multiple that two or more numbers share.

The LCM of 4 and 5 is 20.

lowest terms a way of writing a fraction so that the numerator and denominator have no common factors other than 1.

M

majority More than $\frac{1}{2}$. More than 50%.

mean The sum of a set of values divided by the number of values in the set.

measure of central tendency A value that represents the centre of a set of data. It can be the mean, median, or mode.

median The middle value when a set of data is arranged in order from least to greatest.

mixed number A number made up of a whole number and a fraction, such as $3\frac{1}{2}$.

mode The most common value in a set of data.

model (noun) A physical model that can be used to represent a situation.

model (verb) To represent the facts and factors of, and the results of, a situation.

multiple The product of a given number and a natural number.

Multiples of 2 are 2, 4, 6, 8, and so on.

N

natural numbers The numbers 1, 2, 3, ... Also called positive integers.

net A single pattern piece that can be folded to form a three-dimensional figure.

non-perfect square A number that cannot be written as the square of a whole number.

***n*th term** An item in a sequence or pattern. The variable, *n* represents the position in the sequence.

number line A line that matches a set of points and a set of numbers one to one.

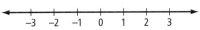

numerator The number of equal parts being considered in the whole or the group.

$\frac{3}{4}$ has numerator 3.

O

obtuse angle An angle that measures more than 90° but less than 180°.

obtuse triangle A triangle containing one obtuse angle.

octagon A polygon with eight sides.

octahedron A polyhedron with eight triangular faces.

opposite angles A pair of equal angles formed by two intersecting lines.

Angles *a* and *c*, and *b* and *d* are pairs of opposite angles.

opposite integers Two integers with the same numeral but different signs.

+2 and −2 are opposite integers.

opposite operation A mathematical operation that undoes a related operation.

ordered pair A pair of numbers, such as (4, 5), used to locate a point on a coordinate grid.

order of operations Proper sequence of steps to evaluate an expression. Use BEDMAS to remember.

B	Brackets
E	Exponents
D	Division and Multiplication,
M	from *left* to *right*
A	Addition and Subtraction,
S	from *left* to *right*

outcome One possible result of a probability experiment.

parallel lines Lines in the same plane that do not intersect.

parallelogram A four-sided figure with both pairs of opposite sides parallel.

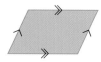

pattern An arrangement of shapes, lines, colours, numbers, symbols, and so on, for which you can predict what comes next.

pentagon A polygon with five sides.

pentagonal prism A prism whose bases are congruent pentagons.

pentagonal pyramid A pyramid with a pentagonal base.

percent Out of 100.

75% means $\dfrac{75}{100}$ or 0.75

percent circle A circle divided into 100 equal sections. Each section represents 1%.

perfect square A number whose square root is a whole number.

4 is a perfect square. $\sqrt{4} = 2$

perimeter The distance around the outside of a two-dimensional shape or figure.

perpendicular lines Lines that intersect at right angles.

pi The ratio of the circumference of a circle to its diameter. Short form is π.

$$\pi = \dfrac{C}{d}$$

pictograph A graph that illustrates data using pictures and symbols.

pie chart A graph in which a circle representing a whole is divided into sections to compare each category to the whole data set. Also called a circle graph.

place value The value given to the place in which a digit appears in a number.

In the number 6172, 6 is in the thousands place, 1 is in the hundreds place, 7 is in the tens place, and 2 is in the ones place.

polygon A two-dimensional closed figure whose sides are line segments.

polyhedron A three-dimensional figure with faces that are polygons. Plural is polyhedra.

population The entire group of people you want to learn about.

power A number in exponential form. Includes a base and an exponent.

predicted probability The chance that something *should* happen. A fraction of the number of ways a favourable outcome can happen to the total number of possible outcomes.

prime factors The prime numbers that are multiplied to give a specific product.

The prime factors of 30 are 2, 3, and 5.
$30 = 2 \times 3 \times 5$

prime number A number that has only two different factors, 1 and itself.

principal Amount of money invested or borrowed.

prism A three-dimensional object with a parallel base and top that are congruent polygons. A prism is named by the shape of its base, for example, rectangular prism, triangular prism.

probability The chance that something will happen.

product A number resulting from multiplication.

proper fraction A fraction in which the denominator is greater than the numerator.

$\frac{5}{8}$ is a proper fraction.

proportion A statement that says two ratios are equal. Can be written in fraction form as

$\frac{1}{4} = \frac{4}{16}$ or in ratio form as 1:4 = 4:16.

Provincial Sales Tax (PST) Money collected by the provincial government on purchases. Rate varies by province.

pyramid A polyhedron with one base and the same number of triangular faces as there are sides on the base.

Pythagorean relationship The relationship between the lengths of the sides of a right triangle.

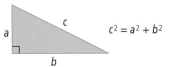

Q

quadrilateral A closed shape with four straight sides.

quotient A number resulting from division.

R

radius The distance from the centre of a circle to the outside edge. Short form is r.

random sample A sample in which everyone in a population has an equal chance of being selected.

rate A comparison of two quantities measured in different units.

120 km in 2 h and $\frac{\$2.97}{\text{kg}}$ are rates.

ratio A comparison of quantities measured in the same units. Can be written in ratio form as 3:4 or in fraction form as $\frac{3}{4}$.

reciprocals Two numbers that have a product of 1.
$\frac{3}{4}$ and $\frac{4}{3}$ are reciprocals.

rectangular prism A prism whose bases are congruent rectangles.

rectangular pyramid A pyramid with a rectangular base.

regular polygon A polygon with all sides equal and all angles equal.

relationship A pattern formed between two sets of numbers.

repeating decimal A decimal with a digit or group of digits that repeats forever. Write the repeating digits with a bar: 0.333... = $0.\overline{3}$.

right angle An angle that measures 90°.

right triangle A triangle containing a 90° angle.

S

sales tax Money collected by a government on purchases. Usually written as a percent.

sample A small group that represents a population.

scalene triangle A triangle with no equal sides or angles.

scientific notation The product of two numbers. The first number is greater than or equal to 1 and less than 10. The second number is a power of 10.

For example, 2.5×10^6.

sequence A pattern of numbers.

similar figures Figures that have the same shape but different size.

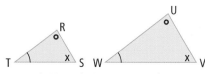

△RST and △UVW are similar.

simple interest An amount earned for money borrowed or lent. Usually expressed as a percent per year.

simulation A probability experiment used to model a real situation.

skeleton A frame formed by joining the edges of a three-dimensional figure.

solution set A list of numbers that make a mathematical statement true.

speed A comparison of distance travelled to time taken.

$$\text{speed} = \frac{\text{distance}}{\text{time}}$$

sphere A round ball-shaped object. All points on its surface are the same distance from a fixed point called the centre.

spreadsheet A software tool for organizing and displaying numerical data.

square-based pyramid A pyramid with a square base.

square (number) The product of two equal factors. Represents the area of a square.

$3 \times 3 = 3^2$

square root (of a number) A factor that multiplies by itself to give that number. Symbol is $\sqrt{\ }$.

Since $9 \times 9 = 81$, the square root of 81 is 9. $\sqrt{81} = 9$

standard form A way of writing a number so that each digit has a place value.

4793 is written in standard form.

statistic A value calculated from a set of data.

stem-and-leaf plot A way of organizing numerical data by representing part of each number as a stem and the other part as a leaf.

straight angle An angle that measures 180°.

supplementary angles Two angles that add to 180°.

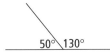

50° 130°

surface area The number of square units needed to cover the outside of an object.

systematic trial A method of solving equations by substituting values for the variable until the correct answer is obtained.

T

table of values A table listing two sets of numbers that may be related.

tally chart A table used to record experimental results or data. Tally marks are used to count the data.

transversal A line that crosses two or more lines.

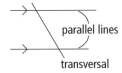

parallel lines

transversal

trapezoid A four-sided figure with exactly one pair of opposite sides parallel.

tree diagram A diagram that shows possibilities as sets of branches.

triangular prism A prism whose bases are congruent triangles.

triangular pyramid A pyramid with a triangular base.

U

unit price A unit rate that involves prices.

$\dfrac{\$3.99}{\text{kg}}$ and $100 per day are unit prices.

unit rate A rate in which the second term is 1.

70 km/h is a unit rate.

V

variable A letter that represents a number or numbers.

In $4x - 1$, the letter x is a variable.

vertex A point at which two or more edges of a figure meet. Plural is vertices.

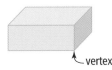

vertex

volume The amount of space occupied by an object. Measured in cubic units.

W

whole numbers The numbers 0, 1, 2, 3, …

X

x-axis The horizontal number line on a coordinate grid.

x-coordinate The first number in the ordered pair describing a point on a coordinate grid.

The point P(2, 5) has x-coordinate 2.

Y

y-axis The vertical number line on a coordinate grid.

y-coordinate The second number in the ordered pair describing a point on a coordinate grid.

The point P(2, 5) has y-coordinate 5.

Z

zero principle The principle that the sum of a pair of opposite integers is zero.

$(+7) + (-7) = 0$

Index

Credits

Photo Credits

t=top; b=bottom; c=centre; l=left; r=right

8-9 © Paul Hutley, Eye Ubiquitous/CORBIS/MAGMA; 12-13 Roland W. Meisel; 15-18 Roland W. Meisel; 20 © Paul Hutley, Eye Ubiquitous/CORBIS/MAGMA; 21 Roland W. Meisel; 22 © NASA/CORBIS/MAGMA; 25 tr Roland W. Meisel, bl © Paul Hutley, Eye Ubiquitous/CORBIS/MAGMA; 26 t Circles #20 © 2002 Michele Hardy, bl & br Roland W. Meisel; 27-28 Roland W. Meisel; 30-31 Roland W. Meisel; 33-35 Screen shots from *The Geometer's Sketchpad*®, Key Curriculum Press, 1150 65th St., Emeryville, CA 94608, 1-800-995-MATH; 36 CP/Montreal Gazette/André Forget; 40 Roland W. Meisel; 42 Roland W. Meisel; 44 Roland W. Meisel; 45 t Roland W. Meisel, b © Philip James Corwin/CORBIS/MAGMA; 46-47 Phil Jason/Stone/Getty Images; 50-51 Roland W. Meisel; 56-57 Screen shots from *The Geometer's Sketchpad*®, Key Curriculum Press, 1150 65th St., Emeryville, CA 94608, 1-800-995-MATH; 58 © Adam Woolfitt/CORBIS/MAGMA; 61 Photodisc Green/Getty Images; 62 Roland W. Meisel; 64 Alec Pytlowany/Masterfile; 68 © PhotoLink/Getty Images; 71 Roland W. Meisel; 75 Phil Jason/Stone/Getty Images; 76 Roland W. Meisel; 78-79 Ron Watts/Firstlight.ca; 88 t Bill Lowry/Ivy Images, b Roland W. Meisel; 91-92 Roland W. Meisel; 98 Roland W. Meisel; 100 Dick Hemingway; 107 Roland W. Meisel; 109 Ron Watts/Firstlight.ca; 110-111 © Mary Steinbacher/Photo Edit; 120 Roland W. Meisel; 131 Roland W. Meisel; 142 Photodisc Green/Getty Images; 145-146 CP/J.P. Moczulski; 150 Roland W. Meisel; 156 Al Harvey/The Slide Farm; 158 Roland W. Meisel; 161 © Image Source/SuperStock; 162 Roland W. Meisel; 170 t Photodisc Green/Getty Images, cr Roland W. Meisel; 178-179 Digital Vision/Firstlight.ca; 179 Roland W. Meisel; 182 Roland W. Meisel; 185 A.G.E. Foto Stock/Firstlight.ca; 186 Photodisc Green/Getty Images; 191 tl © Royalty-Free/CORBIS/MAGMA, br Roland W. Meisel; 192 Roland W. Meisel; 195 Roland W. Meisel; 197 Roland W. Meisel; 198 © Steve Vidler/SuperStock; 203 Thinkstock/Getty Images; 207 Roland W. Meisel; 208-209 © Royalty-Free/CORBIS/MAGMA; 208 © Karl Weatherly/CORBIS/MAGMA; 209 Roland W. Meisel; 212-213 Roland W. Meisel; 220 Roland W. Meisel; 224 © Royalty-Free/CORBIS/MAGMA; 230 t Roland W. Meisel, br Marco Di Lauro/Getty Images; 231 Roland W. Meisel; 235 t © Royalty-Free/CORBIS/MAGMA, b NASA/Johnson Space Center; 240-241 Natural Moments Photography/Firstlight.ca; 242 Don Ford; 246 Roland W. Meisel; 247 c Screen shot from TABS+, © 2002 Apex Software, cr Roland W. Meisel; 251 Roland W. Meisel; 257 Roland W. Meisel; 262 Larry Macdougal/Firstlight.ca; 270 Jim Wehtje/Getty Images; 272 © Royalty-Free/CORBIS/MAGMA; 276-277 © Michael Newman/Photo Edit; 280 © Pierre Vauthey/CORBIS SYGMA/MAGMA; 282 Roland W. Meisel; 286 © David Young-Wolff/Photo Edit; 292 Roland W. Meisel; 297 Screen shots from Fathom™; 298 © Michael Newman/Photo Edit; 299 Screen shots from E-STAT and CANSIM databases, Statistics Canada; 301 Screen shots from E-STAT and CANSIM databases, Statistics Canada; 302 Roland W. Meisel; 303 Screen shot from E-STAT and CANSIM databases, Statistics Canada; 304-306 Screen shots from ApplesWorks 6. Copyright © 2004 Apple Computers, Inc. All rights reserved; 314-315 Digital Vision/Firstlight.ca; 318 Dan Kenyon/Taxi/Getty Images; 328 Roland W. Meisel; 333 © Tony Freeman/Photo Edit; 334 © Jon Feingersh/Masterfile; 344-345 © Royalty-Free/CORBIS/MAGMA; 348 l Photodisc Blue/Getty Images, r © James Marshall/CORBIS/MAGMA;

359 © Julie Houck/CORBIS/MAGMA; 363 Jeff Rotman/Photo Researchers, Inc.; 364 Victor Last/Geographical Visual Aids; 368 Roland W. Meisel; 372 Roland W. Meisel; 379 Schafer & Hill/Stone/Getty Images; 381 Dr. George Gornacz/Science Photo Library; 384-385 © Neil Rabinowitz/CORBIS/MAGMA; 388 CP/AP Photo/Elaine Thompson; 394 Roland W. Meisel; 399 Bill Ivy/Ivy Images; 400 Roland W. Meisel; 405 © Royalty-Free/CORBIS/MAGMA; 416 Roland W. Meisel; 418-419 © C/B Productions/CORBIS/MAGMA; 420-421 Roland W. Meisel; 422 © Freelance Consulting Services Pty Ltd/CORBIS/MAGMA; 423 Roland W. Meisel; 427 Screen shot from *The Geometer's Sketchpad*®, Key Curriculum Press, 1150 65th St., Emeryville, CA 94608, 1-800-995-MATH; 433 Screen shot from *The Geometer's Sketchpad*®, Key Curriculum Press, 1150 65th St., Emeryville, CA 94608, 1-800-995-MATH; 439 Screen shot from *The Geometer's Sketchpad*®, Key Curriculum Press, 1150 65th St., Emeryville, CA 94608, 1-800-995-MATH; 440 Al Harvey/The Slide Farm; 445 t Photodisc Green/Getty Images, c Roland W. Meisel; 447 Roland W. Meisel; 449 Roland W. Meisel.

Statistics Canada information is used with permission of Statistics Canada. Users are forbidden to copy this material and/or redisseminate the data, in an original or modified form, for commercial purposes, without the expressed permission of Statistics Canada. Information on the availability of the wide range of date from Statistics Canada can be obtained from Statistics Canada's Regional Offices, its World Wide Web site at http://statcan.ca, and its toll-free access number 1-800-263-1136

Illustration Credits

Ben Hodson: xiv, 3, 4, 6, 135, 166, 199, 201, 273, 332, 409
Tina Holdcroft Enterprises Inc.: 7, 96, 114, 125, 131, 197, 206, 277, 324, 328, 329, 330, 331, 411

Technical Art

Tom Dart, Greg Duhaney, Kim Hutchinson, Alana Lai, Claire Milne, and Adam Wood of First Folio Resource Group, Inc.